P9-BJU-529
SCOREBUILDERS

Scorebuilders' PT Review Course Manual

Scott M. Giles PT, DPT, MBA
Founder, Scorebuilders

Review Course Participants Save 20% on Scorebuilders' Products!

School Coupon Code
PACIFIC2023

Record your school coupon code here.
Use the coupon code to save 20% at www.scorebuilders.com.

COURSE
SIGN IN

For additional information on our review products for physical therapists and physical therapist assistants, please contact Scorebuilders.

Scorebuilders
175 Innovation Way
Scarborough, Maine 04074

Phone: (207) 885-0304
Fax: (207) 883-8377
Website: www.scorebuilders.com
Email: info@scorebuilders.com

Please visit us on the following social networking sites by searching for Scorebuilders.

Scorebuilders

@scorebuildersme

@scorebuilders

CONTENTS

Appendix

Examination Basics

WELCOME TO
SCOREBUILDERS' REVIEW COURSE
SCOREBUILDERS
EST. 1989
Review Courses
SCOREBUILDERS

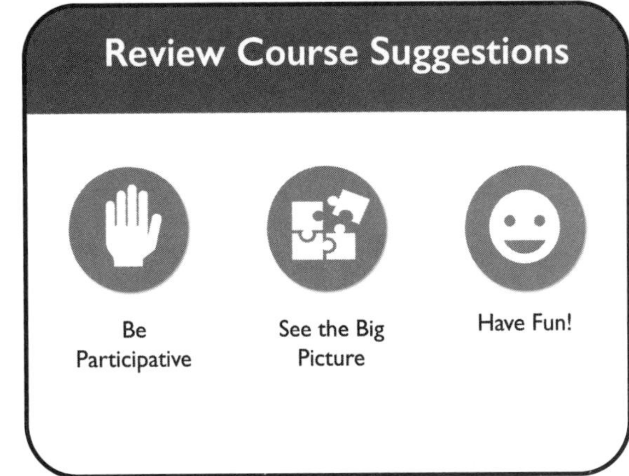
Review Course Suggestions
Be Participative
See the Big Picture
Have Fun!

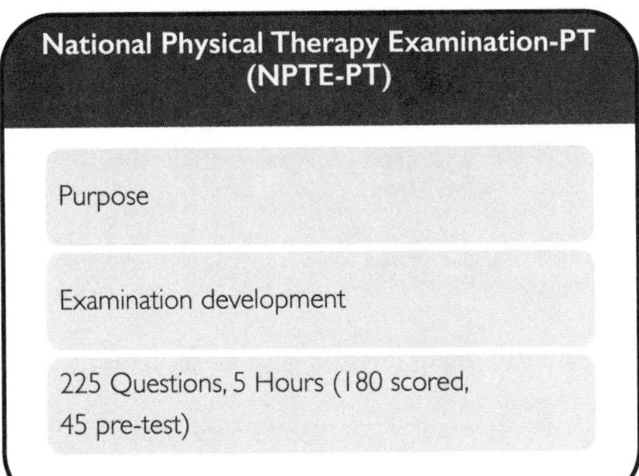
National Physical Therapy Examination-PT (NPTE-PT)
Purpose
Examination development
225 Questions, 5 Hours (180 scored, 45 pre-test)

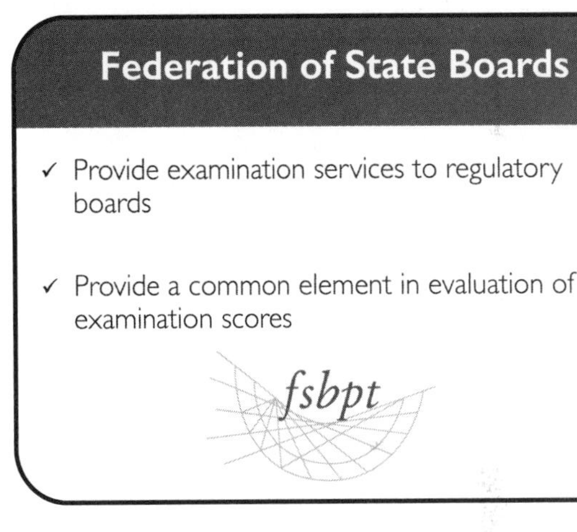
Federation of State Boards
✓ Provide examination services to regulatory boards
✓ Provide a common element in evaluation of examination scores
fsbpt

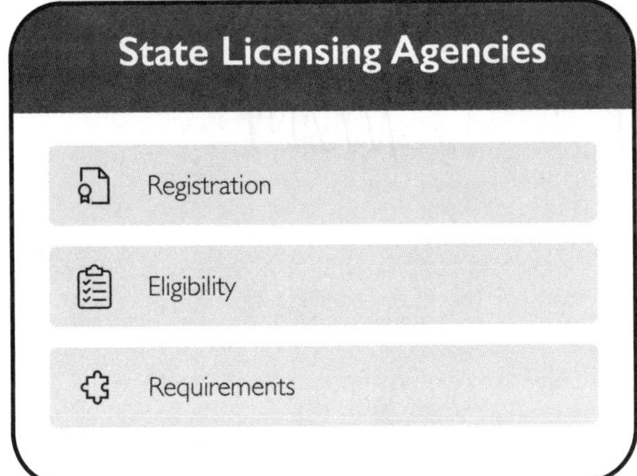
State Licensing Agencies
Registration
Eligibility
Requirements

FSBPT Fixed Date Testing

- ✓ Offered four sets of dates per year
- ✓ Administered at Prometric Centers

Challenges

- ✓ Need to conform to fixed date testing schedule
- ✓ Limited seat availability at selected Prometric Centers
- ✓ Eligibility for Approval to Test (ATT) status varies in some jurisdictions

Opportunities

- ✓ Testing schedule allows candidates to more definitively plan
- ✓ Intensity of studying can be modified based on selected fixed date

Important Deadlines

- ✓ NPTE-PT registration - Approximately 5 weeks before the fixed date
- ✓ Jurisdictional approval - No later than 7 days after the registration deadline
- ✓ Seats released - 21 days prior to the fixed date
- ✓ Scores reported - Approximately one week after the fixed date

Resources

- Candidate Handbook
- NPTE-PT Registration Process
- FSBPT Resources
- Physical Therapy Compact
- Prometric Availability

Recommendations

- ✓ Complete state application and register with FSBPT as soon as eligibility permits
- ✓ Secure an appointment at a Prometric Center immediately after receiving ATT status
- ✓ Select am or pm appointment based on individual preference

Fixed Date Testing Information and Resources

NPTE-PT Fixed Date Testing

2024: January 23/24, April 24/25, July 24/25, October 29/30
2025: January 28/29, April 29/30, July 29/30, October 28/29

Resources

Candidate Handbook

The handbook www.fsbpt.org/Free-Resources/NPTE-Candidate-Handbook offers a wide array of information on all aspects of becoming licensed as a physical therapist.

NPTE-PT Registration Process

Explore a broad overview of the NPTE-PT registration process www.pt.fsbpt.net/UserJourneyMap.

FSBPT Resources

A wide range of resources can be assessed through the FSBPT website www.fsbpt.org/Free-Resources.

Physical Therapy Compact

Stay up to date on the continually expanding Physical Therapy Compact www.ptcompact.org/.

Prometric Availability

Up to the minute seat availability can be accessed at www.prometric.com/fsbpt.

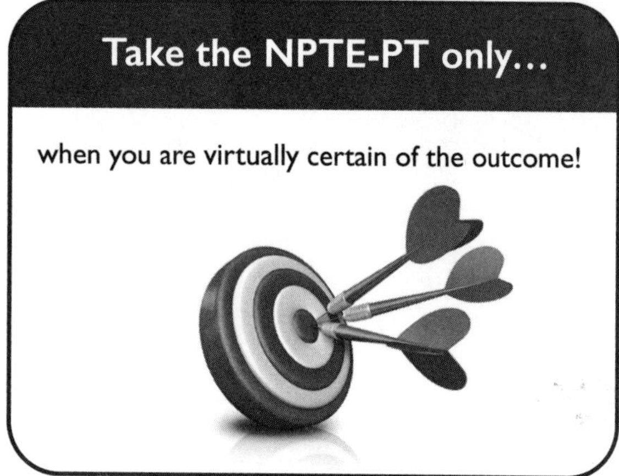
Take the NPTE-PT only...
when you are virtually certain of the outcome!

Take the time to celebrate passing the NPTE-PT!

Types of Questions

- Level 1
- Level 2
- Level 3

Level 1 - Core

✓ Level 1 questions require candidates to possess basic foundational academic knowledge.

✓ Remediation of Level 1 questions occurs through academic review of entry-level content through text books, review books, and flash cards.

10%

Level 2 - Synthesis

✓ Level 2 questions require candidates to integrate numerous pieces of information or to apply knowledge in a given clinical scenario.

✓ Remediation of Level 2 questions occurs by increasing flexibility with academic content and by carefully analyzing decision making processes when answering applied examination questions.

75-80%

Level 3 - Interpretation

✓ Level 3 questions require candidates to systematically analyze and often interpret information to determine an appropriate course of action. The questions tend to have some degree of subjectivity and candidates are required to assign varying degrees of importance to different variables.

✓ Remediation of Level 3 questions occurs by continuing to refine decision making processes when answering examination questions and differentiating between good, better, and best options.

10-15%

Item Requirements

- Items should not test straight memorization, but rather deductive reasoning
- The distracters (the other three answer options) must be plausible and attractive
- The item must be neither too easy nor too difficult

Scoring

- Based on the number of questions answered correctly
- Identify best answer
- No penalty associated with guessing
- Criterion-referenced
- Candidate performance

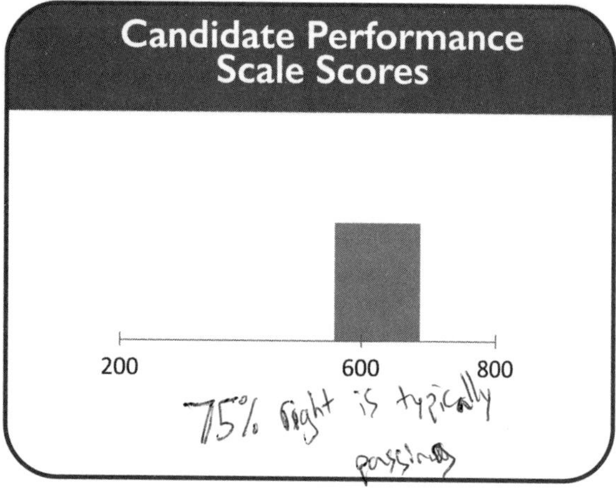
Candidate Performance Scale Scores
200
600
800
75% right is typically passing

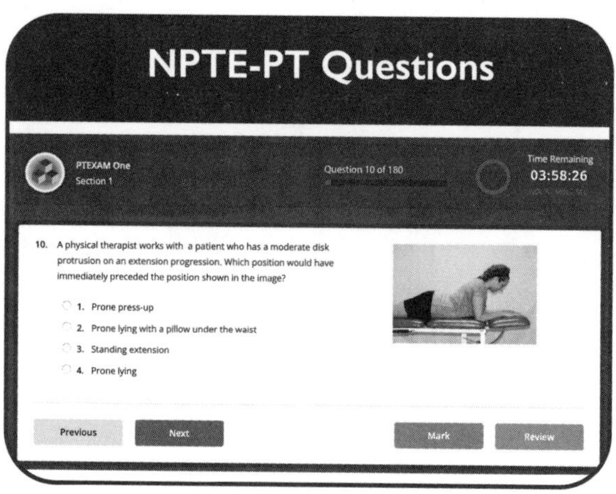
NPTE-PT Questions
PTEXAM One
Section 1
Question 10 of 180
Time Remaining
03:58:26
10. A physical therapist works with a patient who has a moderate disk protrusion on an extension progression. Which position would have immediately preceded the position shown in the image?
1. Prone press-up
2. Prone lying with a pillow under the waist
3. Standing extension
4. Prone lying
Previous
Next
Mark
Review

1st Time Candidates U.S. Accredited PT Programs

Content Outline: 2018-2023

Pass Rate
91%

1st Time Candidates U.S. Accredited PT Programs

Content Outline: 2024-2028

Pass Rate
?

FSBPT Security Agreement

"It is illegal and unethical to recall (memorize) and share questions that are on the NPTE-PT or to solicit questions that are on the NPTE-PT from candidates who have taken the examination."

Activity 1
Are You Ready to Rumble?

1. A physical therapist completing an entry in a medical record notices that a patient exercising independently in the gym is significantly deviating from the standard technique when using a piece of progressive resistive equipment. Assuming the therapist observing the patient is not the therapist of record, which of the following actions would be the **MOST** appropriate immediate response?

   ○ 1. Continue to observe the patient, but do not intervene
   ○ 2. Instruct the patient to stop the exercise and attempt to locate the patient's therapist
   ○ 3. Instruct the patient how to perform the exercise correctly
   ○ 4. Select an alternate progressive resistive exercise for the patient

○ Correct
○ Incorrect
☐ Academic
☐ Decision Making
☐ Test Taking

Level 3

2. A patient is informed that their condition is terminal shortly before a scheduled physical therapy session. During the session the patient asks the physical therapist if they believe the physician's assessment is accurate. What is the **MOST** appropriate therapist response?

   ○ 1. Physicians are not infallible
   ○ 2. Your present condition is serious
   ○ 3. Channel your energy towards getting better
   ○ 4. Focus on your therapy goals

○ Correct
○ Incorrect
☐ Academic
☐ Decision Making
☐ Test Taking

Level 3

3. A physical therapist examines a patient's subtalar range of motion. When goniometrically assessing subtalar range of motion, where should the moving arm of the goniometer be positioned?

   ○ 1. Over the posterior midline of the calcaneus
   ○ 2. Over the anterior aspect of the ankle midway between the malleoli
   ○ 3. Over the posterior aspect of the ankle between the malleoli
   ○ 4. Over the anterior midline of the second metatarsal

○ Correct
○ Incorrect
☐ Academic
☐ Decision Making
☐ Test Taking

Level 1

- ● Correct
- ○ Incorrect
  - ☐ Academic
  - ☐ Decision Making
  - ☐ Test Taking

Level 2

4. A physical therapist applies ultrasound at 1.3 W/cm^2 for 7 minutes to the posterior knee of a patient positioned in prone. The patient has diminished knee extension due to soft tissue shortening following an arthroscopic surgical procedure. If the goal is to improve knee extension range of motion, when should stretching of the knee occur?

○ 1. Immediately before the administration of ultrasound
○ 2. Immediately before and during the administration of ultrasound
○ 3. During the administration of ultrasound
○ 4. During and immediately after the administration of ultrasound

- ○ Correct
- ● Incorrect
  - ☐ Academic
  - ☒ Decision Making
  - ☐ Test Taking

Level 3

5. A physical therapist examines a seven-year-old child rehabilitating from injuries sustained in a motor vehicle accident. During the examination the mother mentions that her child often complains of sharp pain in the right leg. Which method would be the **MOST** appropriate to gain additional information on the child's pain?

○ 1. Ask the child to quantify their pain using a visual analogue pain scale
○ 2. Ask the child to describe the pain they are experiencing
○ 3. Ask the child to rate their pain on a subjective pain scale from 0-10
○ 4. Ask the mother to describe the exact location and severity of her child's pain

- ● Correct
- ○ Incorrect
  - ☐ Academic
  - ☐ Decision Making
  - ☐ Test Taking

Level 2

6. A patient that required a mechanical ventilator for two weeks following a near drowning incident is cleared to gradually decrease use of the device. Which measured value would indicate a sign of distress during the weaning process?

○ 1. Respiratory rate of 38 breaths per minute
○ 2. Tidal volume of 350 milliliters
○ 3. Pulse oximetry measured at 91 percent
○ 4. Heart rate change of 10 beats per minute over baseline

7. A physical therapist examines the medical record of a patient diagnosed with chronic obstructive pulmonary disease. The record contains the results of several lung volumes including inspiratory reserve volume and expiratory reserve volume. Which of the following additional measures is necessary in order to determine vital capacity?

- ○ 1. Inspiratory capacity
- ○ 2. Tidal volume
- ○ 3. Residual volume
- ○ 4. Total lung capacity

Spirogram, memorize how to draw chart

○ Correct
○ Incorrect
☐ Academic
☐ Decision Making
☐ Test Taking

Level 1

8. A physical therapist attempts to obtain information on a patient's response to exercise by assessing pulse rate immediately after an exercise session. Which of the following techniques would provide the therapist with the desired information?

- ○ 1. Determine the pulse rate using the brachial artery for 10 seconds and multiply by six
- ○ 2. Determine the pulse rate using the femoral artery for 15 seconds and multiply by four
- ○ 3. Determine the pulse rate using the radial artery for 30 seconds and multiply by two
- ○ 4. Determine the pulse rate using the carotid artery for 60 seconds

○ Correct
○ Incorrect
☐ Academic
☐ Decision Making
☐ Test Taking

Level 2

9. A physical therapist is treating a patient with a right transtibial amputation. When ambulating with a patellar-tendon bearing socket, the patient complains of discomfort on the patella. Which action is the **MOST** appropriate to decrease the patient's discomfort?

- ○ 1. Add a shoe lift to the left leg
- ○ 2. Add a one-ply sock to the residual limb and reapply the prosthesis
- ○ 3. Discontinue ambulation
- ○ 4. Place a piece of foam over the patella and reapply the prosthesis

○ Correct
○ Incorrect
☐ Academic
☐ Decision Making
☐ Test Taking

Level 2

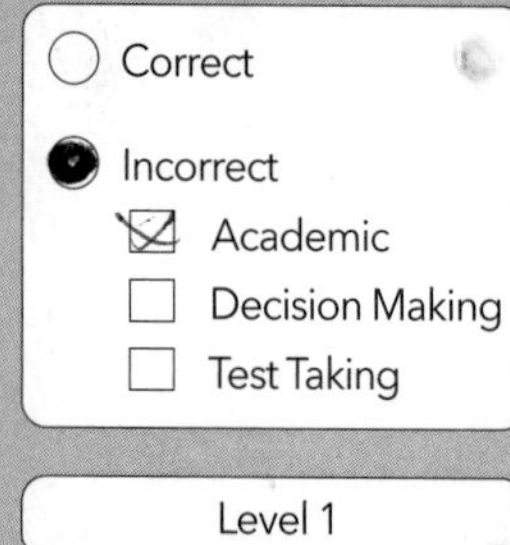
Correct
Incorrect
Academic
Decision Making
Test Taking

Level 1

10. A physical therapist employed in an acute care hospital is informed by a nurse that a Swan-Ganz catheter has recently been utilized on a patient status post cardiac surgery. What is the **PRIMARY** use of this type of catheter?

1. Monitor pulmonary artery pressure
2. Monitor intracranial pressure
3. Administer medication
4. Measure oxygen saturation of blood

PERFORMANCE ANALYSIS

Are You Ready to Rumble?

10 Questions
Time (10:00)

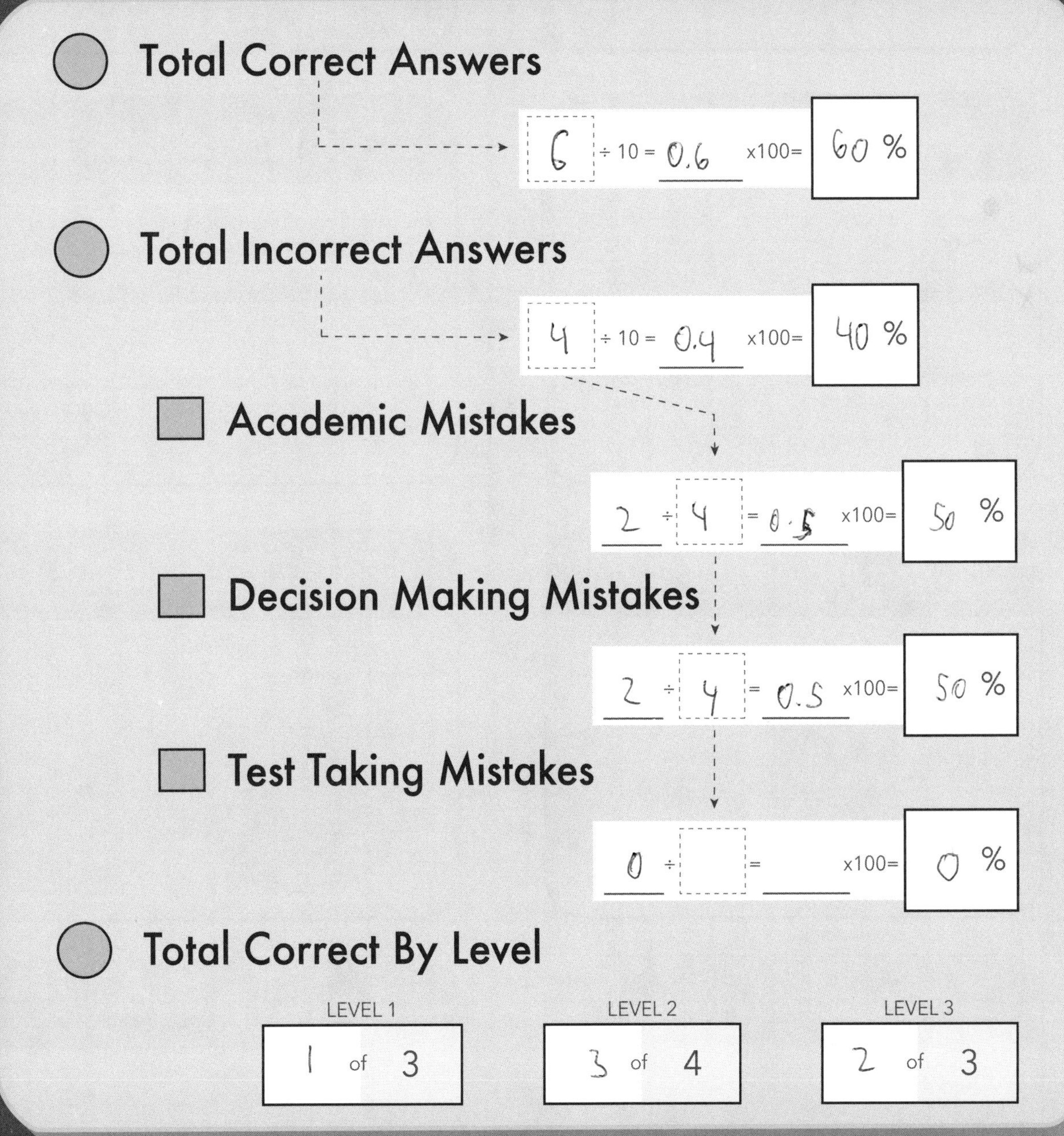

Total Correct Answers
6 ÷ 10 = 0.6 x100= 60 %
Total Incorrect Answers
4 ÷ 10 = 0.4 x100= 40 %
Academic Mistakes
2 ÷ 4 = 0.5 x100= 50 %
Decision Making Mistakes
2 ÷ 4 = 0.5 x100= 50 %
Test Taking Mistakes
0 ÷ = x100= 0 %
Total Correct By Level
LEVEL 1
1 of 3
LEVEL 2
3 of 4
LEVEL 3
2 of 3

"Some people will dream of success... While others will wake up and work hard."

— Anonymous

Sources to Improve Your Score

Academic

Decision Making

Test Taking

Academic Mistakes

- ✓ Characterized by insufficient academic knowledge to select the correct response
- ✓ Remediated by meticulous academic review of relevant physical therapy information
- ✓ Adequate breadth and depth is necessary to consistently answer applied questions

Decision Making Mistakes

- ✓ Characterized by an inability to select the correct response despite correctly comprehending the question and possessing the requisite academic knowledge
- ✓ Remediated by careful self assessment of individual tendencies (e.g., conservative, aggressive, inability to identify subtle nuances)

Test Taking Mistakes

- ✓ Characterized by a failure to select the correct response due to the inability to accurately analyze the actual question. Test taking mistakes occur despite sufficient academic knowledge and appropriate decision making
- ✓ Remediated by formal adoption of a task approach and addressing deficiencies in concentration and/or endurance

Incorrect Item Analysis - Early

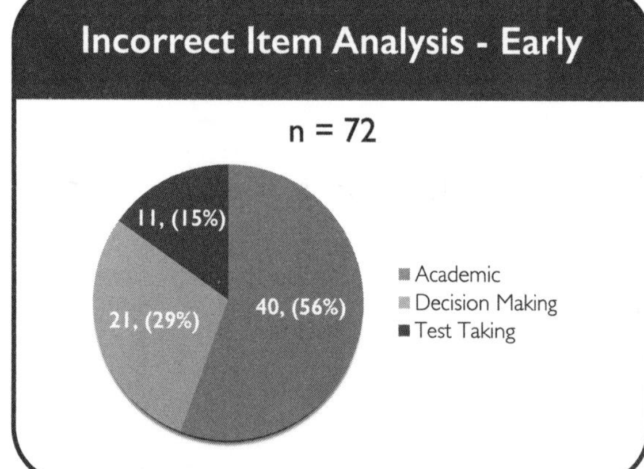

n = 72
40, (56%)
21, (29%)
11, (15%)
Academic
Decision Making
Test Taking

Incorrect Item Analysis - Late

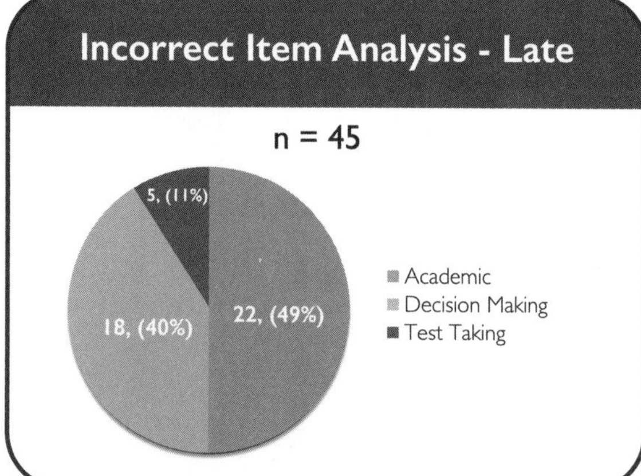

n = 45
22, (49%)
18, (40%)
5, (11%)
Academic
Decision Making
Test Taking

Incorrect Item Analysis

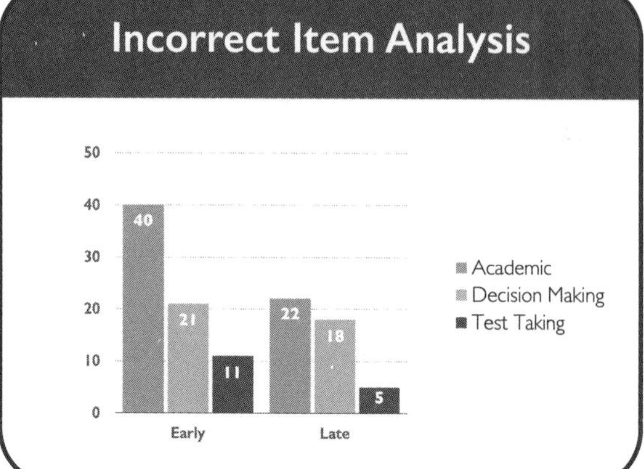

50
40
30
20
10
0
40
21
11
22
18
5
Early
Late
Academic
Decision Making
Test Taking

Special Services/Options

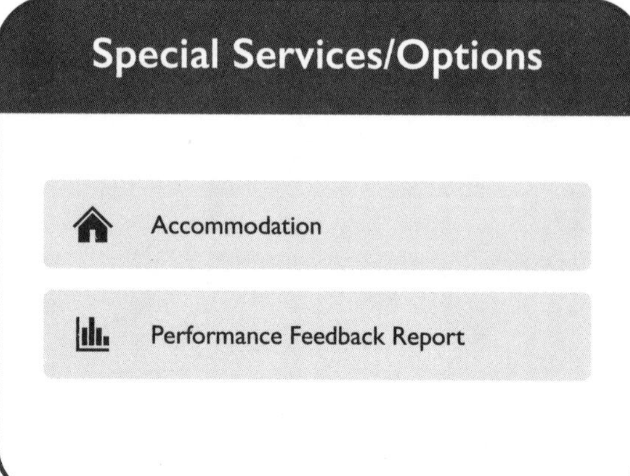

Accommodation
Performance Feedback Report

Multiple-Choice Questions

Components of a multiple-choice question

Item — An item refers to an individual multiple-choice question and the corresponding potential answers.

Stem — The stem refers to the statement that asks the question.

Options — Options refer to the potential answers to the question asked. One option in each item will be the "best answer" while the others are distracters.

Task Approach

1. Read the stem carefully to become familiar with the information and to determine the command words that indicate the desired action
2. Read the stem again and identify relevant words or groups of words based on the identified command words

   **Make sure you understand what the item is asking prior to moving to the next step*

3. Attempt to generate an answer to the stem
4. Examine each option completely before moving to the next option
5. Attempt to identify the best option

   *** Additional steps may not be necessary*

6. Utilize deductive reasoning strategies

> **Caution!** Deductive reasoning strategies can assist candidates to improve examination scores without direct knowledge of subject matter, however, should only be utilized when academic knowledge is not sufficient to answer an examination item.

Common Pitfalls

1. Failure to identify priority terms (e.g., first, least, initial, best)
2. Inability to identify selected information as extraneous
3. Tendency to answer a question based solely on an individual patient or a policy/procedure from a given clinical facility
4. Forming a premature conclusion prior to fully examining all of the presented information
5. Making basic questions unnecessarily complex
6. Demanding perfection and therefore experiencing unnecessary anxiety

Tips for Progressing through the Examination

1. Answer questions you are comfortable with first before dealing with more complex questions
2. Avoid spending too much time on any given question
3. If you do not know the answer to a given question attempt to identify answers that are incorrect

Activity 2
Back to Basics

Correct
Incorrect
Academic
Decision Making
Test Taking

Level 3

1. A physical therapist employed in an outpatient physical therapy clinic notices that a patient referred to a group exercise program for osteoarthritis has been slow to engage in group activities and often seems disinterested. Which therapist action would be the **MOST** immediate to increase the patient's level of participation?

   1. Continue to encourage the patient to participate
   2. Develop a reward program for the patient based on their level of participation
   3. Discuss the purpose of the program and the potential consequences of not participating with the patient
   4. Consult with the patient's referring physician

Correct
Incorrect
Academic
Decision Making
Test Taking

Level 2

2. A physical therapist examines a patient with a venous stasis ulcer. Which statement would be **MOST** consistent with the clinical presentation of this type of ulcer?

   1. Subjective reports of pain are diminished by dependency
   2. Pulses are absent in the immediate area of the ulcer
   3. Located on the lower leg, proximal to the medial malleolus
   4. Irregular edges with poor granulation tissue

Correct
Incorrect
Academic
Decision Making
Test Taking

Level 2

3. A physical therapist uses mechanical spinal traction to temporarily increase the size of the intervertebral foramen on a patient diagnosed with foraminal stenosis. Which of the following spinal positions would **BEST** accomplish the therapist's objective?

   1. Neutral and extension
   2. Neutral and flexion
   3. Extension and flexion
   4. Hyperextension and hyperflexion

Correct
Incorrect
Academic
Decision Making
Test Taking

Level 2

4. A physical therapist examines a patient with suspected temporomandibular joint dysfunction. The therapist believes that the patient's clinical presentation is consistent with an anterior disk dislocation that does not reduce during joint translation. Which finding is **MOST** characteristic of this scenario?

   1. Excessive crepitation during mouth opening and closing
   2. Restricted mouth opening
   3. Loud click or pop during mouth opening
   4. Constant pain

5. A physical therapist asks a physical therapist assistant to instruct an existing patient in ascending and descending the stairs with axillary crutches. During the training session the patient falls and fractures their hip. Which individual would be **MOST** liable for this incident?

- ○ 1. Referring physician
- ○ 2. Patient
- ● 3. Physical therapist
- ○ 4. Physical therapist assistant

○ Correct
● Incorrect
☐ Academic
☒ Decision Making
☐ Test Taking

Level 3

6. A physical therapist instructs a patient diagnosed with emphysema in pursed-lip breathing. What is the **PRIMARY** purpose of this intervention?

- ○ 1. Increase respiratory rate
- ● 2. Maintain open airways
- ○ 3. Normalize alveolar gas exchange
- ○ 4. Increase accessory muscle use

● Correct
○ Incorrect
☐ Academic
☐ Decision Making
☐ Test Taking

Level 1

7. A patient diagnosed with rheumatoid arthritis over ten years ago has visible deformities in their wrists and hands. The patient reports difficulty performing activities such as putting on the gas cap of their vehicle and turning the dial to start the washing machine. Assuming the patient is right handed, what range of motion limitation is **MOST** likely responsible for the patient's described functional limitations?

- ● 1. Wrist ulnar deviation
- ○ 2. Wrist radial deviation
- ○ 3. Wrist flexion
- ○ 4. Wrist extension

● Correct
○ Incorrect
☐ Academic
☐ Decision Making
☐ Test Taking

Level 3

8. A physical therapist completes an examination on a 28-year-old female recovering from an upper extremity fracture. During the examination the therapist identifies several objective findings that lead the therapist to believe the patient may be a victim of domestic abuse. What is the **MOST** appropriate initial action by the therapist?

- ○ 1. Report the findings to the local authorities
- ○ 2. Refer the patient to a counseling center
- ○ 3. Schedule a meeting with the woman and her spouse
- ● 4. Ask the patient about her current home life

● Correct
○ Incorrect
☐ Academic
☐ Decision Making
☐ Test Taking

Level 3

Correct
Incorrect
Academic
Decision Making
Test Taking

Level 2

9. A patient rehabilitating from a T2 spinal cord injury complains of a pounding headache and blurred vision while completing an exercise program in supine on a mat table. The patient is sweating profusely and has a pulse rate of 50 beats per minute. What is the **MOST** immediate physical therapist response?

1. Maintain the patient in a supine position and monitor blood pressure
2. Place the patient in an upright position and check the catheter
3. Document the subjective and objective information in the medical record
4. Contact the nursing staff to discuss the patient's condition

Correct
Incorrect
Academic
Decision Making
Test Taking

Level 1

10. A physical therapist performs suctioning on a patient in the medical intensive care unit. When is the **MOST** appropriate time to perform the actual suctioning?

1. While passing the catheter into the trachea
2. While the catheter is being withdrawn
3. When moving the catheter up and down
4. Prior to stimulating a cough

Correct
Incorrect
Academic
Decision Making
Test Taking

Level 3

11. A physical therapist assistant works with a patient rehabilitating from a medial meniscectomy. While observing the patient complete a leg press exercise, the assistant feels the patient is struggling more than usual and is concerned that the patient may alter their technique in an attempt to successfully complete the activity. Which of the following actions by the assistant would be the **MOST** appropriate?

1. Attempt to contact the supervising physical therapist to discuss the situation
2. Decrease the weight used on the leg press exercise
3. Decrease the number of sets for the leg press exercise
4. Discontinue the exercise session

Correct
Incorrect
Academic
Decision Making
Test Taking

Level 3

12. A female physical therapist prepares to examine an adult male diagnosed with spinal stenosis. During the examination the therapist decides that it may be prudent to have another individual in the treatment room prior to beginning a positional assessment of the patient's sacrum. Which individual is the **MOST** appropriate to witness the assessment activity?

1. Administrative assistant
2. Member of the patient's family
3. Physical therapy aide
4. Physical therapist

13. A physical therapist works on mobility training with a patient diagnosed with T2 paraplegia. Which of the following devices would serve as the patient's **PRIMARY** mode of mobility?

● 1. Manual wheelchair
○ 2. Power wheelchair
○ 3. Manual and power wheelchairs
○ 4. Wheelchair and knee-ankle-foot orthoses

● Correct
○ Incorrect
☐ Academic
☐ Decision Making
☐ Test Taking

Level 2

14. A patient recently diagnosed with terminal cancer discusses their future plans with a physical therapist. The patient indicates that if they dedicate themselves to a daily exercise program it will be possible to attend their grandson's college graduation next year. Which stage of death and dying is **BEST** characterized in this scenario?

○ 1. Denial
● 2. Bargaining
○ 3. Depression
○ 4. Acceptance

● Correct
○ Incorrect
☐ Academic
☐ Decision Making
☐ Test Taking

Level 2

15. A physical therapist utilizes a handheld neuromuscular electrical stimulation unit to treat a patient with disuse muscle atrophy of the quadriceps. After observing a series of muscle contractions, the therapist decides to alter the pulse rate and width. Which of the following actions should occur before altering the existing parameters?

○ 1. Reposition the electrodes on the quadriceps
○ 2. Obtain informed consent from the patient
○ 3. Check the strength of the battery
● 4. Decrease the intensity of the current

● Correct
○ Incorrect
☐ Academic
☐ Decision Making
☐ Test Taking

Level 2

16. A physical therapist observes a five-month-old infant in supine with their legs elevated and the hips positioned in hip flexion, abduction, and lateral rotation. Which observation would represent the **MOST** advanced volitional movement in this position?

○ 1. Reaching of the hand to the ipsilateral knee
● 2. Reaching of the hand to the ipsilateral foot
○ 3. Reaching of the hand to the contralateral knee
✓ 4. Reaching of the hand to the contralateral foot

○ Correct
● Incorrect
☐ Academic
☐ Decision Making
☒ Test Taking

Level 2

Correct
Incorrect
Academic
Decision Making
Test Taking

Level 2

17. A physical therapist treats a patient with Parkinson's disease. Based on the diagnosis, which intervention would be the **MOST** appropriate to include in the plan of care?

1. Small amplitude movements to increase motor control
2. Reaching activities utilizing a standing frame
3. External cues and feedback to improve arm swing during gait
4. Facilitation techniques to increase tone in the extremities

Correct
Incorrect
Academic
Decision Making
Test Taking

Level 1

18. A female patient recently diagnosed with an endocrine system disorder informs a physical therapist that their condition is seven times more common in females than it is in males. Which medical condition is **MOST** consistent with the described incidence?

1. Paget's disease
2. Addison's disease
3. Amyotrophic lateral sclerosis
4. Graves' disease

Correct
Incorrect
Academic
Decision Making
Test Taking

Level 3

19. A physical therapist records the blood pressure of a patient with their arm positioned above the level of the heart. What impact would this have on the obtained measurement in comparison to a more traditional measurement of blood pressure?

1. The obtained systolic and diastolic values would be higher
2. The obtained systolic and diastolic values would be lower
3. The obtained systolic value would be higher and the diastolic value would be lower
4. The obtained systolic value would be lower and the diastolic value would be higher

Correct
Incorrect
Academic
Decision Making
Test Taking

Level 1

20. A physical therapist decides to administer Spurling's test to a patient with suspected cervical spine pathology. As part of the testing procedure, the therapist applies compression with the head in an extended and rotated position. Which finding would be **MOST** indicative of a positive test in the described position?

1. Pain throughout the neck region
2. Radiating pain into the limb on the same side as the head rotation
3. Radiating pain into the limb on the opposite side as the head rotation
4. Radiating pain into both limbs

PERFORMANCE ANALYSIS

Back to Basics

20 Questions
Time (20:00)

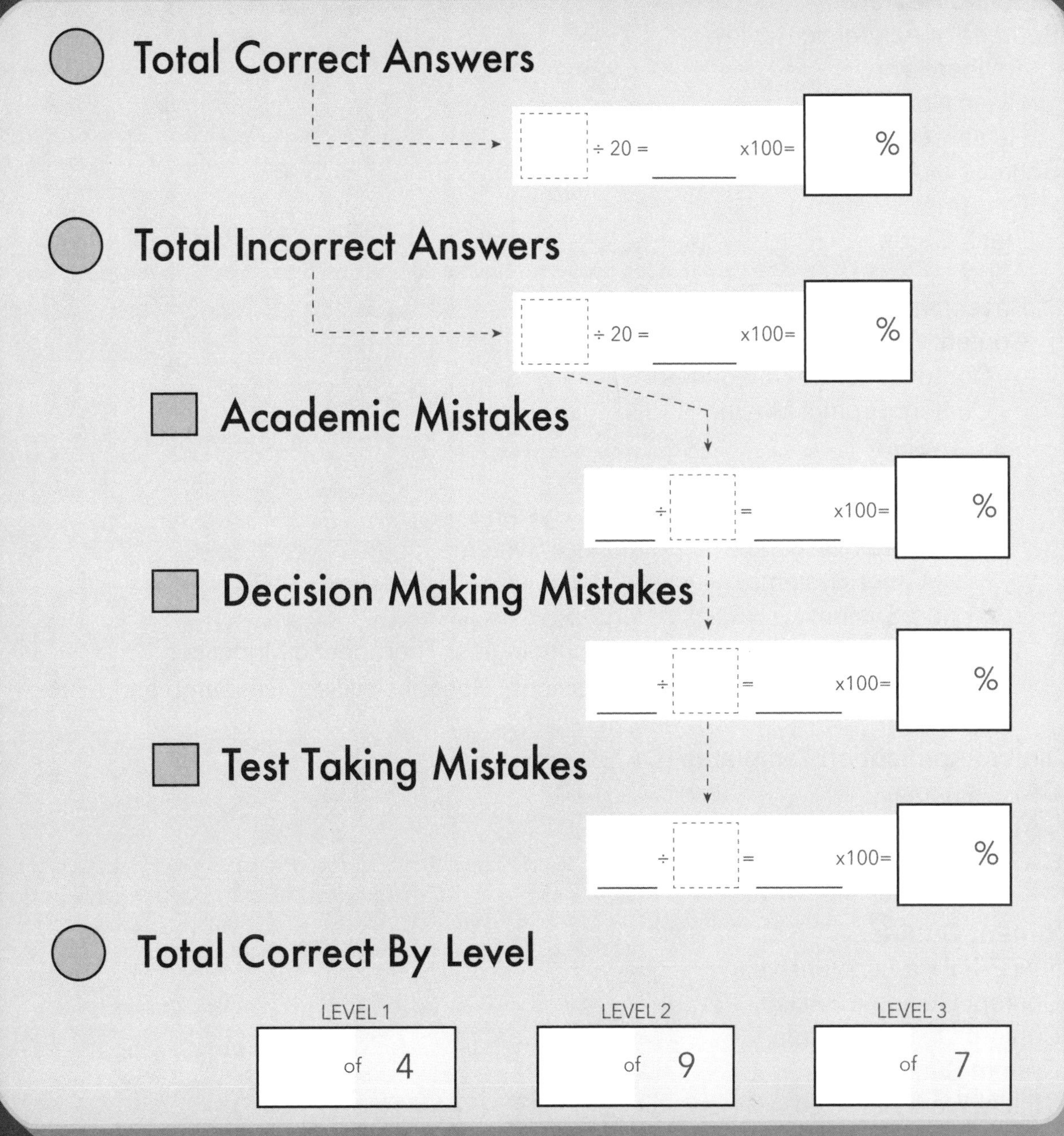

Total Correct Answers
÷ 20 =
x100=
%
Total Incorrect Answers
÷ 20 =
x100=
%
Academic Mistakes
÷
=
x100=
%
Decision Making Mistakes
÷
=
x100=
%
Test Taking Mistakes
÷
=
x100=
%
Total Correct By Level
LEVEL 1
of 4
LEVEL 2
of 9
LEVEL 3
of 7

"Everyone who got where he is had to begin where he was."

— Robert Louis Stevenson

THE BIG PICTURE

I. Sample Examinations

- Types of Questions
- Golden Rules
- Target Scores
- Resources

II. Academic Review

- Sources of Academic Review
  - Textbooks
  - Class Notes
  - Review Books
- Sources of Active Learning
  - Classmates
  - Flash Cards
  - Apps
  - Basecamp
  - Content Prompts
    - Content Prompt Categories
    - Content Prompt Master
      - System
        - Musculoskeletal System
        - Neuromuscular and Nervous Systems
        - Cardiovascular and Pulmonary Systems
        - Other Systems
      - Non-System
        - Equipment, Devices, and Technologies; Therapeutic Modalities
        - Safety and Protection; Professional Responsibilities; Research and EBP

III. Clinical Application Templates (CAT)

- CAT Diagnoses
- CAT Masters
- CAT Samples

IV. Content Outline

- NPTE-PT Practice Analysis
- Content Outline Exercise
- Content Outline Summary
- System Summary
- Critical Work Activities

V. Study Plan

- Building a Study Plan
- Sample Study Plans

VI. Challenges and Solutions

Sample Examinations

Assess... Assess... Assess

Sample Examinations are active assessment activities designed to determine the relative mastery of a candidate using multiple-choice questions.

Sample Examinations allow candidates to:

- Identify strengths and weaknesses in system specific and content outline areas
- Assess time management skills on full length sample examinations
- Compare performance of sample examination scores versus established target scores
- Determine current portfolio of mistakes (i.e., academic, decision making, test taking)

Sample Examinations

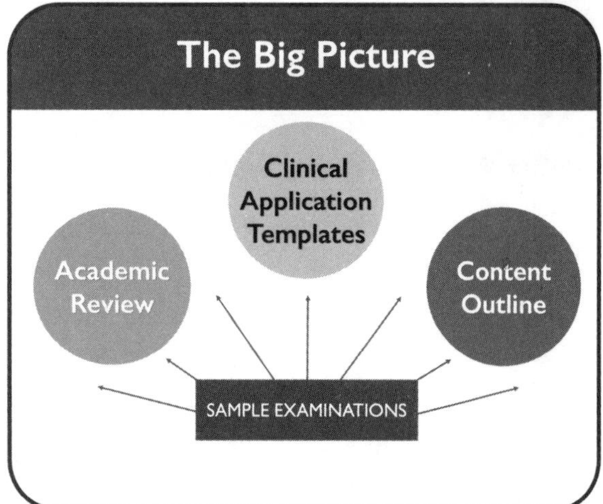
The Big Picture
Clinical Application Templates
Academic Review
Content Outline
SAMPLE EXAMINATIONS

Sample Examinations

Full length, single sitting examinations

- strengths and weaknesses
- time management skills
- score in relation to target score
- areas of mistakes (academic, decision making, test taking)

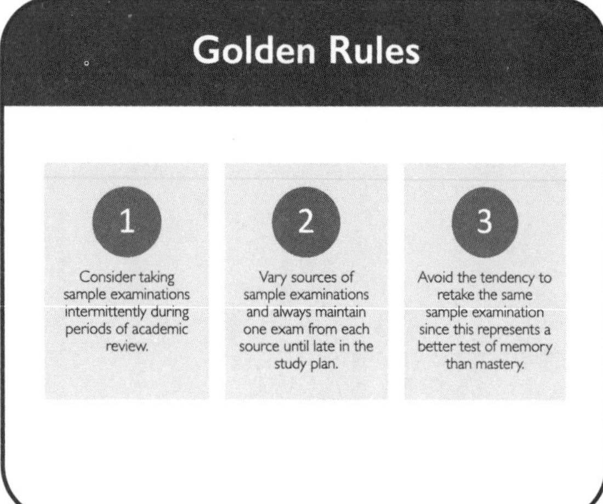
Golden Rules
1
Consider taking sample examinations intermittently during periods of academic review.
2
Vary sources of sample examinations and always maintain one exam from each source until late in the study plan.
3
Avoid the tendency to retake the same sample examination since this represents a better test of memory than mastery.

Target Scores

Goal: Meet or Exceed Target Scores

- ✓ Establishing target scores provides candidates with a general sense of the relative difficulty of different sample examinations.
- ✓ Candidates should attempt to consistently meet or exceed established target scores with multiple sources of sample examinations.
- ✓ Consistently achieving target scores using multiple sources increases the probability that a candidate will pass the NPTE-PT.

Warning!

- A decision to take the NPTE-PT should always be based on a variety of quantitative and qualitative data.
- Candidates must resist the urge to take the NPTE-PT until they are virtually certain of the outcome.

PTEXAM: The Complete Study Guide

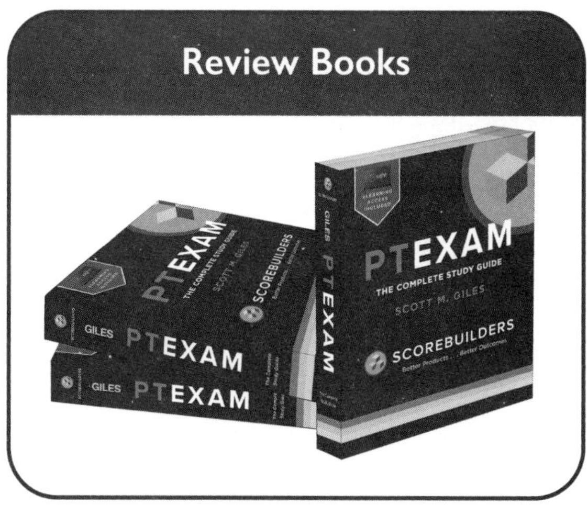
Review Books
PTEXAM
THE COMPLETE STUDY GUIDE
SCOTT M. GILES
SCOREBUILDERS
GILES PTEXAM

Type of Resource: Review book
Author: Scott Giles PT, DPT, MBA
Company: Scorebuilders

20% discount for course attendees
Learn more on our website!

Features

- Comprehensive academic review with full color and hundreds of images.
- Active learning activities including chapter essentials and proficiency exercises.
- Three full-length examinations updated for the 2024 blueprint with expansive explanation of answers and cited resources for the correct and incorrect options.
- Video discussions compare and contrast good, better, and best options for selected examination questions.
- Edition Guarantee provides students with formal updates through the "What's New!" section of our eLearning site - **Insight**.

Target Score

Greater than or equal to 130 on each of the three examinations

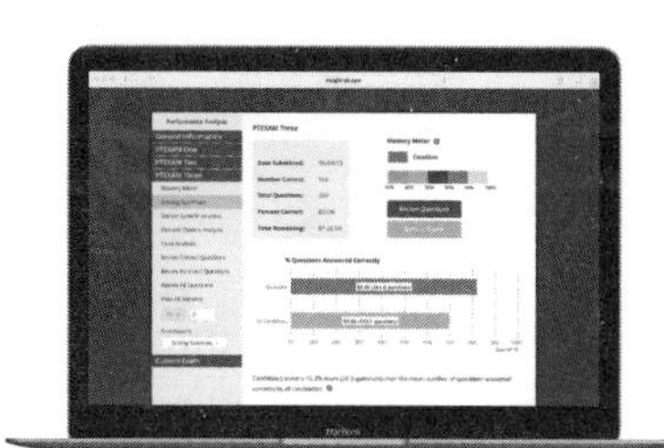

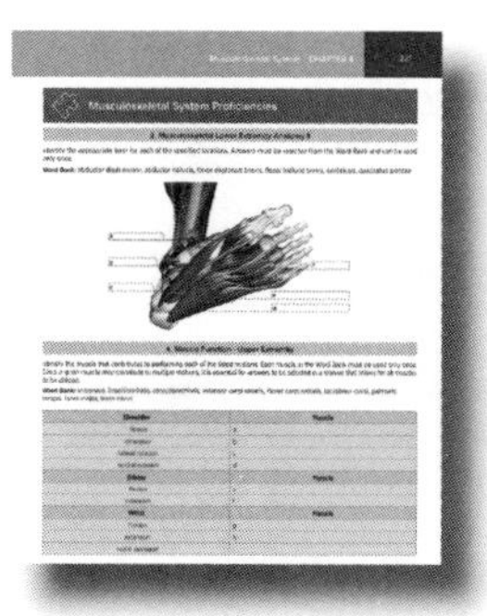

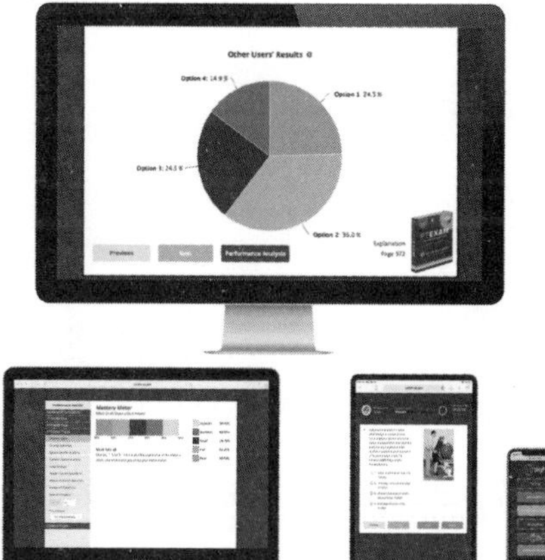

insight

What's New!

Online Advantage - Student Version

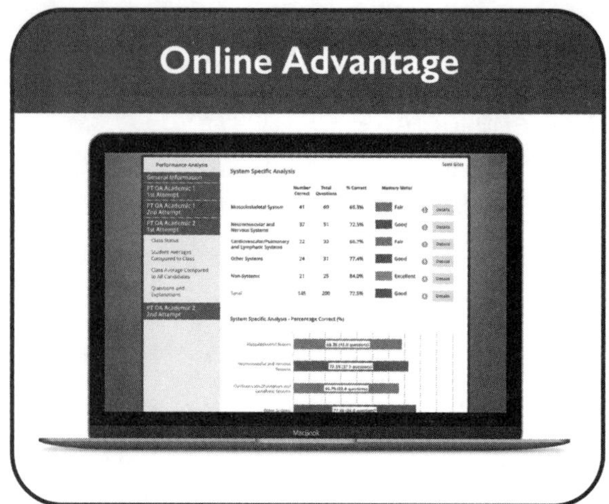
Online Advantage

Type of Resource: Web-based exams
Authors: 20 invited contributors
Company: Scorebuilders

20% discount for course attendees
Learn more on our website!

An ideal test drive prior to the NPTE-PT! The questions utilized in Online Advantage are different than questions utilized in other Scorebuilders' products, including Online Advantage - Academic Version.

Features

- Full-length web-based exams weighted to the exact exam blueprint specifications.
- Multiple-choice questions reflective of the difficulty level of the actual exam with explanation of answers.
- Sophisticated performance analysis generates summary reports that identify both areas of strength and weakness.
- Leaderboards, academic focus areas, and item analysis assist students to identify appropriate remedial activities.

Target Score

Greater than or equal to the mean for each of the two examinations

LEADERBOARD
RANK
#321 of 2,899
% RANK
88.9%
System Specific Leaderboard
ONLINE
ADVANTAGE

PEAT - Practice Exam and Assessment Tool

fsbpt

Type of Resource: Web-based exams
Company: Federation of State Boards of Physical Therapy

Learn more on the FSBPT's website.

Features

- Two exams utilizing the same format as the actual exam.
- Performance report by system areas and content areas.

Target Score

Specified on each performance report

FUN FACT:

The typical student preparing for the NPTE-PT takes between **5** and **9** full-length sample examinations using **3** or **4** unique sources.

Academic Review

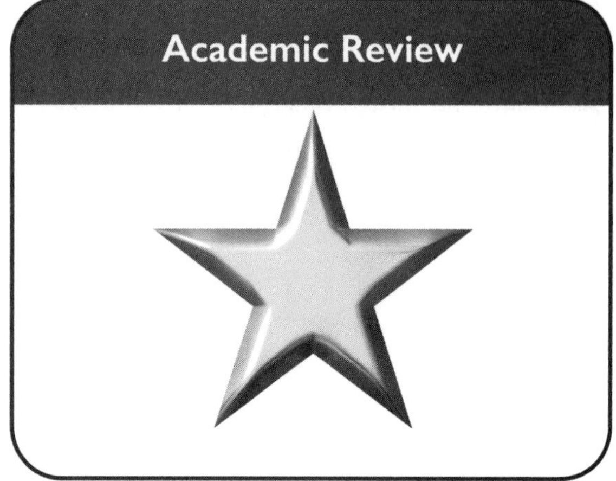
Academic Review

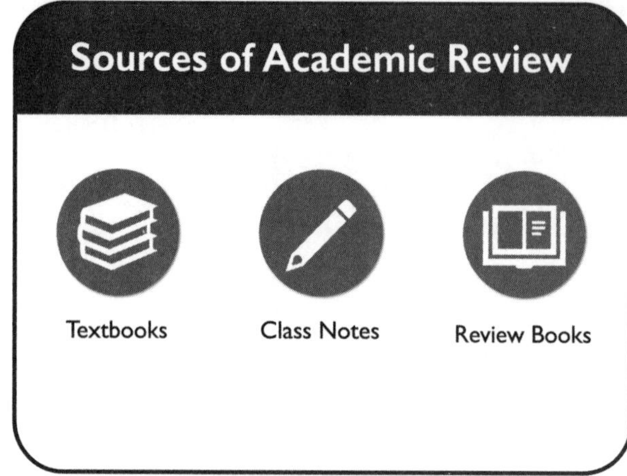
Sources of Academic Review
Textbooks
Class Notes
Review Books

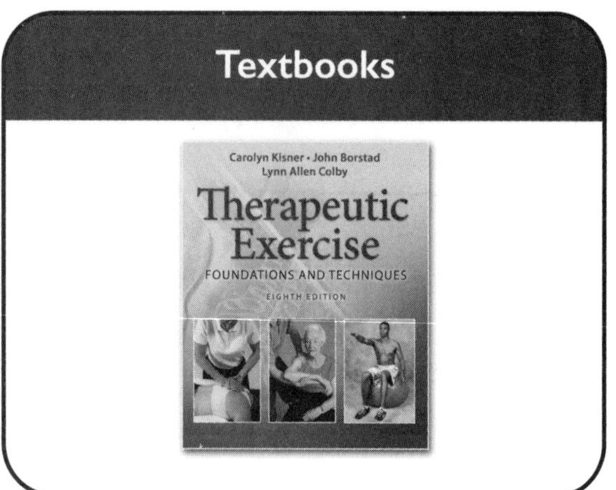
Textbooks
Carolyn Kisner • John Borstad
Lynn Allen Colby
Therapeutic Exercise
FOUNDATIONS AND TECHNIQUES
EIGHTH EDITION

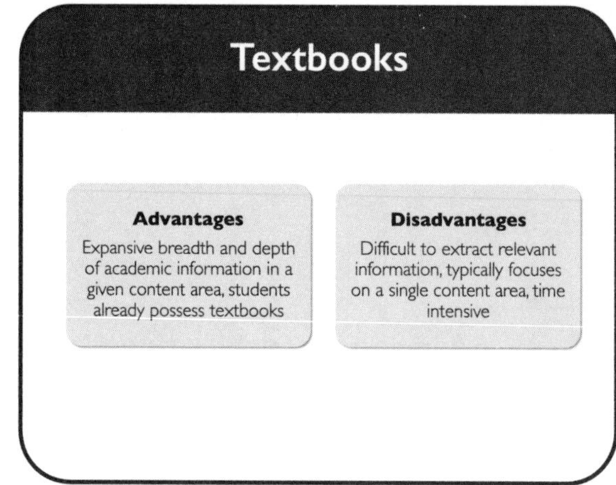
Textbooks
Advantages
Expansive breadth and depth of academic information in a given content area, students already possess textbooks
Disadvantages
Difficult to extract relevant information, typically focuses on a single content area, time intensive

Class Notes

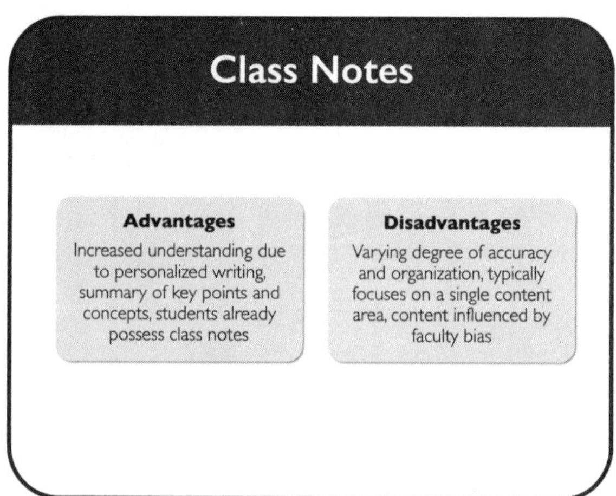
Class Notes
Advantages
Increased understanding due to personalized writing, summary of key points and concepts, students already possess class notes
Disadvantages
Varying degree of accuracy and organization, typically focuses on a single content area, content influenced by faculty bias

Review Books

PTEXAM
THE COMPLETE STUDY GUIDE
SCOTT M. GILES
SCOREBUILDERS
GILES PTEXAM
GILES PTEXAM

Review Books

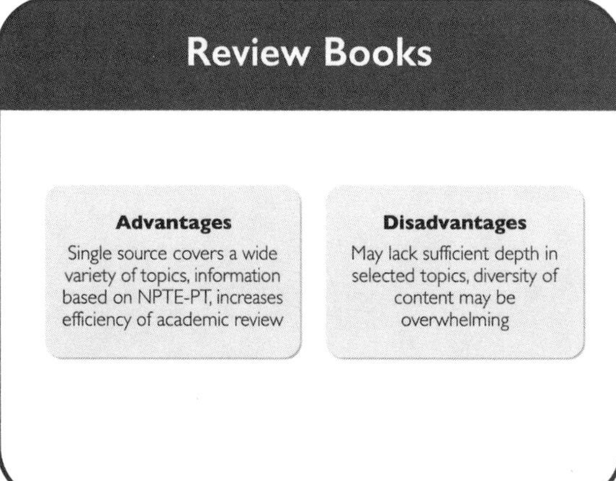

Advantages

Single source covers a wide variety of topics, information based on NPTE-PT, increases efficiency of academic review

Disadvantages

May lack sufficient depth in selected topics, diversity of content may be overwhelming

Passive Learning

Traditional sources of academic review (i.e., textbooks, class notes, review books) promote passive learning.

Passive and Active Learning

Passive Learning + Active Learning = Increased ROI

ROI = Return on Investment

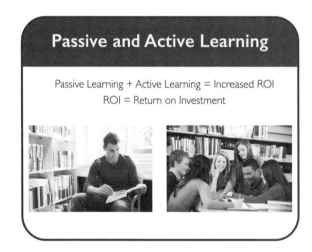

Sources of Active Learning

- Classmates
- Flash Cards
- Apps
- Basecamp
- Content Prompts

Classmates

Classmates

Advantages

Common goal, different strengths and weaknesses, unique clinical education experiences, familiarity with study partners, increased accountability

Disadvantages

Schedule and geographic constraints, requires preplanning and structured study sessions, social distractions

Flash Cards

Flash Cards

Individually created or commercially produced flash cards assist candidates to improve their command of core academic content.

Advantages

Increased understanding due to personalized writing, summary of key points and concepts

Disadvantages

May lack appropriate level of breadth and depth, varying degree of accuracy and organization

Apps

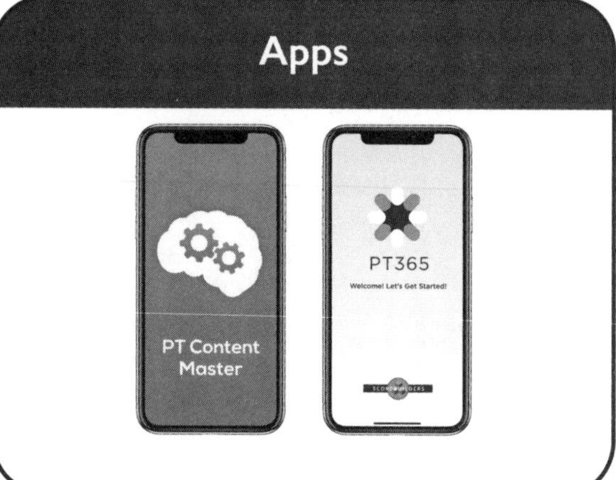
PT Content Master
PT365
Welcome! Let's Get Started!

Apps

Mobile devices that are capable of running interactive applications designed for physical therapists.

Advantages

Portable devices provide convenient access, interactive platform promotes frequent use, enhances use of multiple learning channels

Disadvantages

Limited access to specific technology for some students

PT Content Master - Flash Cards

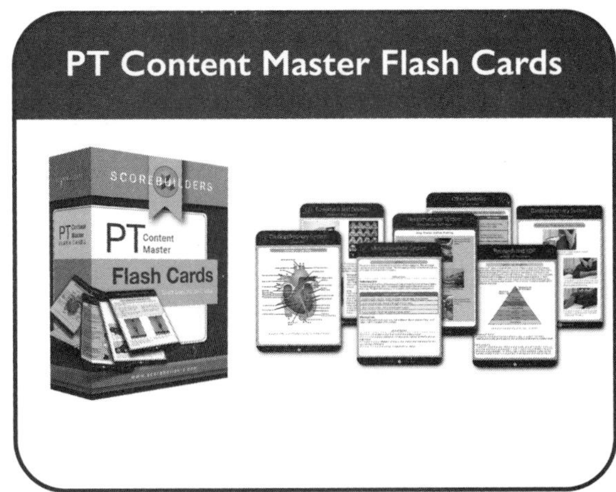
PT Content Master Flash Cards
SCOREBUILDERS
PT Content Master
Flash Cards

Type of Resource: Flash Cards
Author: Scott Giles PT, DPT, MBA
Company: Scorebuilders
Cards: 200 double-sided cards

20% discount for course attendees
Learn more on our website!

Features

- 200 double-sided flash cards covering essential physical therapy academic content.
- Vibrant colors and visually pleasing layouts make the flash cards an ideal method to review academic content.
- The cards are organized into nine unique categories: Musculoskeletal System; Neuromuscular and Nervous Systems; Cardiovascular/Pulmonary and Lymphatic Systems; Other Systems; Equipment and Devices; Therapeutic Modalities; Safety and Professional Roles; Teaching and Learning; and Research and Evidence-Based Practice.

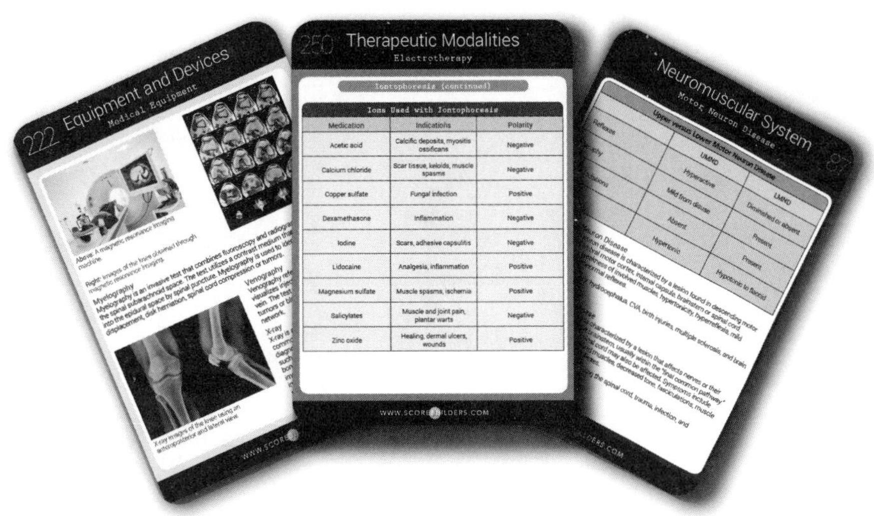
222 Equipment and Devices
Medical Equipment
250 Therapeutic Modalities
Electrotherapy
Iontophoresis (continued)
Ions Used with Iontophoresis
Medication
Indications
Polarity
Acetic acid
Calcific deposits, myositis ossificans
Negative
Calcium chloride
Scar tissue, keloids, muscle spasms
Negative
Copper sulfate
Fungal infection
Positive
Dexamethasone
Inflammation
Negative
Iodine
Scars, adhesive capsulitis
Negative
Lidocaine
Analgesia, inflammation
Positive
Magnesium sulfate
Muscle spasms, ischemia
Positive
Salicylates
Muscle and joint pain, plantar warts
Negative
Zinc oxide
Healing, dermal ulcers, wounds
Positive
WWW.SCOREBUILDERS.COM
Neuromuscular System
Motor Neuron Disease

Physical Therapy Content Master - App

PT Content Master App
PT Content Master

Type of Resource: Apple/Android App
Author: Scott Giles PT, DPT, MBA
Company: Scorebuilders

Learn more on our website!

Features

- Content review mode explores academic content in nine unique systems and non-systems categories. Candidates can scroll through menus in each category and select academic areas requiring remediation.
- Assessment mode consists of 750 multiple-choice questions designed to assess a candidate's level of mastery with the information presented in the content review mode. Candidates receive a formal score report detailing their performance in each category.

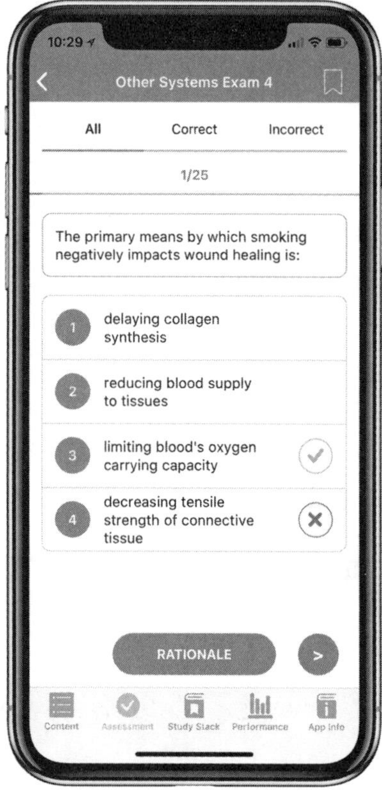
10:29
Other Systems Exam 4
All
Correct
Incorrect
1/25
The primary means by which smoking negatively impacts wound healing is:
1 delaying collagen synthesis
2 reducing blood supply to tissues
3 limiting blood's oxygen carrying capacity
4 decreasing tensile strength of connective tissue
RATIONALE
Content
Assessment
Study Stack
Performance
App Info

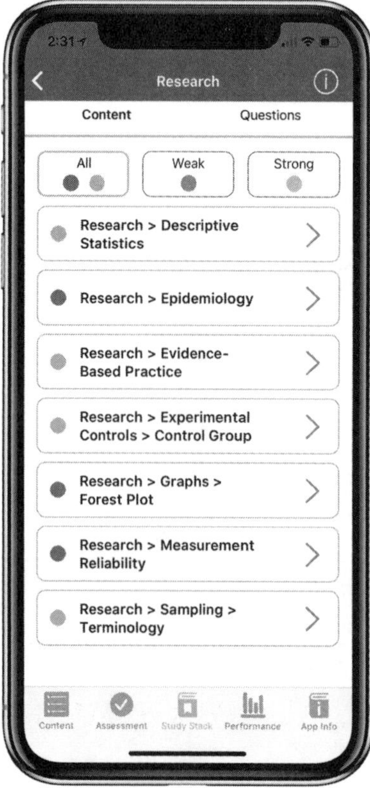
2:31
Research
Content
Questions
All
Weak
Strong
Research > Descriptive Statistics
Research > Epidemiology
Research > Evidence-Based Practice
Research > Experimental Controls > Control Group
Research > Graphs > Forest Plot
Research > Measurement Reliability
Research > Sampling > Terminology
Content
Assessment
Study Stack
Performance
App Info

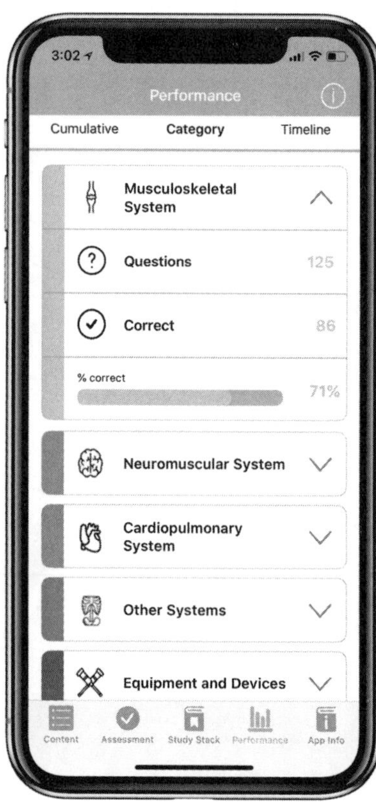
3:02
Performance
Cumulative
Category
Timeline
Musculoskeletal System
Questions 125
Correct 86
% correct 71%
Neuromuscular System
Cardiopulmonary System
Other Systems
Equipment and Devices
Content
Assessment
Study Stack
Performance
App Info

PT365 - App

PT365 App
PT365
Your Daily PT Vitamin!

Type of Resource: Apple/Android App
Author: Scott Giles PT, DPT, MBA
Company: Scorebuilders
Price: Free!

Learn more on our website!

Features

- App provides users with a unique daily opportunity to assess their mastery of essential physical therapy content through multiple-choice questions.
- App provides users with a method to track their individual performance over time and to compare their results to the relative performance of other users.
- Complete explanation of both correct and incorrect options is offered for all questions.

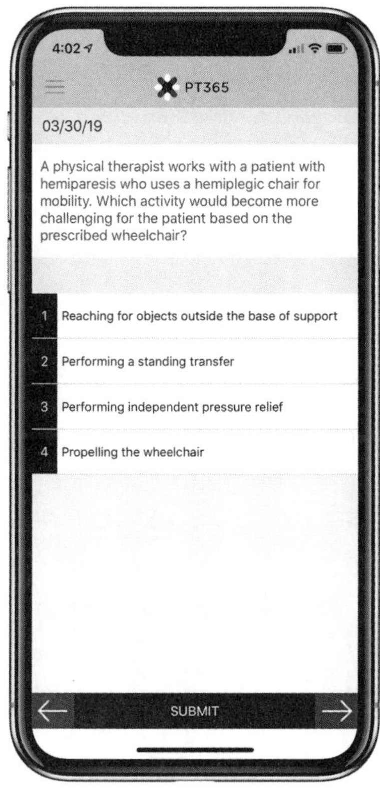
4:02
PT365
03/30/19
A physical therapist works with a patient with hemiparesis who uses a hemiplegic chair for mobility. Which activity would become more challenging for the patient based on the prescribed wheelchair?
1 Reaching for objects outside the base of support
2 Performing a standing transfer
3 Performing independent pressure relief
4 Propelling the wheelchair
SUBMIT

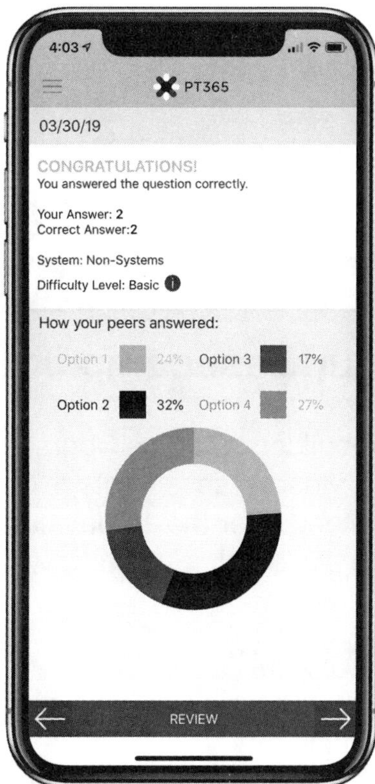
4:03
PT365
03/30/19
CONGRATULATIONS!
You answered the question correctly.
Your Answer: 2
Correct Answer:2
System: Non-Systems
Difficulty Level: Basic
How your peers answered:
Option 1 24% Option 3 17%
Option 2 32% Option 4 27%
REVIEW

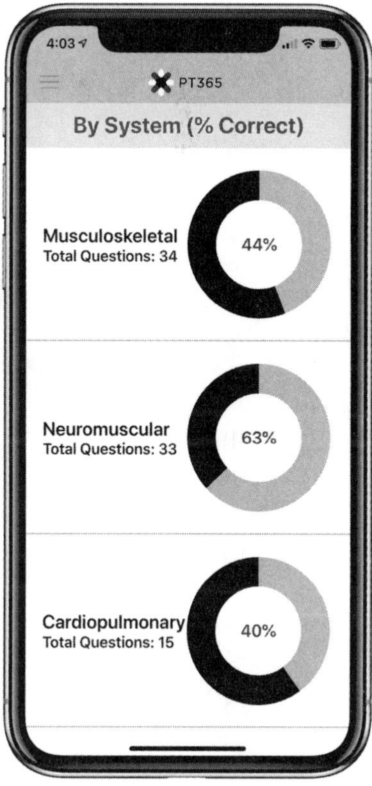
4:03
PT365
By System (% Correct)
Musculoskeletal
Total Questions: 34
44%
Neuromuscular
Total Questions: 33
63%
Cardiopulmonary
Total Questions: 15
40%

Basecamp - Academic Review

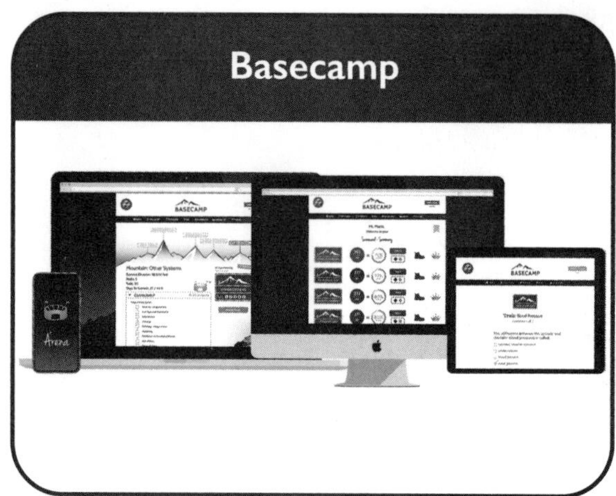
Basecamp

Type of Resource: Web-based Academic Tool
Author: Scott Giles PT, DPT, MBA
Company: Scorebuilders

15 days FREE access with your course manual; Extension options available at a 20% discount

Learn more on our website!

Features

- Assignments to promote mastery of core academic content.
- 140 assessment videos (over 50 hours).
- Thousands of flash cards to review your knowledge.
- 6,000 content driven questions with explanations.
- Competitive games allow students to compete against classmates.
- Interactive calendar tracks progress.
- Sophisticated scorecard section summarizes performance.
- Free access to the Basecamp Arena app.

RECEIVE FREE BASECAMP ACCESS!

Start Your Basecamp Journey Today!

All students attending a Scorebuilders' Review Course receive 15 days of **FREE** Basecamp access. Use the assignments, video assessments, exams, and flash cards to enhance your mastery of core academic content. After the 15 days, students can purchase extensions using their 20% review course discount!

Assignments

Flash Cards

Videos

A+

Exams

GETTING STARTED WITH BASECAMP

MUSCULOSKELETAL
Peaks: 1 2 3 4 5

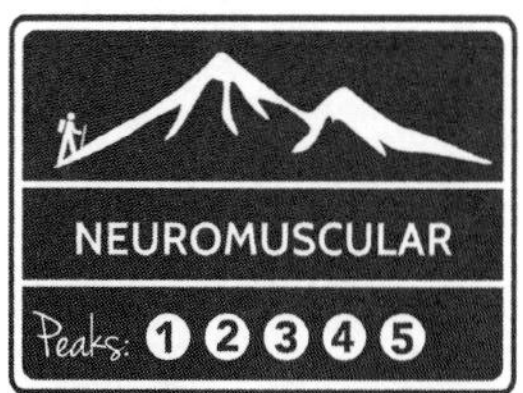
NEUROMUSCULAR
Peaks: 1 2 3 4 5

CARDIOPULMONARY
Peaks: 1 2 3 4 5

OTHER SYSTEMS
Peaks: 1 2 3 4 5

NON-SYSTEMS
Peaks: 1 2 3 4 5

BASECAMP takes students on a journey through five Mountains (Musculoskeletal, Neuromuscular, Cardiopulmonary, Other Systems, Non-Systems) and 140 Trails (e.g., Special Tests, Cardiac - Pathology, Motor Learning, Research Concepts). Each Trail integrates specific assignments from our best-selling review book **PTEXAM: The Complete Study Guide**. Students have the opportunity to assess their trail mastery by watching videos and answering multiple-choice questions. Collectively, **BASECAMP** includes over 50 hours of videos, thousands of flash cards, and 6,000 questions. The **Basecamp Arena app** provides students with a unique mobile experience where they can spontaneously connect and compete with friends while mastering educational content.

Sophisticated Fun!

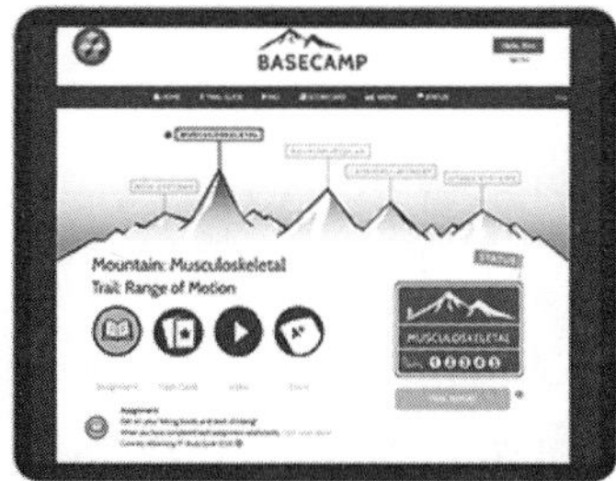
BASECAMP
Mountain: Musculoskeletal
Trail: Range of Motion

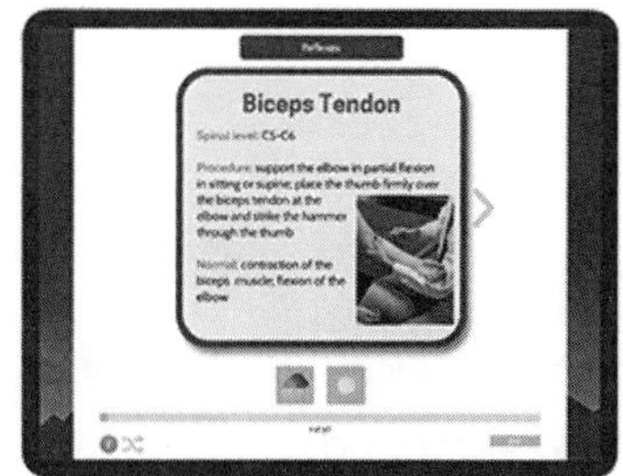
Biceps Tendon

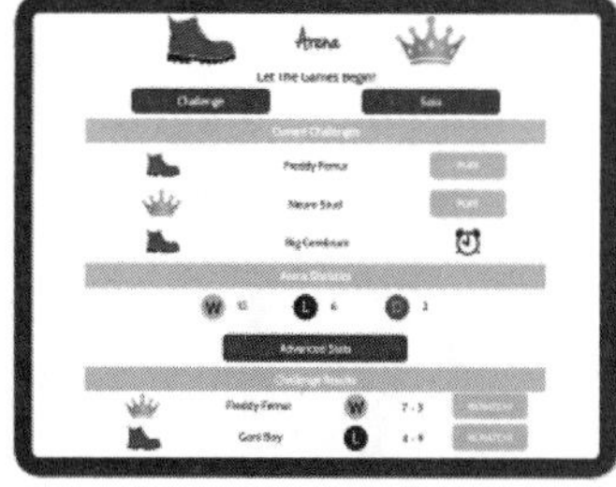

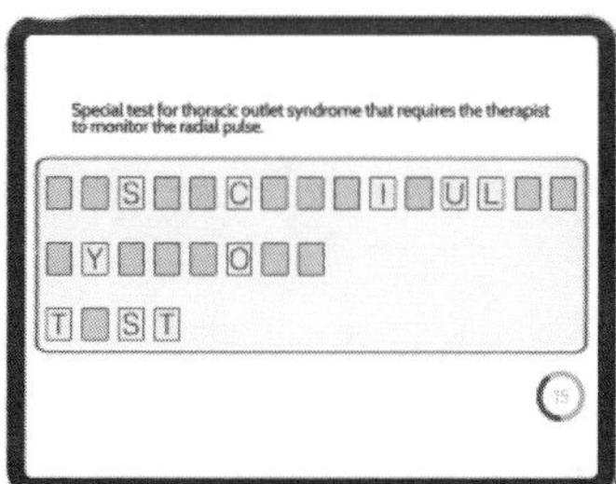
Special test for thoracic outlet syndrome that requires the therapist to monitor the radial pulse.

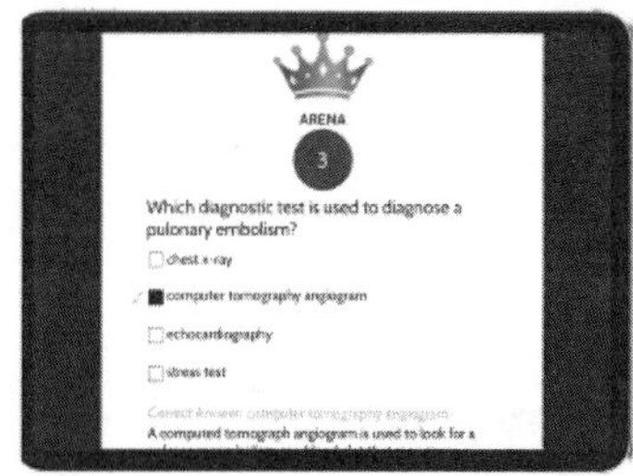
ARENA
Which diagnostic test is used to diagnose a pulonary embolism?

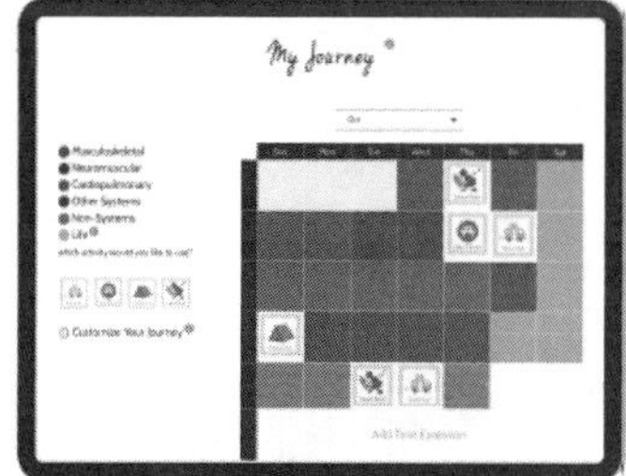
My Journey

Start Climbing!

Mastery of critical core academic content allows students to quickly progress to the higher level decision-making and analysis skills required to be successful on the National Physical Therapy Examination (NPTE-PT)!

Content Prompts

On the Road to Mastery!

Content Prompts allow candidates to determine if they possess talking knowledge of relevant academic content in system and non-system areas.

Content Prompts assist candidates to:

- Promote increased breadth and depth of core academic content
- Establish a reinforcing loop for previously reviewed academic content
- Discover potentially relevant academic content not previously reviewed
- Increase flexibility applying academic content in unique scenarios

Content Prompts

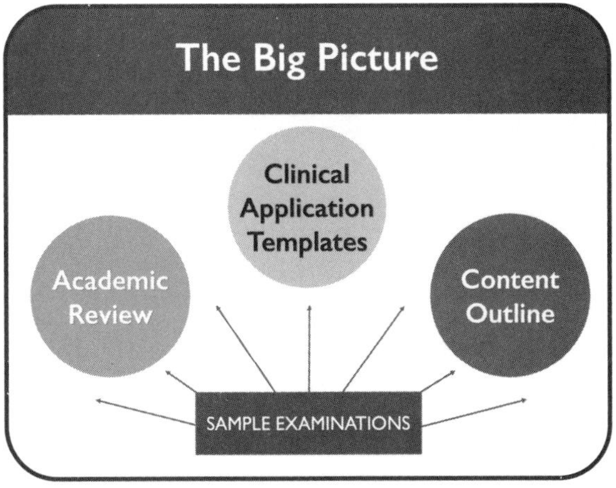

The Big Picture
Clinical Application Templates
Academic Review
Content Outline
SAMPLE EXAMINATIONS

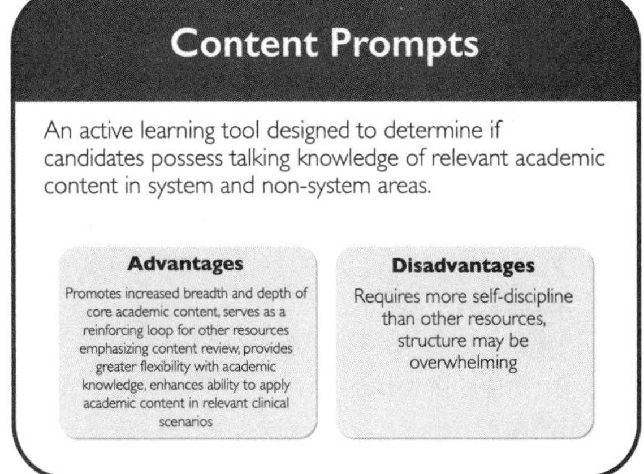

Content Prompts
An active learning tool designed to determine if candidates possess talking knowledge of relevant academic content in system and non-system areas.
Advantages
Promotes increased breadth and depth of core academic content, serves as a reinforcing loop for other resources emphasizing content review, provides greater flexibility with academic knowledge, enhances ability to apply academic content in relevant clinical scenarios
Disadvantages
Requires more self-discipline than other resources, structure may be overwhelming

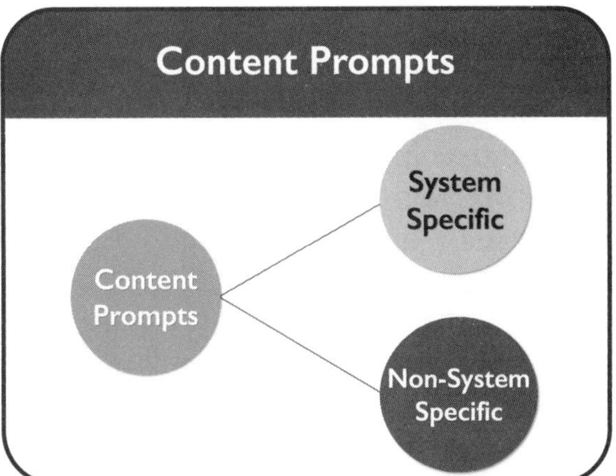

Content Prompts
Content Prompts
System Specific
Non-System Specific

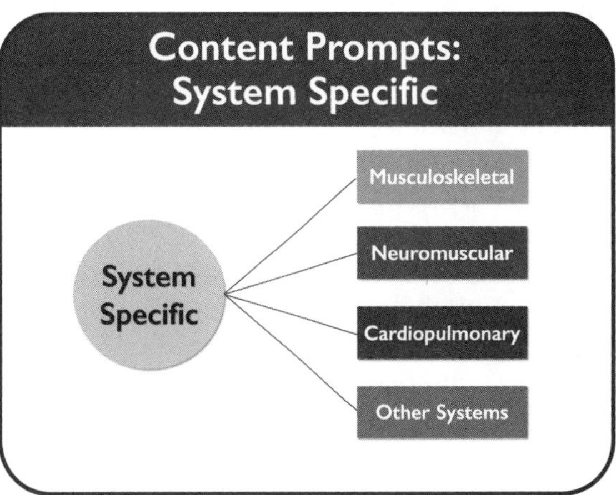

Content Prompts: System Specific
System Specific
Musculoskeletal
Neuromuscular
Cardiopulmonary
Other Systems

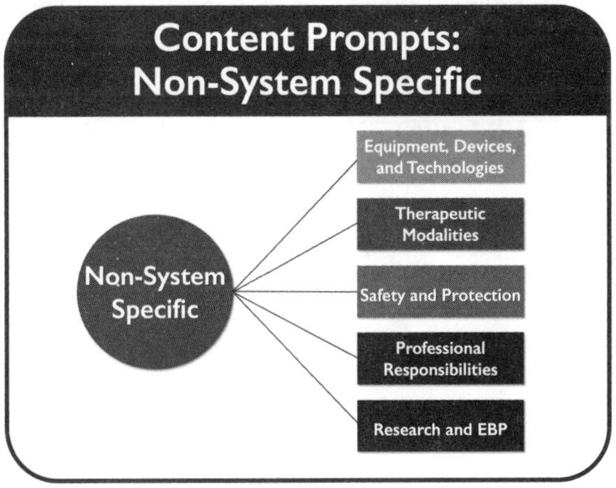

Content Prompts: Non-System Specific
Non-System Specific
Equipment, Devices, and Technologies
Therapeutic Modalities
Safety and Protection
Professional Responsibilities
Research and EBP

Let's Explore

Content Prompt Categories

Musculoskeletal System

Active-passive insufficiency
Arthrokinematics-osteokinematics
Body composition
Capsular patterns
Circumferential measurements
Close packed-open packed positions
Dynamometry
End-feel
Gait
Joint play
Joint receptors
Levels of limb amputations
Manual muscle testing
Mobilization
Muscles - origin, insertion, action, innervation
Musculoskeletal pharmacology
Orthopedic special tests
Pain
Palpation
Planes of the body
Postural awareness training
Postural stabilization training
Posture
Range of motion
Resistance training
Stretching
Types of fractures

Neuromuscular & Nervous Systems

Anatomy of the brain
APGAR
Apraxia
ASIA Impairment Scale
Autonomic nervous system
Balance
Bobath
Brachial plexus
Brunnstrom's stages of recovery
Central nervous system
Communication
Cranial nerves
Deep tendon reflexes
Dermatomes
Diagnostic testing
Glasgow Coma Scale
Limbic system
Mental status
Motor learning
Myotomes
Neuromuscular pharmacology
Normal development
Perceptual training
Peripheral nervous system
Proprioceptive neuromuscular facilitation (PNF)
Rancho Los Amigos Cognitive Functioning Scale
Reflexes
Sensation
Somatic nervous system
Spasticity
Spinal cord level of lesion and functional outcomes
Spinal tracts
Synergy patterns
Upper versus lower motor neuron disease

Cardiovascular and Pulmonary Systems

Anatomy of the heart
Anatomy of the lungs
Arterial blood gases
Blood pressure
Breath sounds-voice sounds
Breathing exercises
Cardiac cycle
Cardiac pharmacology
Cardiac rehabilitation
Cough enhancement techniques
Diagnostic tools for cardiac dysfunction
Electrocardiogram
Exercise participation
Exercise prescription
Heart rate
Heart sounds
Laboratory values
Metabolic equivalents
Peripheral pulses
Postural drainage
Pulmonary function tests
Pulmonary pharmacology
Rate of perceived exertion (RPE) scale
Relaxation techniques
Respiration rate
Risk factors for cardiac disease
Sputum analysis
Suctioning
Target heart rate

Other Systems

Integumentary System

Anatomy of the integumentary system
Burn classification
Debridement
Dressings
Integumentary pharmacology
Physiology of the integumentary system
Positioning
Risk factors for developing wounds
Rule of nines
Scar management
Splinting
Stages of pressure injuries
Stages of wound healing
Types of grafts
Wound characteristics

Metabolic and Endocrine Systems

Anatomy of the endocrine system
Endocrine pathology
Endocrine pharmacology
Functions of the metabolic system
Metabolic pathology

Gastrointestinal System

Anatomy of the gastrointestinal system
Gastrointestinal examination
Gastrointestinal pharmacology
Gland organ pathology
Lower gastrointestinal pathology
Upper gastrointestinal pathology

Genitourinary System

Anatomy of the genital system
Anatomy of the renal system
Effects of exercise on the renal system
Genital pathology
Genitourinary examination
Genitourinary pharmacology
Renal pathology

Lymphatic System

Anatomy of the lymphatic system
Functions of the lymphatic system
Lymphedema
Complete decongestive therapy

System Interactions

Impact of comorbidities
Impact of psychological and mental conditions
Pathologies and conditions affecting multiple systems

Non-Systems

Equipment, Devices, and Technologies

Adaptive devices
Assistive devices
Gait patterns
Gait training
Orthoses
Prosthetics
Tubes, lines, and medical equipment
Wheelchair prescription
Wheelchair training

Therapeutic Modalities

Aquatics
Biofeedback
Continuous passive motion
Cryotherapy
Electrical equipment care and maintenance
Electrical stimulation
Electromyography
Hydrotherapy
Intermittent compression
Iontophoresis
Massage
Principles of heat transfer
Superficial heat
Traction – mechanical/manual
Ultrasound

Safety and Protection

Abuse
Bed mobility
Body mechanics
Cardiopulmonary resuscitation
Emergency care procedures
Ergonomics
Guarding technique
Infection control
Levels of weight bearing
Pressure relief activities
Transfers

Professional Responsibilities

Accessibility standards
Advanced directives
Americans with Disabilities Act (ADA)
APTA documents
Classical conditioning
Cultural influence
Delegation
Disablement models
Documentation
Domains of learning
Draping
Ethical principles
Federal legislation affecting children with disabilities
Feedback
Health behavior models
Health care professions
Health insurance
Individual Education Plan (IEP)
Informed consent
Maslow's Hierarchy of Needs
Operant conditioning
Psychological disorders
Risk management program
Stages of dying
Teaching methods
Team models

Research and Evidence-Based Practice

Descriptive statistics
Inferential statistics
Levels of measurement
Normal distribution
Qualitative research
Quantitative research
Reliability
Research design
Research studies
Sampling
Sensitivity-specificity
Statistical charts and diagrams
Validity
Variables

Assigning Mastery

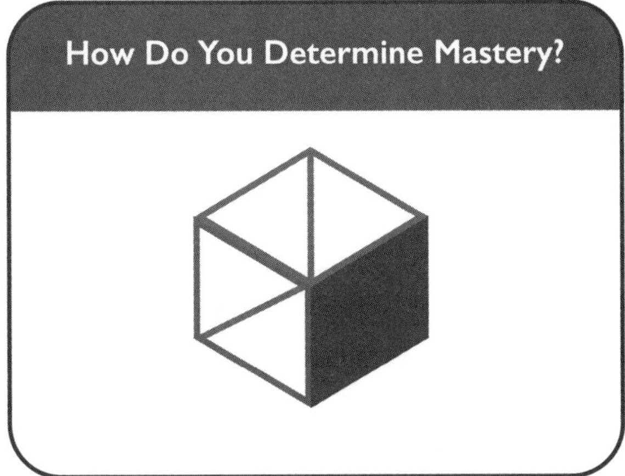
How Do You Determine Mastery?

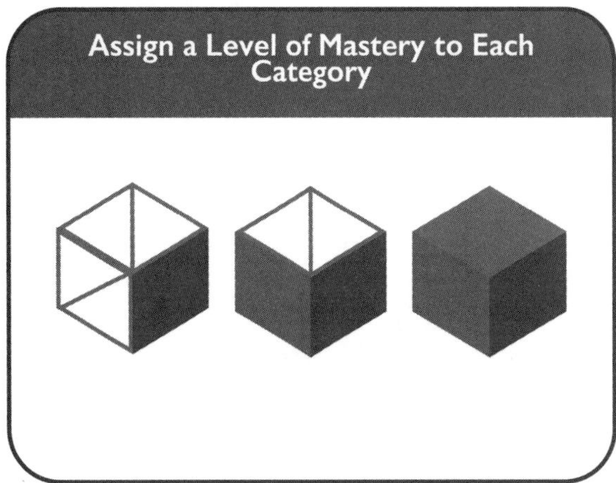
Assign a Level of Mastery to Each Category

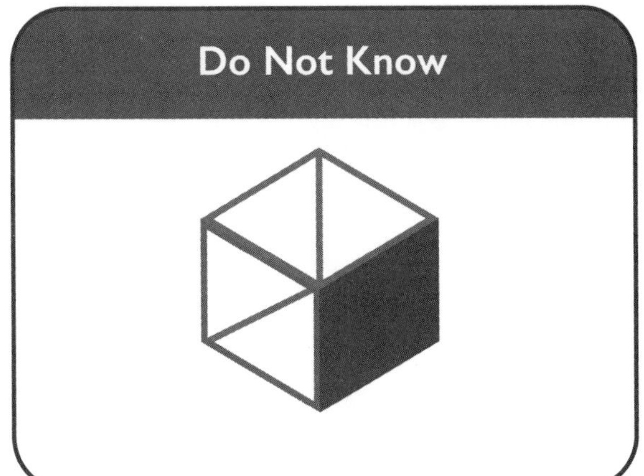
Do Not Know

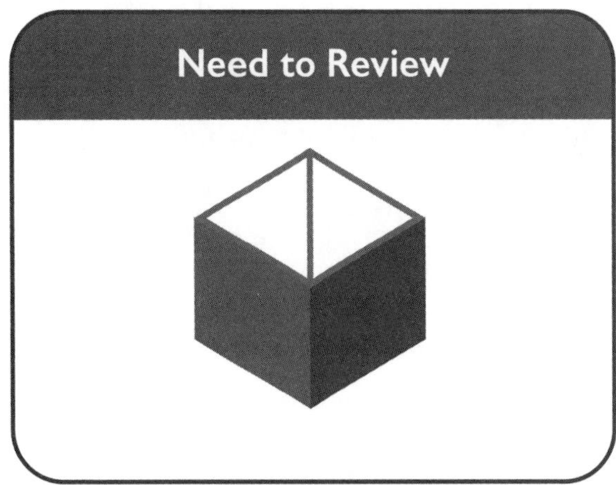
Need to Review

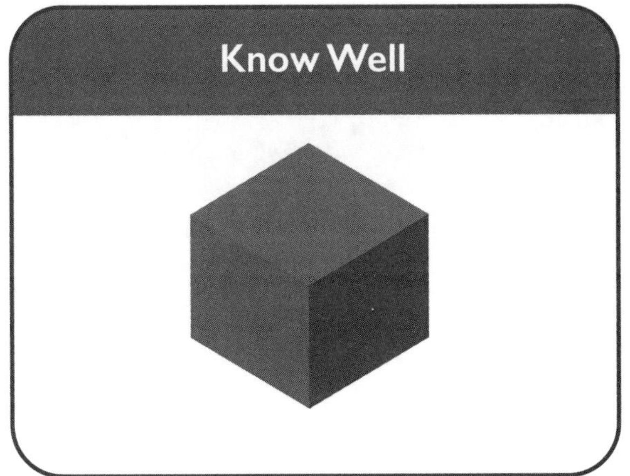
Know Well

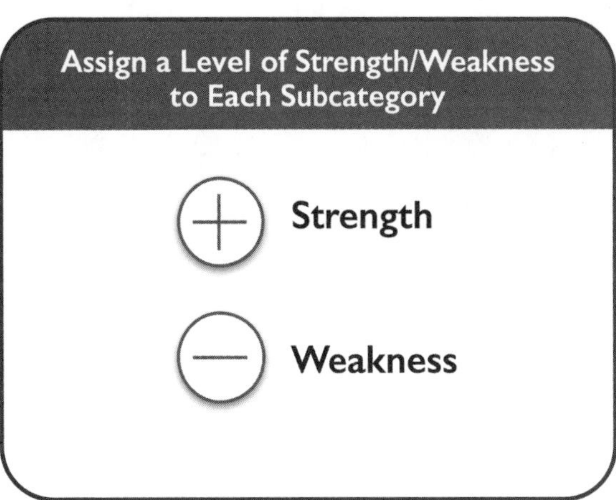
Assign a Level of Strength/Weakness to Each Subcategory
Strength
Weakness

Strength Promotes the Achievement of Mastery

Weakness Inhibits the Achievement of Mastery

Early

Range of Motion

- ⊖ Normal range of motion
  - ⊕ Upper extremity joints
  - ⊕ Lower extremity joints
  - ⊖ Spine (cervical, thoracic, lumbar)
  - ⊖ Temporomandibular joint
- ⊕ Active versus passive range of motion
- ⊖ Recommended sequence for goniometry
- ⊕ Patient position
- ⊕ Stabilization
- ⊕ End-feel
- ⊖ Palpation of bony landmarks
- ⊖ Alignment of goniometer
  - ⊖ Fulcrum (axis)
  - ⊖ Stationary arm
  - ⊖ Moving arm
- ⊕ Documentation of range of motion
- ⊕ Reliability
  - ⊕ Intratester
  - ⊕ Intertester
- ⊕ Validity

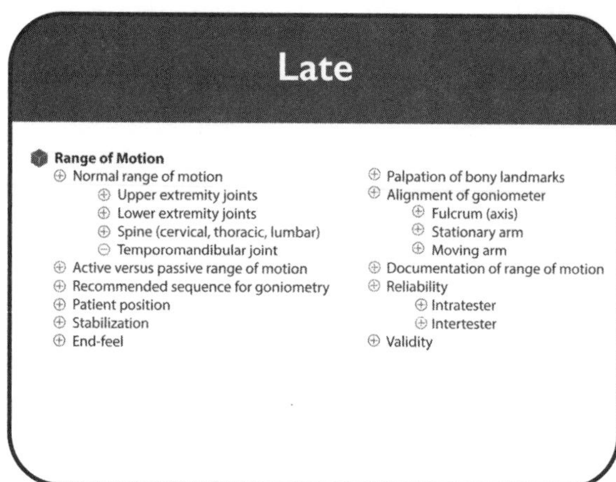
Late
Range of Motion
⊕ Normal range of motion
⊕ Upper extremity joints
⊕ Lower extremity joints
⊕ Spine (cervical, thoracic, lumbar)
⊖ Temporomandibular joint
⊕ Active versus passive range of motion
⊕ Recommended sequence for goniometry
⊕ Patient position
⊕ Stabilization
⊕ End-feel
⊕ Palpation of bony landmarks
⊕ Alignment of goniometer
⊕ Fulcrum (axis)
⊕ Stationary arm
⊕ Moving arm
⊕ Documentation of range of motion
⊕ Reliability
⊕ Intratester
⊕ Intertester
⊕ Validity

Musculoskeletal System

Active-Passive Insufficiency
- Length-tension relationship
- Active insufficiency
  - Definition
  - Example
- Passive insufficiency
  - Definition
  - Example
- One-joint muscle
  - Testing methods (range, strength)
- Two-joint muscle
  - Testing methods (range, strength)

Arthrokinematics-Osteokinematics
- Arthrokinematics
  - Definition
  - Types of motion
    - Roll
    - Slide
    - Spin
- Convex-concave rule
  - Convex moving on concave
    - Direction of slide
    - Direction of roll
  - Concave moving on convex
    - Direction of slide
    - Direction of roll
- Osteokinematics
  - Definition
  - Specific joints and their planar motions
- Examples of specific joints and their arthrokinematic and osteokinematic motions

Body Composition
- Definition
- Purpose
- Densitometry measurement tools
  - Hydrostatic weighing
    - Archimedes' principle
    - Advantages-disadvantages
- Anthropometric measurement tools
  - Body mass index
    - Procedure
    - Health risk
    - Normative values
    - Advantages-disadvantages
  - Waist-to-hip circumference
    - Procedure
    - Disease risk values
    - Advantages-disadvantages
  - Skinfold measurements
    - Procedure
    - 7 sites
    - Advantages-disadvantages
- Bioelectric impedance
  - Procedure
  - Equipment
  - Positioning of electrodes
  - Advantages-disadvantages

Capsular Patterns
- Definition
- Identification of capsular pattern by joint
  - Upper extremity
  - Lower extremity
  - Spine and pelvis
- Diagnoses associated with capsular patterns

Circumferential Measurements
- Indications
  - Edema
  - Atrophy/hypertrophy
  - Waist-to-hip ratio
- Patient positioning
- Palpation of landmarks
- Procedure
- Comparison to uninvolved side

Close Packed-Open Packed Positions
- Definition of close packed
  - Amount of congruence
  - Amount of ligamentous stretch
  - Relationship to anatomical position
- Purpose of utilizing close packed position

- ○ Identification of close packed position
  - ○ Upper extremity
  - ○ Lower extremity
  - ○ Spine and pelvis
- ○ Definition of open packed
  - ○ Amount of congruence
  - ○ Amount of ligamentous stretch
  - ○ Relationship to anatomical position
- ○ Purpose of utilizing open packed position
- ○ Identification of open packed position
  - ○ Upper extremity
  - ○ Lower extremity
  - ○ Spine and pelvis

Dynamometry

- ○ Definition
- ○ Position
  - ○ Subject
  - ○ Limb
  - ○ Dynamometer
- ○ Stabilization
- ○ Testing position
- ○ Bilateral comparison
  - ○ Upper extremity
  - ○ Lower extremity
- ○ Contraction type
  - ○ Isometric
  - ○ Concentric
  - ○ Eccentric
- ○ Muscle performance characteristics
  - ○ Power
  - ○ Endurance
- ○ Isometric dynamometry
  - ○ Procedures
  - ○ Advantages-disadvantages
- ○ Grip dynamometer
  - ○ Adjustable hand spacing
  - ○ Bell curve
  - ○ Fatigue
  - ○ Advantages-disadvantages
- ○ Reliability
- ○ Validity

End-Feel

- ○ Type of range of motion
- ○ Quality of range of motion
  - ○ Capsular
  - ○ Noncapsular
- ○ Amount of range of motion
  - ○ Hypermobility
  - ○ Hypomobility
- ○ Normal end-feel
  - ○ Definition and example
    - ○ Soft
    - ○ Firm
    - ○ Hard
- ○ Abnormal end-feel
  - ○ Definition and example
    - ○ Soft
    - ○ Firm
    - ○ Hard
    - ○ Empty
- ○ Clinical relevance

Gait

- ○ Rancho Los Amigos terminology
  - ○ Weight acceptance
    - ○ Initial contact
    - ○ Loading response
  - ○ Single limb support
    - ○ Midstance
    - ○ Terminal stance
  - ○ Swing limb advancement
    - ○ Pre-swing
  - ○ Initial swing
    - ○ Midswing
    - ○ Terminal swing
- ○ Traditional terminology
  - ○ Stance phase
    - ○ Heel strike
    - ○ Foot flat
    - ○ Midstance
    - ○ Heel off
    - ○ Toe off
  - ○ Swing phase
    - ○ Acceleration
    - ○ Midswing
    - ○ Deceleration

- Range of motion required
  - Stance phase
    - Ankle, knee, hip
  - Swing phase
    - Ankle, knee, hip
- Muscle strength/activation
  - Stance phase
  - Swing phase
- Common gait patterns associated with medical diagnoses
- Contributions to abnormal gait
  - Range of motion restrictions
  - Muscle weakness
  - Malalignment
  - Paralysis
- Energy costs during ambulation
- Temporal variables
  - Stance time
  - Single support time
  - Double support time
  - Stride duration
  - Step duration
  - Cadence
- Distance variables
  - Stride length
  - Step length
  - Width of base of support
  - Degree of toe out

Joint Play

- Procedure
- Grades of available joint play (0-6)
- Preparation
  - Positioning
  - Stabilization
- Clinical relevance

Joint Receptors

- Deep sensory receptors
  - Ruffini endings
  - Paciniform endings
  - Golgi ligament endings
  - Free nerve endings
- Location
- Sensitivity
- Primary distribution

Levels of Limb Amputations

- Upper limb
  - Digital
  - Partial hand
  - Wrist disarticulation
  - Transradial
  - Elbow disarticulation
  - Transhumeral
  - Shoulder disarticulation
  - Forequarter (scapulothoracic)
- Lower limb
  - Partial toe
  - Toe disarticulation
  - Partial foot/ray resection
  - Transmetatarsal
  - Syme's
  - Long transtibial
  - Transtibial
  - Short transtibial
  - Knee disarticulation
  - Long transfemoral
  - Transfemoral
  - Short transfemoral
  - Hip disarticulation
  - Hemipelvectomy
  - Hemicorporectomy

Manual Muscle Testing

- Purpose
- Benefits
- Limitations
- Positioning
  - Against gravity
  - Gravity eliminated
- Hand placement
  - Stabilizing hand
  - Mobilizing hand
- Direction of force
- Grades
  - Normal (5)
  - Good plus (4+)
  - Good (4)
  - Good minus (4-)

- ○ Fair plus (3+)
- ○ Fair (3)
- ○ Fair minus (3-)
- ○ Poor plus (2+)
- ○ Poor (2)
- ○ Poor minus (2-)
- ○ Trace (1)
- ○ Zero (0)

○ One-joint muscles
○ Two-joint muscles
○ Substitution
○ Possible reasons for muscle weakness
- ○ Nerve involvement
- ○ Disuse atrophy
- ○ Stretch weakness
- ○ Pain and fatigue

Mobilization

- ○ Purpose
- ○ Indications
- ○ Contraindications
- ○ Potential adverse reactions
- ○ Manual therapy approaches
  - ○ Cyriax
  - ○ Kaltenborn
  - ○ Maitland
- ○ Principles and rules
- ○ Assessment of joint play
  - ○ Loose packed position
- ○ Tissue stops and abnormal range
- ○ Convex-concave rule
  - ○ Roll
  - ○ Glide
- ○ Grading scale
  - ○ Hypomobile
  - ○ Hypermobile
- ○ Movement
  - ○ Quality
  - ○ Quantity
  - ○ End-feel
- ○ Positioning and stabilization
- ○ Mobilizing force
- ○ Traction or distraction
- ○ Gliding or oscillation
- ○ Graded oscillation techniques
  - ○ Definition and technique
    - ○ Grade 1
    - ○ Grade 2
    - ○ Grade 3
    - ○ Grade 4
    - ○ Grade 5 (thrust)

Muscles – Origin, Insertion, Action, Innervation

- ○ Major muscles
  - ○ Upper extremity
  - ○ Lower extremity
  - ○ Spine, trunk, pelvis
- ○ Origin and insertion
- ○ Action
- ○ Innervation

Musculoskeletal Pharmacology

- ○ For each category
  - ○ Purpose
  - ○ Mechanism
  - ○ Side effects
- ○ Drug categories
  - ○ Nonopioid agents
  - ○ Opioid agents
  - ○ Glucocorticoid agents
  - ○ Disease-modifying antirheumatic agents

Orthopedic Special Tests

- ○ Test name
- ○ Purpose of test
- ○ Method for performing test
- ○ Positive findings

Pain

- ○ Types of pain
  - ○ Acute
  - ○ Chronic
- ○ Pain behaviors
- ○ Peripheral nerve pathways
  - ○ A-delta fibers
  - ○ C-fibers
- ○ Central pathways
  - ○ Neurotransmitters

- ○ Pain-spasm-pain cycle
- ○ Lateral spinothalamic tract
- ○ Anterior spinothalamic tract

○ Pain modulation
- ○ Gate control theory
- ○ Endorphins
- ○ Psychological central control mechanisms

○ Pain description
- ○ Onset
- ○ Description
- ○ Intensity
- ○ Duration
- ○ Pattern
- ○ Aggravating factors
- ○ Relieving factors

○ Pain patterns
- ○ Vascular
- ○ Neurogenic
- ○ Musculoskeletal
- ○ Emotional

○ Pain types
- ○ Cutaneous
- ○ Deep somatic
- ○ Visceral
- ○ Neuropathic
- ○ Referred

○ Pain assessment
- ○ Body mapping
- ○ Visual analogue scale
- ○ Numerical rating scale
- ○ McGill pain scale
- ○ Waddell's nonorganic signs
- ○ Questionnaires
  - ○ Diagrammatic
  - ○ Qualitative
  - ○ Temporal
  - ○ Intensity-related

○ Rationale for physician referral

○ Pain management approaches
- ○ Pharmacological
- ○ Physical agents
- ○ Multidisciplinary pain treatment programs

Palpation

○ Purpose

○ Characteristics
- ○ Temperature
- ○ Contour
- ○ Symmetry
- ○ Mobility
- ○ Elasticity
- ○ Moisture
- ○ Thickness
- ○ Tenderness
- ○ Pulses
- ○ Texture

○ Structures
- ○ Skin
- ○ Subcutaneous tissues
- ○ Tendon
- ○ Blood vessels
- ○ Nerves
- ○ Muscle
- ○ Ligament
- ○ Bone

Planes of the Body

○ Anatomic position

○ Cardinal planes
- ○ Sagittal plane
- ○ Frontal plane (coronal)
- ○ Transverse plane

○ Anatomical reference axes
- ○ Frontal axis (coronal)
- ○ Sagittal axis
- ○ Longitudinal axis

○ Sagittal plane movements

○ Frontal plane movements

○ Transverse plane movements

○ Multi-planar movements

Postural Awareness Training

○ Definition

○ Purpose

○ Center of mass

○ Reactive control

○ Proactive anticipatory control

○ Adaptive postural control

- Postural sway
- Strengthening

Postural Stabilization Training

- Indications
- Contraindications
- Equipment needed
- Progression
  - Early training/protection phase
  - Basic training/controlled motion phase
  - Intermediate to advanced training/ return to function phase
- Kinesthetic training
  - Goal
  - Proprioceptive awareness
  - Posture/positioning
- Flexibility/mobility
  - Goal
  - Stretching techniques
- Muscle performance
  - Goal
  - Core muscle control
  - Dynamic stabilization
  - Strengthening
  - Muscle endurance

Posture

- Observation
- Surface landmarks
- Effect of gravity
- Plumb line
- Correct posture
  - Definition
  - Factors affecting correct posture
- Faulty posture
  - Definition
  - Causes
    - Positional
    - Structural
- Common spinal deformities
  - Kyphosis-lordosis posture
  - Flat-back posture
  - Sway-back posture
  - Scoliosis

Range of Motion

- Normal range of motion
  - Upper extremity joints
  - Lower extremity joints
  - Spine (cervical, thoracic, lumbar)
  - Temporomandibular joint
- Active versus passive range of motion
- Recommended sequence for goniometry
- Patient position
- Stabilization
- End-feel
- Palpation of bony landmarks
- Alignment of goniometer
  - Fulcrum (axis)
  - Stationary arm
  - Moving arm
- Documentation of range of motion

Resistance Training

- Indications
- Contraindications
- Guiding principles
  - Overload
  - SAID (specific adaptation to imposed demands)
  - Reversibility
- Muscle performance
  - Strength
  - Power
  - Endurance
- Physiologic effects
  - Fatigue
  - Age related
- Physiologic adaptations
  - Neural
  - Skeletal muscle
    - Hypertrophy
    - Hyperplasia
    - Muscle fiber type
  - Connective tissue
    - Tendons, ligaments, and connective tissue
    - Bone

- Intensity
  - Sub-maximal versus maximal load
  - Strength training zone
- Muscle contractions
  - Isotonic
    - Concentric
    - Eccentric
  - Isometric
- Parameters
  - Repetition and sets
  - Muscle strength
  - Muscle endurance
  - Frequency
  - Duration
  - Rest interval
- Manual versus mechanical
  - Isometric
    - Purpose
    - Limitations
    - Muscle setting
    - Stabilization
      - Rhythmic stabilization
      - Alternating isometrics
      - Dynamic stabilization
  - Isokinetic
    - Purpose
    - Limitations
    - Characteristics
      - Constant velocity
      - Range of training velocities
      - Fiber type recruitment
      - Specificity
- Open chain exercise
  - Definition
  - Examples
  - Clinical significance
- Closed chain exercise
  - Definition
  - Examples
  - Clinical significance

Stretching

- Purpose
- Indications
- Contraindications
- Terminology
  - Flexibility
  - Extensibility
  - Dynamic flexibility
  - Passive flexibility
  - Contracture
- Mechanical response to stretch
  - Elasticity
  - Viscoelasticity
  - Plasticity
  - Stress-strain curve
  - Creep
  - Stress-relaxation
- Neurophysiologic response to stretch
  - Muscle spindle
  - Golgi tendon organ
- Determinants of stretching
  - Intensity
  - Duration
  - Speed
  - Frequency
- Mode of stretch
  - Manual
  - Self-stretching
  - Mechanical
  - Joint mobilization
  - Neural mobilization
  - Selective stretching
  - Hold-relax
  - Contract-relax
  - Antagonist contraction
- Utilization of modalities to facilitate stretching

Types of Fractures

- Definition
- Classification by extent
  - Complete
  - Incomplete
- Classification by configuration
  - Oblique
  - Transverse
  - Spiral
  - Comminuted
- Classification by relationship of fragments to one another
  - Non-displaced

- Displaced
- Classification by site
  - Intra-articular
  - Epiphyseal
  - Metaphyseal
  - Diaphyseal
- Classification by relationship to external environment
  - Closed (simple)
  - Open (compound)
- Phases of healing
- Clinical versus complete union
- Factors influencing weight bearing status
- Complications
  - Delayed union
  - Malunion
  - Non-union

Neuromuscular and Nervous Systems

Anatomy of the Brain

- For each structure
  - Location
  - Function
- Forebrain
  - Telencephalon
    - Cerebrum
    - Hippocampus
    - Basal ganglia
    - Amygdala
  - Diencephalon
    - Thalamus
    - Hypothalamus
    - Subthalamus
    - Epithalamus
- Midbrain
  - Tectum
  - Tegmentum
- Hindbrain
  - Metencephalon
    - Cerebellum
    - Pons
  - Myelencephalon
    - Medulla oblongata
- Cerebral cortex
  - Frontal lobe
  - Parietal lobe
  - Temporal lobe
  - Occipital lobe
- Cerebellum
  - Right and left hemispheres
- Ventricular system and the flow of CSF
- Blood supply of the brain
  - Circle of Willis
  - Anterior cerebral artery
  - Middle cerebral artery
  - Posterior cerebral artery
  - Vertebral-basilar artery

APGAR

- Purpose
- Assessment
  - Heart rate
  - Respiratory effort
  - Muscle tone
  - Reflex irritability
  - Skin color
- Scoring
- Interpretation of results

Apraxia

- Types
  - Ideomotor apraxia
  - Ideational apraxia
  - Constructional apraxia
  - Verbal apraxia
- For each type
  - Testing
  - Characteristics
  - Intervention

ASIA Impairment Scale

- Purpose
- Procedure
- Components
  - Motor
  - Sensory
- Indications
  - Complete lesion
  - Incomplete lesion
- Interpretation of results

Autonomic Nervous System

- Purpose
- Divisions
  - Sympathetic
  - Parasympathetic
- Normal function
- Dysfunction
- Clinical relevance

Balance

- Components of functional balance
  - Sensory
  - Motor
  - Cognition
- Muscles active during quiet stance

- ○ Peripheral feedback
  - ○ Muscle spindles
  - ○ Golgi tendon organs
  - ○ Joint and cutaneous receptors
  - ○ Visual and auditory systems
- ○ Balance systems
  - ○ Somatosensory
    - ○ Vibration and pressure testing
    - ○ Standing on varying surfaces
  - ○ Vestibular
    - ○ Dix-Hallpike maneuver
    - ○ Nystagmus
    - ○ Vestibulo-ocular reflex
  - ○ Visual
    - ○ Field cuts
    - ○ Hemianopsia
- ○ Intervention
  - ○ Method of challenging each system
  - ○ Perturbations
  - ○ Balance tests and measures
    - ○ Berg Balance Scale
    - ○ Clinical Test of Sensory Integration and Balance (CTSIB)
    - ○ Fregly-Graybiel Ataxia Test Battery
    - ○ Fugl-Meyer Sensorimotor Assessment
    - ○ Functional Reach Test
    - ○ Romberg Test
    - ○ Timed Up and Go (TUG) Test
    - ○ Tinetti Performance Oriented Mobility Assessment
  - ○ Motor strategies
    - ○ Ankle
    - ○ Hip
    - ○ Stepping
    - ○ Suspensory
- ○ Clinical relevance

Bobath

- ○ Neurodevelopmental treatment
  - ○ Purpose
  - ○ Practice
- ○ Role of postural reflexes and control
- ○ Positioning
  - ○ Reflex inhibiting postures
- ○ Synergistic movements
- ○ Handling techniques
  - ○ Facilitatory
  - ○ Inhibitory
  - ○ Key points of control
- ○ Sensory stimulation
  - ○ Kinesthetic
  - ○ Proprioceptive
  - ○ Tactile
  - ○ Vestibular
- ○ Strategies for motor learning
- ○ Clinical relevance

Brachial Plexus

- ○ Structure
  - ○ 5 Roots
    - ○ Ventral rami C5-T1
  - ○ 3 Trunks
    - ○ Superior
    - ○ Middle
    - ○ Inferior
  - ○ 2 Divisions of each trunk
    - ○ Anterior
    - ○ Posterior
  - ○ 3 Cords
    - ○ Lateral
    - ○ Medial
    - ○ Posterior
  - ○ 5 Major branches (nerves)
    - ○ Origin of each
    - ○ Course of each
- ○ Brachial plexus injuries
  - ○ Etiology
    - ○ Disease
    - ○ Stretching
    - ○ Wounds
    - ○ Birth injuries
  - ○ Clinical signs
    - ○ Paralysis
    - ○ Paresthesia
  - ○ Injuries to the superior parts of the brachial plexus
    - ○ Waiter's tip position

- Erb's palsy
    - Backpacker's palsy
    - Compression of cords of the plexus
  - Injuries to the inferior parts of the brachial plexus
    - Clawhand
    - Klumpke's palsy

Brunnstrom's Stages of Recovery

- Purpose
- Practice
- Number of stages
- Characteristics of each stage
- Active isolated movement
- Upper and lower extremity synergy patterns
- Treatment goals for each stage
- Positive effects of spasticity
- Negative effects of spasticity
- Techniques for sensory stimulation
  - Stretch
  - Tapping
  - Stroking
  - Pressure
  - Warmth
- Clinical relevance

Central Nervous System

- Purpose
  - Integration/coordination of information
- Anatomy
  - Brain and spinal cord
  - Meninges
  - Cerebrospinal fluid
- Cerebral hemisphere dominance and function
- Normal function
- Dysfunction
- Predictable patterns of impairment
  - Specific lobe or structure
  - Specific blood supply
- Clinical relevance

Communication

- Definition
- Components of communication
- Pathology
  - Area of lesion
  - Right hemisphere versus left hemisphere
  - Focal versus diffuse
- Impairments
  - Expressive versus receptive
  - Signs and symptoms
- Types of communication disorders
  - Aphasia
    - Fluent
      - Wernicke's
      - Conduction
    - Non-fluent
      - Broca's
      - Global
  - Aprosody
  - Dysarthria

Cranial Nerves

- Structure
- Name and number
- Function
- Type of nerve
  - Sensory
  - Motor
  - Sensorimotor
- Methods of testing
  - Positive results
  - Negative results
- Cranial nerve injuries
  - Etiology
  - Characteristics
  - Intervention

Deep Tendon Reflexes

- Definition
- Equipment required for testing
- Common deep tendon reflexes
  - Innervation level
  - Testing procedure
  - Normal response
- Reflex grading
- Hyperreflexia
- Hyporeflexia

Dermatomes

- Definition
- Skin innervation
- Organization and overlap
  - Upper extremities
  - Lower extremities
  - Trunk
- Sensory integrity testing
  - Light touch
  - Sharp/dull
  - Two-point discrimination
- Interpretation of results
- Common diagnoses resulting in dermatomal damage
- Clinical relevance

Diagnostic Testing

- For each category
  - Purpose
  - Indications
  - Contraindications
- Types
  - Cerebral angiography
  - Computed tomography
  - Electroencephalogram
  - Electromyography
  - Lumbar puncture
  - Magnetic resonance imaging
  - Nerve conduction velocity
  - Positron emission tomography
- Clinical relevance

Glasgow Coma Scale

- Purpose
- Scoring activities
  - Eye opening
  - Best motor response
  - Verbal response
- Total score (minimum and maximum)
- Severity
  - Mild
  - Moderate
  - Severe
- Prediction of outcome

Limbic System

- Purpose
  - Mood
  - Processing
  - Memory
  - Motivation
- Anatomy
- Clinical relevance

Mental Status

- Levels of arousal
  - Alert
  - Lethargic
  - Obtunded
  - Stupor
  - Coma
- Factors that influence arousal/ attention
- Specific tests
  - Mini-Mental State
  - Montreal Cognitive Assessment
  - Short Portable Mental Status
- Types of attention
  - Selective
  - Sustained
  - Divided
  - Alternating
- Levels of orientation
  - Person
  - Place
  - Time
  - Situation

- Types of memory
  - Declarative
  - Procedural
- Types of memory impairments
  - Retrograde amnesia
  - Anterograde amnesia
  - Confusion
  - Delirium

Motor Learning
- Stages of motor learning
  - Cognitive
  - Associative
  - Autonomous
- Associated terms
  - Acquisition
  - Retention
  - Transfer
- Types of practice
  - Part
  - Whole
  - Blocked
  - Random
  - Massed
  - Distributed
- Types of feedback
  - Intrinsic
  - Extrinsic
    - Knowledge of results
    - Knowledge of performance
- Verbal training
- Demonstration
- Feedback schedule
- Environment
- Clinical examples for each stage of motor learning

Myotomes
- Definition
- Muscle innervation
  - Upper extremities
    - C4 - T1
  - Lower extremities
    - L2 - S1
  - Trunk
- Testing positions
- Sequence of testing for efficiency
- Interpretation of results
- Common diagnoses or injuries resulting in myotomal damage
- Clinical relevance

Neuromuscular Pharmacology
- For each category
  - Purpose
  - Mechanisms
  - Side effects
- Drug categories
  - Antiepileptic agents
  - Antispasticity agents
  - Cholinergic agents
  - Dopamine replacement agents
  - Muscle relaxant agents

Normal Development
- Theories of development
- Domains of development
  - Motor
    - Gross
    - Fine
  - Cognitive
  - Social/emotional
- Developmental milestones/skill achievement
  - Prenatal
  - Infancy
  - Childhood
  - Adolescence
  - Adulthood
  - Older adulthood
- Developmental sequence
- Age appropriate reflexes and integration

Perceptual Training

- Definition of perception
- Examination
  - Sensory deficits
  - Cognitive deficits
  - Perceptual deficits
  - Visual deficits
- Primary perceptual deficits
  - Body schema and image
    - Unilateral neglect
    - Anosognosia
    - Somatoagnosia
  - Spatial relationship
    - Form discrimination
    - Position in space
    - Depth and distance
  - Agnosia
    - Tactile agnosia
    - Auditory agnosia
  - Apraxia
    - Ideational apraxia
    - Ideomotor apraxia
    - Constructional apraxia
- Theoretical frameworks
  - Retraining approach
  - Sensory integrative approach
- Clinical relevance

Peripheral Nervous System

- Purpose
- Anatomy
  - 12 pairs - cranial nerves
  - 31 pairs - spinal nerves
- Characteristics
  - Myelinated
  - Unmyelinated
  - Afferent
  - Efferent
  - Somatic
  - Visceral
  - Myotome
  - Dermatome
- A fibers
  - Alpha
  - Beta
  - Delta
  - Gamma
- B fibers
- C fibers
- Peripheral nerve testing
- Normal function
- Dysfunction/injury
  - Neurapraxia
  - Axonotmesis
  - Neurotmesis
- Clinical relevance

Proprioceptive Neuromuscular Facilitation (PNF)

- Purpose
- Practice
  - Verbal commands
  - Manual contacts
- Diagonal patterns
  - Upper extremity versus lower extremity
    - D1 flexion
    - D2 flexion
    - D1 extension
    - D2 extension
- Developmental sequence
- Levels of motor control
  - Mobility
  - Stability
  - Controlled mobility
  - Skill
- PNF exercise techniques
  - Alternating isometrics
  - Contract-relax
  - Hold-relax active movement
  - Repeated contractions
  - Rhythmic initiation
  - Rhythmic rotation
  - Rhythmic stabilization
  - Timing for emphasis
- Clinical relevance

Rancho Los Amigos Cognitive Functioning Scale

- Purpose
- Characteristics and goals for each level
  - No response
  - Generalized response
  - Localized response
  - Confused-agitated
  - Confused-inappropriate
  - Confused-appropriate
  - Automatic-appropriate
  - Purposeful-appropriate
  - Purposeful-appropriate: Stand-by assistance on request
  - Purposeful-appropriate: Modified independent
- Clinical relevance

Reflexes

- Definition
- For each primitive reflex
  - Testing procedure
  - Expected response
  - Normal age of response
- Primitive reflexes
  - Asymmetrical tonic neck
  - Body righting acting on the body
  - Body righting acting on the head
  - Crossed extension
  - Flexor withdrawal
  - Galant
  - Moro
  - Neck righting acting on the body
  - Optical righting
  - Palmar grasp
  - Plantar grasp
  - Positive support
  - Protective extension
  - Rooting
  - Startle
  - Symmetrical tonic neck
  - Tonic labyrinthine
  - Walking (stepping)
- For each deep tendon reflex
  - Testing procedure
  - Anticipated response
- Deep tendon reflexes
  - Biceps brachii
  - Brachioradialis
  - Triceps
  - Patellar tendon
  - Achilles
- For each superficial reflex
  - Testing procedure
  - Anticipated response
- Superficial reflexes
  - Abdominal
  - Corneal
  - Cremasteric
  - Gag
  - Plantar
- Clinical relevance

Sensation

- Definition
- Organization
  - Upper extremities
  - Lower extremities
  - Trunk
- Types of sensation
  - Superficial
    - Sharp/dull
    - Temperature
    - Light touch
  - Deep
    - Vibration
    - Proprioception
    - Kinesthesia
  - Cortical (combined)
    - Stereognosis
    - Two-point discrimination
    - Barognosis
- Procedure for sensory testing
  - Sensations to test
  - Order of testing
  - Methods of testing
  - Tools for assessing sensation
    - Cotton
    - Semmes-Weinstein filaments
    - Test tubes
    - Tuning fork
- Interpreting findings

- Common diagnoses resulting in sensory deficits
- Clinical relevance

Somatic Nervous System

- Purpose
- Anatomy
  - Peripheral and motor nerve fibers
- Normal function
  - Relay of neural information
  - Sensory
  - Motor
  - Five major senses
- Dysfunction
- Clinical significance

Spasticity

- Definition
- Examination
  - Observation
  - Passive range of motion
  - Active range of motion
  - Velocity dependent
- Patterns of spasticity
  - Synergistic postures
  - Clasp-knife phenomenon
  - Exaggerated tendon jerk
  - Clonus
  - Rigidity
    - Cog-wheel phenomenon
    - Lead pipe rigidity
    - Decorticate rigidity
    - Decerebrate rigidity
- Modified Ashworth Scale
- Terminology
  - Spastic hemiparesis
  - Spastic diplegia
  - Spastic tetraplegia
  - Spastic paralysis
- Medical conditions associated with spasticity
- Intervention
  - Positioning
  - Inhibitory techniques
  - Range of motion
- Pharmacological intervention
- Medical/surgical procedures
- Clinical relevance

Spinal Cord Level of Lesion and Functional Outcomes

- Clinical presentation for each level
- Anticipated functional outcomes for each level
  - Complete spinal cord injury
    - C1-C4
    - C5
    - C6
    - C7
    - C8-T1
    - T4-T6
    - T9-T12
    - L2-L3
    - L4-L5
  - Incomplete spinal cord injury
    - Incomplete lesion
    - Cord syndromes
- Clinical relevance

Spinal Tracts

- For each tract
  - Motor or sensory
  - Normal function
  - Characteristics of impairment
- Major ascending tracts
  - Fasciculus cuneatus (posterior or dorsal column)
  - Fasciculus gracilis (posterior or dorsal column)
  - Spinothalamic tract (anterior and lateral)
- Major descending tracts
  - Corticospinal tract (anterior and lateral)
  - Reticulospinal tract
- Clinical relevance

Synergy Patterns

- Upper extremity
  - Components of synergy pattern
    - Flexion
    - Extension
- Lower extremity
  - Components of synergy pattern
    - Flexion
    - Extension
- Strongest patterns
- Associated medical diagnoses and conditions
- Assessment
  - Tone
    - Spastic
    - Flaccid
  - Clonus
  - Raimiste's phenomenon
  - Homolateral limb synkinesis
- Intervention
  - Neurodevelopmental treatment
  - Proprioceptive neuromuscular facilitation
  - Task-oriented approach
  - Modalities

Upper versus Lower Motor Neuron Disease

- Upper motor neuron disease
  - Definition
  - Clinical presentation
  - Goals/focus of intervention
  - Examples/diagnoses
- Lower motor neuron disease
  - Definition
  - Clinical presentation
  - Goals/focus of intervention
  - Examples/diagnoses
- Clinical relevance

Cardiovascular and Pulmonary Systems

Anatomy of the Heart

- Apex of the heart
- Base of the heart
- Endocardium
- Epicardium
- Myocardium
- Pericardium
- Arteries of the heart
  - Left coronary
  - Left anterior descending
  - Right coronary
  - Posterior descending
- Chambers
  - Left atrium
  - Right atrium
  - Left ventricle
  - Right ventricle
- Conduction system
  - SA node
  - AV node
  - Bundle of His
  - Purkinje fibers
- Nerves that innervate the heart
- Valves
  - Aortic valve
  - Pulmonary valve
  - Bicuspid (mitral)
  - Tricuspid
- Major vessels attached to the heart
  - Aorta
  - Superior vena cava
  - Inferior vena cava
  - Pulmonary veins
- Path of blood flow in and out of the heart
  - Pulmonary circuit
  - Systemic circuit

Anatomy of the Lungs

- Right lung
  - Right upper lobe
    - Apical
    - Anterior
    - Posterior
  - Right middle lobe
    - Medial
    - Lateral
  - Right lower lobe
    - Superior
    - Anterior basal
    - Lateral basal
    - Posterior basal
    - Medial basal
- Left lung
  - Left upper lobe
    - Apical posterior
    - Anterior
    - Superior lingular
    - Inferior lingular
  - Left lower lobe
    - Superior
    - Anterior medial basal
    - Lateral basal
    - Posterior basal
- Fissures
  - Oblique
  - Horizontal (transverse)
- Pulmonary circulation
- Bronchial circulation

Arterial Blood Gases

- Purpose
- Locations accessed
- Normal values
  - Arterial pH
  - Partial pressure carbon dioxide (PCO_2)
  - Partial pressure oxygen (PO_2)
  - Oxygen saturation (% SAT)
  - Bicarbonate concentration (HCO_3)
- Complications of acid-base imbalance
  - Respiratory – signs and symptoms
    - Acidosis
    - Alkalosis
  - Metabolic – signs and symptoms
    - Acidosis
    - Alkalosis
- Clinical significance of each finding

Blood Pressure
- Capillary pressure
  - Diastolic
  - Systolic
- Classifications
  - Hypertension
  - Hypotension
- Equipment
  - Sphygmomanometer
  - Stethoscope
- Measuring blood pressure
  - Cuff size
  - Estimation of systolic
  - Deflation rate
  - Determining systolic/diastolic
  - Korotkoff's sounds
- Determinants
  - Cardiac output
  - Peripheral resistance
- Resting blood pressure
  - Normal values
  - Adults versus children
  - Abnormal values
- Blood pressure response to exercise
  - Normal
  - Abnormal
- Factors influencing blood pressure
  - Exercise
  - Smoking
  - Body weight
  - Stress
  - Medications

Breath Sounds - Voice Sounds
- Definition
- Equipment
- Procedure
- Normal breath sounds
  - Bronchial
  - Vesicular
- Decreased breath sounds
  - Adventitious sounds
    - Crackles
    - Wheezes
    - Rhonchi
- Voice transmission tests
  - Bronchophony
  - Egophony
  - Whispered pectoriloquy

Breathing Exercises
- Goals for breathing retraining
- Positioning for relief of dyspnea
  - In bed
  - Sitting
  - Standing
  - Fowler's position
  - Semi-Fowler's position
- Breathing exercises
  - Purpose and procedure for each
    - Pursed-lip breathing
    - Diaphragmatic breathing
    - Paced breathing
    - Segmental breathing
    - Thoracic mobility exercises
    - Inspiratory hold maneuver
    - Incentive spirometry
    - Inspiratory muscle training

Cardiac Cycle
- Conduction system
  - Sinoatrial node (SA node)
  - Inter-nodal fiber bundles
    - Purkinje fibers
  - Atrioventricular node (AV node)
  - Atrioventricular bundle
    - Bundle of His
- Action potential
  - Generation
  - Pathway
  - Ectopic focus
- Two phases of the cardiac cycle
  - Systole
  - Diastole
- Atrial systole
  - P wave
  - Retrograde blood flow
  - Ventricular end-diastolic volume
  - S4 and ventricular hypertrophy

- Isovolumetric contraction
  - QRS complex
  - S1
- Rapid ejection
  - Ejection fraction
- Reduced ejection
  - Ventricular repolarization
  - T wave
- Isovolumetric relaxation
  - S2
  - End-systolic volume
  - Stroke volume
    - Preload
    - Afterload
    - Contractility
- Rapid ventricular filling
  - S3 and ventricular dilation
- Reduced ventricular filling
  - Diastasis
- Length of cardiac cycle
- Heart rate
  - Normal versus abnormal values
    - Resting
    - Exertional

Cardiac Pharmacology

- For each category
  - Purpose
  - Mechanism
  - Side effects
- Drug categories
  - Alpha adrenergic antagonist agents
  - Angiotensin-converting enzyme (ACE) inhibitor agents
  - Angiotensin II receptor antagonist agents
  - Antiarrhythmic agents
  - Anticoagulant agents
  - Antihyperlipidemia agents
  - Antithrombotic (antiplatelet) agents
  - Beta blocker agents
  - Calcium channel blocker agents
  - Diuretic agents
  - Nitrate agents
  - Positive inotropic agents
  - Thrombolytic agents

Cardiac Rehabilitation

- Indications
- Contraindications
- Interdisciplinary team
- Risk factors for exercise
  - Low-risk patients
  - Moderate-risk patients
  - High-risk patients
- Phases
  - Setting
  - Duration
  - Frequency
  - Intensity
  - Monitoring
  - Activities
  - Goals
  - Calculation of target heart rate
  - Benefits of program
- Grading scales
  - Angina
  - Dyspnea
  - Rate of perceived exertion
- Acceptable range for vital signs
- Abnormal exercise responses
  - Symptoms for termination of exercise
- Outcome measures
- Discharge criteria

Cough Enhancement Techniques

- Purpose
- Indications
- Contraindications
- Types of cough
- Effective cough
- Positioning
- Technique
  - Assisted
  - Self-assisted
  - Splinting
  - Huffing

Diagnostic Tools for Cardiac Dysfunction

- Categories of diagnostic tools
  - Clinical laboratory tests
    - Arterial blood gas
    - Prothrombin time
    - Serum enzymes
    - Cholesterol screen
  - Non-invasive diagnostic testing
    - CT scan
    - Holter monitoring
    - Echocardiography
    - Graded exercise test
  - Invasive diagnostic testing
    - Angiography
    - Bronchoscopy
    - Cardiac catheterization
    - Pharmacologic stress test
    - Positron emission tomography (PET)
- Positive findings for specific dysfunction

Electrocardiogram

- Indications
- Contraindications
- Electrode placement
  - Leads V1-V6 (6 chest leads)
  - Leads I, II, III, aVR, aVL, aVF (6 limb leads)
- Waveforms
- Normal ECG reading
- Abnormal ECG readings
- Interpretation of results

Exercise Participation

- Health screening
  - PAR-Q and You
  - Coronary artery disease risk factors
  - Major signs and symptoms suggestive of cardiovascular and pulmonary disease
- Risk stratification for cardiac patients
- Pre-test clinical evaluation
  - Medical history
  - Physical examination
  - Laboratory testing
- Method of exercise
- Treatment parameters
  - Frequency
  - Duration
  - Intensity
  - Repetitions
  - Sets
  - Rest period
  - Type of muscle contraction
  - Strength versus endurance

Exercise Prescription

- Indications
- Contraindications
- Components of a training session
  - Warm-up
  - Activity phase
  - Cool down
- Cardiovascular fitness
  - Mode
  - Intensity
  - Duration
  - Frequency
- Specificity of training
- Rate of progression stages
- Maintenance and supervision of program
- Exercise for patients with cardiac pathology
  - Inpatient and outpatient programs
    - Mode
    - Intensity
    - Duration
    - Frequency
    - Types
    - Rate of progression
    - Resistance training
    - Maintenance and supervision of program
- Exercise for patients with pulmonary pathology
  - Mode
  - Intensity

- Duration
- Frequency
- Breathing strategies
- Alternative modes to exercise training
- Maintenance and supervision of program

- Exercise for specific populations
  - Children
  - Pregnant women
  - Elderly
  - Diabetes
  - Obesity
  - Peripheral vascular disease
  - Hypertension

Heart Rate

- Normal values
  - Infant
  - Child
  - Adult
- Bradycardia
- Tachycardia
- Maximum heart rate
- Resting heart rate
- Calculation
  - By palpation
  - With electrocardiogram strip
- Target heart rate (Karvonen formula)

Heart Sounds

- Auscultation
  - Equipment
  - Placement
- Cardiac cycle
  - Systole
  - Diastole
- Normal/abnormal heart sounds
  - S1
    - Mitral and tricuspid valve
    - Association/cause
  - S2
    - Aortic and pulmonic valve
    - Association/cause
  - S3
    - Ventricular gallop
    - Association/cause
  - S4
    - Atrial gallop
    - Association/cause
- Abnormal heart sounds
  - Systolic murmur
  - Diastolic murmur

Laboratory Values

- Serum enzymes
  - Creatine phosphokinase (CPK-MB)
  - Lactic dehydrogenase (LDH-1)
- Blood lipids
  - Total cholesterol
  - High-density lipoproteins (HDL)
  - Low-density lipoproteins (LDL)
  - Triglycerides
- Complete blood cell count
  - Red blood cells
  - Hemoglobin
  - Hematocrit
  - White blood cells
  - Platelets
- Coagulation profile
  - Prothrombin time (PT)
  - Partial thromboplastin time (PTT)
- Electrolyte levels
  - Sodium (Na^+)
  - Potassium (K^+)
- Serum glucose
  - Normal
  - Hypoglycemia
  - Hyperglycemia
- Arterial blood gases (ABG)
  - pH
  - PaO_2
  - $PaCO_2$
  - HCO_3

Metabolic Equivalents

- Definition
- Physical activity recommendations
- Use in exercise prescription
- Intensity of exercise (METS)
  - Light
  - Moderate
  - Vigorous

Peripheral Pulses

- Locations for peripheral pulse palpation
  - Upper extremity
    - Brachial
    - Radial
    - Carotid
    - Ulnar
  - Lower extremity
    - Femoral
    - Popliteal
    - Posterior tibial
    - Dorsalis pedis
- Procedure
  - Appropriate digits for palpation
  - Note all of the following
    - Rhythm
    - Volume
    - Quality
  - Method of calculating rate
- Grades of pulse
- Normative values
  - Variations of pulses
  - Age
  - Position of body
- Considerations related to diminished pulses
  - Right-sided heart failure
  - Bilateral peripheral edema
  - Diabetes
  - Peripheral vascular disease
- Ankle-brachial index
  - Purpose
  - Doppler ultrasound
  - Procedure
    - Normal values
    - Abnormal values
  - Clinical relevance

Postural Drainage

- Indications
- Contraindications
- Equipment
- Positioning
  - Upper lobes
    - Anterior apical segments
    - Posterior apical segments
    - Anterior segments
    - Posterior segments
    - Lingular segments
  - Middle lobe
    - Right middle segment
  - Lower lobes
    - Basal segments
    - Lateral segments
    - Superior segments
- For each category
  - Indications
  - Contraindications
  - Technique
- Categories of airway clearance
  - Percussion
  - Vibration
- Other airway clearance techniques
  - Huffing
  - Active cycle of breathing
  - Coughing
  - Autogenic drainage
  - High frequency airway oscillation
- Complications of retained secretions

Pulmonary Function Tests

- Lung volume and capacity
  - Spirometry
    - Tidal volume
    - Inspiratory reserve volume
    - Expiratory reserve volume
    - Vital capacity
    - Inspiratory capacity
    - Residual volume

- Gas flow rates
  - Forced vital capacity
  - Forced expiratory volume
  - Forced expiratory volume in one second
- Normal values for common pulmonary measures
- Interpretation of pulmonary function tests
  - Obstructive lung disease
  - Restrictive lung disease

Pulmonary Pharmacology

- For each category
  - Purpose
  - Mechanism
  - Side effects
- Drug categories
  - Antihistamine agents
  - Anti-inflammatory agents
  - Bronchodilator agents
  - Expectorant agents
  - Mucolytic agents

Rate of Perceived Exertion (RPE) Scale

- Purpose
- Advantages
- Disadvantages
- Different scales (Borg)
  - 6-20 scale
  - 0-10 scale
- Corresponding values to level of exertion
- Correlation between RPE and heart rate
- Relationship to fatigue level
- Scenarios to use RPE

Relaxation Techniques

- Purpose
- Indications
- Physiological effects
- Sources of stress
- Effects of stress
- Aspects of relaxation procedures
  - Environment
  - Individual
  - Therapist
- Methods of relaxation
  - Physical approaches
  - Mental approaches
    - Self-awareness
    - Imagery
    - Visualization
    - Autogenic training
    - Meditation
- Limitations
- Outcome measures

Respiration Rate

- Definition
- Measurement methods
- Purpose of monitoring
- Normal values
- Abnormal values
  - Interpretation of abnormal values
- Breathing patterns
  - Orthopnea
  - Bradypnea
  - Tachypnea
  - Dyspnea
  - Apnea
  - Cheyne-Stokes
  - Eupnea
  - Paradoxical
  - Kussmaul's

Risk Factors for Cardiac Disease

- Major risk factors
  - Modifiable
    - Cigarette smoking
    - Hypertension
    - Hypercholesterolemia
    - Physical inactivity
  - Non-modifiable
    - Heredity
    - Male sex
    - Increased age
- Minor risk factors
  - Diabetes
  - Obesity
  - Family history
  - Stress
- Clinical relevance

Sputum Analysis

- Description
  - Color
    - Pink/Red
    - Yellow/Green
    - Brown/Black
    - White/Gray
    - Rust
  - Consistency
    - Viscous
    - Thick/tenacious
  - Odor
    - Fetid
  - Contents
    - Blood
    - Other
  - Quantity
    - Normal versus abnormal
  - Acute versus chronic production
- Types of abnormal sputum
  - Mucoid
  - Mucopurulent
  - Hemoptysis
  - Purulent
  - Frothy
- Medical conditions and characteristic sputum production

Suctioning

- Purpose
- Indications
- Contraindications
- Equipment
- Auscultation of lung sounds
- Sequence of suctioning procedure
- Sputum characteristics
- Potential complications
- Outcome assessment

Target Heart Rate

- Definition
- Purpose
- Formulas
- Predicted maximal heart rate
- Target heart rate range
- Target heart rate for patients with cardiac pathology

Other Systems

Integumentary System

Anatomy of the Integumentary System

- Skin
  - Epidermis
  - Dermis
  - Subcutaneous layer
- Hair
- Nails
- Glands
  - Sweat glands
  - Sebaceous glands

Burn Classification

- Types of burns
  - Thermal
  - Radiation
  - Chemical
  - Electrical
- At risk populations
  - Geriatric
  - Pediatric
  - Psychosocial disorders
- Depth of damage
  - Duration
  - Intensity
  - Skin thickness
  - Area exposed
  - Vascularity
  - Age
- Classification
  - For each classification of burn
    - Layer(s) of skin involved
    - Mechanism of burn
    - Skin appearance
    - Blanching
    - Sensation
    - Associated pain
    - Healing time and mechanism
  - Superficial burn
  - Superficial partial-thickness burn
  - Deep partial-thickness burn
  - Full-thickness burn
  - Subdermal burn
- Burn wound zones
  - Zone of coagulation
  - Zone of stasis
  - Zone of hyperemia

Debridement

- Purpose
- Indications
- Contraindications
- Characteristics of necrotic tissue
  - Slough
  - Eschar
- Selective debridement
  - Sharp
  - Autolytic
  - Enzymatic
- Non-selective debridement
  - Whirlpool
  - Wet-to-dry dressing
  - Wound cleansing
  - Wound irrigation
  - Chemical debridement
  - Pulsatile lavage
- General procedure
  - Positioning
  - Draping
  - Personal protective equipment required
  - Medical asepsis
  - Instruments and equipment
  - Technique
  - Frequency and duration
- Clinical relevance

Dressings

- Purpose
- Indications
- Contraindications
- Selection considerations
  - Location of wound
  - Wound stage
  - Cavities
  - Necrosis
  - Drainage

- Wound edges
- Epithelialization
- Granulation
- Incontinence
- Infection
- Types of dressings
  - For each dressing
    - Description
    - Advantages
    - Disadvantages
    - Procedure
    - Medical asepsis
  - Gauze (woven and unwoven)
  - Wet-to-dry
  - Impregnated gauze
  - Transparent films
  - Hydrocolloids
  - Hydrogels
  - Foams
  - Alginates
  - Absorptive fillers
  - Composite dressings
  - Collagen
  - Biological dressings
  - Dressings containing active agents

Integumentary Pharmacology

- For each category
  - Purpose
  - Mechanisms
  - Side effects
- Drug categories
  - Antibiotic agents
  - Analgesic agents
  - Antimicrobial agents
  - Immunosuppressive agents
  - Topical agents

Physiology of the Integumentary System

- Thermoregulation
- Protection
- Vitamin synthesis
- Excretion of sweat
- Sensation

Positioning

- Definition
- Prevention of primary/secondary impairments
  - Examination
    - Range of motion
    - Pain and discomfort
    - Edema
    - Pressure sores
    - Contracture
    - Skin breakdown
- Bony prominences that contribute to pressure sores
- Common contracture locations
- Instruction and education
  - Role of physical therapist
  - Role of other health care providers/ family
- Techniques for positioning
  - Supine
  - Prone
  - Sidelying
  - Semi-Fowler
  - Trendelenburg
- Pressure relief activities
  - Turning schedule
  - Prevention of shear forces
- Equipment
  - Cushions
  - Wedges
  - Electric bed
  - Pillows
  - Tilt tables
  - Wheelchairs
    - Tilt in space
    - Reclining

Risk Factors for Developing Wounds

- Arterial insufficiency
- Venous insufficiency
- Infection
- Pressure and shear
- Neuropathy
- Mobility
- Age

Rule of Nines
- Purpose
- Total body surface area
  - Anterior and posterior portions
- Percent body area in the adult versus the child
  - Head
  - Upper extremities
  - Trunk
  - Genitals
  - Lower extremities
- Lund and Browder Chart comparison

Scar Management
- Scar formation
  - Process
- Scars
  - Definition and characteristics of each
    - Normal
    - Hypertrophic
    - Keloid
- Healing time
- Intervention
  - Pressure garments
  - Massage and creams
    - Vitamin E
    - Sun block
    - Silicone gel
  - Ultrasound
  - Electrical stimulation
  - Pharmacological
- Aesthetic appearance
  - Surgical
    - Skin graft
    - Tissue expansion

Splinting
- Definition
- Anatomical considerations
- Purpose
- Indications
- Contraindications
- Goals of proper splinting technique
  - Rest
  - Protection
  - Prevention of deformity
  - Substitution
- Types of splints
  - Static
  - Dynamic
- Splinting materials
  - Thermoplastic
  - Non-thermoplastic

Stages of Pressure Injuries
- Description of stages 1-4
- Prognosis
- Staging
  - Variations in staging for darker skin
  - Implication of eschar
  - Benefits of staging
  - Limitations of staging
- Clinical implications
- Precautions

Stages of Wound Healing
- Inflammatory phase
  - Vascular response
  - Cellular response
  - Chemical mediators of inflammation
- Proliferative phase
- Remodeling phase
- Factors affecting tissue repair
- Clinical relevance based on phase
- Length of healing time based on type of wound

Types of Grafts
- Indications
- Contraindications
- For each specific type
  - Advantages
  - Disadvantages
  - Precautions and contraindications post graft
- Specific types
  - Autograft
  - Allograft (homograft)

- Xenograft (heterograft)
- Skin substitutes
- Split-thickness graft
- Full-thickness graft
- Sheet graft
- Mesh graft

Wound Characteristics

- Classification of wound
  - Etiology
  - Specific classifications
    - Red-Yellow-Black system
    - Wagner Ulcer Grade Classification Scale
    - NPUAP Stages 1-4
- Wound examination
  - Location
  - Mechanism of injury
  - Dimensions
    - Length
    - Width
    - Depth
  - Drainage
    - Type
    - Consistency
    - Color and odor
  - Tunneling, undermining, contraction
- Periwound examination
  - Pulses
  - Hair/nail growth
  - Sensation/pain
  - Edema
  - Ecchymosis
- Clinical indicators of wound infection

Metabolic and Endocrine Systems

Anatomy of the Endocrine System

- Hormones secreted, function, and dysfunction of each
  - Hypothalamus
  - Thyroid gland
  - Pituitary gland
  - Parathyroid glands
  - Pancreas
  - Adrenal glands
  - Ovaries
  - Testes

Endocrine Pathology

- Examples
  - Graves' disease
  - Diabetes mellitus
  - Addison's disease
  - Cushing's syndrome

Endocrine Pharmacology

- For each category
  - Purpose
  - Mechanisms
  - Side effects
- Drug categories
  - Replacement therapy
  - Hyperfunction therapy

Functions of the Metabolic System

- Processes of creating energy
  - Anabolism
  - Catabolism
- Metabolic rate
  - Factors that influence rate

Metabolic Pathology

- Examples
  - Mitochondrial disease
  - Osteomalacia
  - Paget's disease
  - Wilson's disease

Gastrointestinal System

Anatomy of the Gastrointestinal System

- Function and dysfunction of each
  - Upper GI
    - Mouth
    - Esophagus
    - Stomach
  - Lower GI
    - Small intestine
      - Duodenum
      - Jejunum
      - Ileum
    - Large intestine
      - Ascending colon
      - Transverse colon
      - Descending colon
      - Sigmoid
      - Rectum
      - Anus
  - Gland organs
    - Gallbladder
    - Liver
    - Pancreas

Gastrointestinal Examination

- Observation
  - Purpose and procedure
  - Pain patterns and location
  - Fatigue
  - Effect of exercise
- Auscultation
  - Purpose and procedure
  - Bowel sounds
  - Vascular sounds
- Palpation
  - Purpose and procedure
  - Upper and lower quadrant palpation
  - Response to palpation (e. g., guarding, rebounding, rigidity)
  - Percussion of abdomen
- Interpretation of findings

Gastrointestinal Pharmacology

- For each category
  - Purpose
  - Mechanisms
  - Side effects
- Drug categories
  - Antacids
  - H+ receptor blockers
  - Proton pump inhibitors
  - Anticholinergics
  - Antibiotics
  - Antidiarrheal agents
  - Laxative agents
  - Emetic agents
  - Antiemetic agents

Gland Organ Pathology

- Examples
  - Jaundice
  - Cirrhosis
  - Hepatitis
  - Cholelithiasis (gallstones)

Lower Gastrointestinal Pathology

- Examples
  - Irritable bowel syndrome
  - Crohn's disease
  - Ulcerative colitis
  - Colon cancer

Upper Gastrointestinal Pathology

- Examples
  - Esophageal cancer
  - Gastroesophageal reflux disease
  - Gastritis
  - Peptic ulcer disease

Genitourinary System

Anatomy of the Genital System

- Function and dysfunction of each
  - Male
    - Prostate
    - Penis
    - Testes
    - Scrotum
    - Pelvic floor musculature
  - Female
    - Uterus
    - Vagina
    - Ovaries
    - Pelvic floor musculature

Anatomy of the Renal System

- Function and dysfunction of each
  - Bladder
  - Ureters
  - Kidneys
  - Urethra

Effects of Exercise on the Renal System

- Considerations with renal disease
- Considerations with urinary incontinence
- Considerations with dialysis

Genital Pathology

- Examples
  - Testicular cancer
  - Prostate cancer
  - Ovarian cancer
  - Uterine cancer
  - Cervical cancer
  - Erectile dysfunction
  - Dyspareunia

Genitourinary Examination

- Observation
  - Purpose and procedure
  - Pain patterns and location
  - Fatigue
  - Abdominal/genital rash
  - Lesions, masses
  - Hernia
  - Edema
- Palpation
  - Purpose and procedure
  - Potential ascites or masses
  - Response to palpation
    - Guarding
    - Rebounding
    - Rigidity
- Percussion of abdomen
  - Purpose and procedure
- Interpretation of findings

Genitourinary Pharmacology

- For each category
  - Purpose
  - Mechanisms
  - Side effects
- Drug categories
  - Antibiotics
  - Cholinergic stimulants
  - Anticholinergic agents
  - Muscle relaxants
  - Diuretic agents
  - Hormone replacement

Renal Pathology

- Examples
  - Glomerulonephritis
  - Acute renal failure
  - Chronic renal failure
  - Hematuria
  - Cystitis
  - Urinary incontinence
    - Stress
    - Urge
    - Overflow
    - Functional

Lymphatic System

Anatomy of the Lymphatic System
- Lymph structures
  - Initial lymph vessels
  - Lymph collectors
  - Lymphatic trunks
  - Deep versus superficial
- Lymph fluid
  - Components
- Lymph nodes
- One-way valves

Functions of the Lymphatic System
- Fluid collection
  - Relationship to venous system
- Protein collection
- Lymph movement
  - Unidirectional flow
  - Role of autonomic nervous system
  - Role of "muscle pump"
- Immune system defense
  - Lymph nodes
  - Thymus
  - Bone marrow
  - Spleen
  - Tonsils
  - Peyer patches (small intestine)

Lymphedema
- Common etiologies
  - Primary versus secondary
- Signs and symptoms
- Staging
  - 0 → 3
- Imaging techniques
  - Direct lymphography
  - Indirect lymphography
  - Lymphoscintigraphy
- Tests and measures
  - Circumferential measurements
  - Volumetric measurements

Complete Decongestive Therapy
- Purpose
- Indications
- Contraindications
- Phase I versus phase II
- Manual lymphatic drainage
  - Purpose
  - Method
- Compression therapy
  - Purpose
  - Bandages versus garments
  - Short-stretch versus long-stretch
  - Appropriate pressure ranges
  - Use of intermittent pneumatic compression devices
- Exercise
  - Purpose
  - Mode
  - Frequency, intensity, duration
  - Exercise order
  - Use of compression
  - Red flags
- Skin care
  - Recommendations

System Interactions

Impact of Comorbidities

- Treatment considerations and expected outcomes
  - Hypertension
  - Diabetes mellitus
  - Obesity
  - Dementia
  - Peripheral vascular disease

Impact of Psychological and Mental Conditions

- Treatment considerations and expected outcomes
  - Anxiety
  - Depression
  - Schizophrenia
  - Affective disorders

Pathologies and Conditions Affecting Multiple Systems

- Treatment considerations and expected outcomes
  - Oncology
  - Psychological disorders
  - Bariatrics
  - Autoimmune disorders
  - Rheumatoid arthritis
  - Systemic lupus erythematosus
  - Fluid and electrolyte imbalances
  - Acid-base imbalances
  - Human immunodeficiency virus
  - Multiple organ dysfunction syndrome

Non-Systems

Equipment, Devices, and Technologies

Adaptive Devices
- ○ Definition
- ○ Types of adaptive devices
  - ○ Features
  - ○ Advantages
  - ○ Disadvantages
- ○ Rationale for prescription
  - ○ Level of dependence
  - ○ Weight bearing status
  - ○ Diagnosis
  - ○ Comorbidities
- ○ Categories for adaptive devices
  - ○ Bathing
  - ○ Personal care
  - ○ Dressing
  - ○ Meal preparation
  - ○ Household tasks
  - ○ Work environment
- ○ Adaptive device examples
  - ○ Long handled reacher
  - ○ Built-up utensil handle
  - ○ Environmental control unit
  - ○ Non-slip surfaces

Assistive Devices
- ○ Definition
- ○ Purpose
- ○ Screening
- ○ For each category
  - ○ Function
  - ○ Measurement
  - ○ Weight bearing
  - ○ Instruction
    - ○ Gait pattern
    - ○ Stairs
    - ○ Curbs
    - ○ Safety awareness
- ○ Assistive device categories
  - ○ Cane
    - ○ Straight
    - ○ Quad
  - ○ Crutches
    - ○ Axillary
    - ○ Lofstrand
  - ○ Walker
    - ○ Standard
    - ○ Rolling
    - ○ Hemi

Gait Patterns
- ○ For each category
  - ○ Assistive device
  - ○ Benefits
  - ○ Weight bearing status
  - ○ Patient instructions
- ○ Gait pattern categories
  - ○ 4-point gait
  - ○ 2-point gait
  - ○ Modified 4-point or 2-point gait
  - ○ 3-point gait
  - ○ Swing-to gait
  - ○ Swing-through gait

Gait Training
- ○ Screening
- ○ Medical record
  - ○ Patient status
  - ○ Laboratory values
  - ○ Diagnosis
  - ○ Mental status
- ○ Contraindications
- ○ Instructions
- ○ Demonstration
- ○ Guarding
  - ○ Positioning
  - ○ Gait belt
- ○ Parallel bar progression
  - ○ Standing balance
  - ○ Weight shifting
  - ○ Stepping
  - ○ Forward progression
  - ○ Turning
  - ○ Backward progression
- ○ Advanced progression
  - ○ Inclines
  - ○ Curb
  - ○ Stairs
  - ○ Uneven surfaces
- ○ Signs and symptoms of distress

Orthoses

- Indications
- Contraindications
- Function
  - Alignment
  - Assist joint motion
  - Relieve weight bearing
  - Protection
  - Tone reducing
- Orthotic assessment
  - Joint mobility
  - Motor function
  - Sensation
  - Cognition
- Types of lower extremity orthoses
  - Foot orthoses (FO)
    - Navicular pad
    - Metatarsal bar
    - Heel wedge/cup
    - Rocker bar
  - Ankle-foot orthoses (AFO)
    - Foot plate
    - Stirrup
      - Solid versus split
    - Ankle control mechanism
      - Solid ankle
      - Posterior leaf spring
      - Anterior stop
      - Posterior stop
  - Knee-ankle-foot orthoses (KAFO)
    - Knee control
      - Hinge offset joint
      - Drop lock
      - Pawl lock with bail release
      - Computer controlled knee joint
  - Hip-knee-ankle-foot orthoses (HKAFO)
    - Hip joint
    - Pelvic band
  - Trunk-hip-knee-ankle-foot orthoses (THKAFO)
    - Lumbosacral orthosis combined with KAFOs
    - Reciprocating gait orthosis
- Lower extremity orthotic training
  - Observation
    - Fit
    - Skin integrity
    - Alignment
  - Mobility training
    - Donning/doffing
    - Transfers
    - Gait
    - Stairs
- Types of trunk orthoses
  - Corset
  - Rigid orthoses
  - Knight-Taylor brace
  - Jewett orthosis
  - Boston brace
  - Milwaukee brace
- Types of cervical orthoses
  - Four-post orthosis
  - Soft foam collar
  - Philadelphia collar
- Major impairments requiring orthoses
  - Congenital defect
    - Cerebral palsy
    - Spina bifida
  - Disease
    - Muscular dystrophy
    - Multiple sclerosis
  - Trauma
    - Spinal cord injury
    - Head injury

Prosthetics

- Indications
- Contraindications
- Prosthetics for ankle/foot disarticulations or Syme's amputation
  - Single axis foot
  - Multi axis foot
  - Hydraulic foot
  - Expandable wall and bladder prosthesis
  - Sleeve suspension Syme's prosthesis
- Socket design
  - Transtibial
    - Patella tendon bearing
    - Total surface bearing

- Transfemoral
  - Quadrilateral
  - Ischial containment
  - Elevated vacuum sockets
- Interface materials
  - Hard socket
  - Socks and sheaths
  - Soft inserts
  - Flexible inner socket
  - Gel liners
- Suspension
  - Transtibial
    - Waist belt or corset
    - Cuff strap
    - Supracondylar/suprapatellar
    - Sleeve
    - Suction
    - Vacuum
  - Transfemoral
    - Pull-in
    - Roll on
    - Shuttle lock system
    - Cushion liner with air expulsion
    - Silesian belt
    - Elevated vacuum
- Limb or pylon design
  - Endoskeletal
  - Exoskeletal
- Prosthetics for knee disarticulation
  - Single axis
  - Polycentric knee
  - Pneumatic
  - Hydraulic
- Upper extremity prosthetics
  - Types
    - Passive or restoration
      - Cable driven
      - Adaptive (activity specific)
      - Electrical
      - Hybrid
- Prosthetic training
  - Observation
    - Fit
    - Skin integrity
    - Alignment
  - Mobility skills

Tubes, Lines, and Medical Equipment

- For each device
  - Function
  - Entrance or location
  - Complications
  - Restrictions
- Feeding devices
  - Nasogastric (NG tube)
  - Gastric tube (G tube)
  - Jejunostomy (J tube)
  - Intravenous feeding system
- Lines/Monitoring devices
  - Arterial line (A-line)
  - Central line
  - Hickman line
  - Intracranial pressure catheter
  - Oximeter
  - Peripherally inserted central catheter
  - Portacath
  - Swan-Ganz (pulmonary artery catheter)
- Ventilators
  - Pressure driven
  - Delivery of breath
- Oxygen therapy
  - Nasal cannula
  - Oronasal mask
  - Tracheostomy mask or catheter
- Ostomy devices
  - Colostomy
  - Urostomy
- Pain control devices
  - Epidural catheter
  - PCA pump (patient controlled analgesia)
- Urinary catheters
  - External
  - Foley
  - Suprapubic

Wheelchair Prescription

- Manual versus power
- Patient considerations
  - Physical abilities

- ◯ Functional abilities
- ◯ Cognition
- ◯ Endurance

◯ Frame considerations
- ◯ Folding
- ◯ Rigid
- ◯ Lightweight
- ◯ Hemi-frame
- ◯ Amputee

◯ Seat and back considerations
- ◯ Sling
- ◯ Solid
- ◯ Cushions
- ◯ Foam
- ◯ Gel
- ◯ Air
- ◯ Molded

◯ Seating systems
- ◯ Support
- ◯ Positioning
- ◯ Comfort
- ◯ Pressure relief

◯ Wheel considerations
- ◯ Quick release wheels
- ◯ Axle placement
- ◯ Casters
- ◯ Tires
  - ◯ Solid
  - ◯ Pneumatic
- ◯ Wheels
  - ◯ Spoke
  - ◯ Mag
- ◯ Push rims
  - ◯ Projections

◯ Brake considerations
- ◯ Push versus pull to lock
- ◯ Extensions

◯ Legrest considerations
- ◯ Rigid with frame
- ◯ Swing away
- ◯ Removable
- ◯ Elevating

◯ Armrest considerations
- ◯ Removable
- ◯ Adjustable height
- ◯ Full versus partial length

◯ Power considerations
- ◯ Joy stick control
- ◯ Sip and puff control
- ◯ Head control
- ◯ Proportional drive
- ◯ Microswitching system

◯ Other considerations
- ◯ Headrest
- ◯ Tilt
- ◯ Trunk supports
- ◯ Recline
- ◯ Anti-tip tubes
- ◯ Seat belts
- ◯ Lap trays
- ◯ Sport/recreation options

◯ Wheelchair measurements
- ◯ Seat width
- ◯ Seat depth
- ◯ Seat height
- ◯ Leg length
- ◯ Arm height
- ◯ Back height

Wheelchair Training

- ◯ Chair propulsion
- ◯ Locks
- ◯ Foot supports
- ◯ Armrests
- ◯ Anti-tip tubes
- ◯ Transfers
- ◯ Level of independence
  - ◯ Wheelies
  - ◯ Curbs
  - ◯ Ramps
- ◯ Vehicle transportation
- ◯ Controlled falls
- ◯ Floor-to-wheelchair transfers
- ◯ Powerchair training
  - ◯ Driving skill
  - ◯ Safety
- ◯ Household propulsion

Therapeutic Modalities

Aquatics
- Purpose
- Indications
- Contraindications
- Properties of water
  - Buoyancy
  - Hydrostatic pressure
  - Viscosity
  - Surface tension
- Heat regulation
- Water temperature
- Physiologic effects of immersion
- Movement through water
- Modifications to weight bearing status
- Special equipment
- Outcome assessment
- Common conditions/diagnoses

Biofeedback
- Purpose
- Indications
- Contraindications
- Instrumentation
- Impedance
- Bandwidth
- Noise level
- Gain
- Ohm's law
- Motor learning
- Feedback
  - Intrinsic
  - Extrinsic
- Muscle physiology
- Neuromuscular re-education
- Outcome assessment
- Common conditions/diagnoses

Continuous Passive Motion
- Purpose
- Indications
- Contraindications
- Physiologic effects
- Risks of immobilization
- Treatment parameters
  - Speed
  - Duration
  - On:off time
  - Safety switch
- Outcome assessment
- Common conditions/diagnoses

Cryotherapy
- Indications
- Contraindications
- Physiologic effects
  - Hemodynamic
  - Neuromuscular
  - Nerve conduction velocity
  - Pain threshold
  - Muscular strength
  - Metabolic rate
- Equipment
- Mechanisms of cooling
- Depth of cooling
- Patient preparation
  - Draping
  - Skin integrity
- Specific agents
  - Cold/ice pack
  - Ice massage
  - Cold compression unit
  - Cold whirlpool
- Normal response
- Abnormal response
- Outcome assessment
- Common conditions/diagnoses

Electrical Equipment Care and Maintenance
- Local, state, and federal operational standards
- Identification of potential problems
- Operation
  - Staff education
  - Operation manuals
- Routine inspections
- Scheduled service on equipment by qualified personnel
- Electrical safety

Electrical Stimulation

- ○ Purpose
- ○ Indications
- ○ Contraindications
- ○ Physiological effects
- ○ Sequence of stimulation (i.e., sensory, motor, pain)
- ○ For each electrical stimulation category
  - ○ Indications
  - ○ Parameters
- ○ Types of electrical stimulation
  - ○ Neuromuscular (NMES)
  - ○ Transcutaneous electrical neuromuscular stimulation (TENS)
    - ○ Acupuncture-like
    - ○ Conventional
    - ○ Brief intense
    - ○ Noxious
  - ○ Functional (FES)
  - ○ Electrical stimulation for wound control and edema
- ○ Type of current
  - ○ Direct (galvanic)
  - ○ Alternating
  - ○ Pulsatile
    - ○ Monophasic
    - ○ Biphasic
  - ○ Russian
  - ○ High-volt
  - ○ Interferential
- ○ Electrodes
  - ○ Placement
  - ○ Size
- ○ Outcome assessment
- ○ Common conditions/diagnoses

Electromyography

- ○ Definition
- ○ Purpose
- ○ Instrumentation
- ○ Electrodes
- ○ Skin resistance
- ○ Sensitivity
- ○ Artifacts
- ○ Insertion activity
- ○ Muscle at rest
  - ○ Spontaneous potentials
- ○ Normal action potentials
  - ○ Phase
  - ○ Polyphasic potentials
  - ○ Interference pattern
- ○ Abnormal action potentials
  - ○ Spontaneous activity
  - ○ Fibrillation potentials
  - ○ Positive sharp waves
  - ○ Fasciculations
  - ○ Repetitive discharges

Hydrotherapy

- ○ Purpose
- ○ Indications
- ○ Contraindications
- ○ Physiologic effects
- ○ Uses of hydrotherapy
  - ○ Superficial heating/cooling
  - ○ Wound care
  - ○ Water exercise
  - ○ Pain control
  - ○ Edema control
- ○ Forms of hydrotherapy
  - ○ Whirlpool
  - ○ Hubbard tank
  - ○ Exercise pool
  - ○ Non-immersion irrigation device
- ○ Application variables
  - ○ Temperature
  - ○ Equipment
  - ○ Frequency
  - ○ Duration
- ○ Outcome assessment
- ○ Common conditions/diagnoses

Intermittent Compression

- ○ Purpose
- ○ Indications
- ○ Contraindications
- ○ Physiologic effects
- ○ Methods of application
- ○ Equipment required

- Types of sleeves
  - Upper extremity
  - Lower extremity
- Inflation/deflation ratio
- Patient positioning
- Treatment procedure
  - Observation
  - Measurements
  - Duration
  - Frequency
- Use of intermittent compression in garment measurement
- Outcome assessment
- Common conditions/diagnoses

Iontophoresis

- Indications
- Contraindications
- Theory
- Type of current
- Primary medications administered
  - Polarity
  - Dosage
  - Side effects
- Current parameters
  - Amplitude
  - Duration
  - Total current dosage
  - Frequency
  - Depth
  - Determining treatment time
  - Number of treatments
- Skin preparation
- Electrodes
  - Size options
  - Polarity
- Electrode placement
  - Delivery electrode (active)
  - Return electrode (dispersive)
  - Distance between electrodes
- Skin response to treatment
  - Normal pH
  - Alkaline reaction
  - Acidic reaction
- Physician prescription
- Outcome assessment
- Common conditions/diagnoses

Massage

- Purpose
- Indications
- Contraindications
- Therapeutic effects
  - Mechanical
  - Reflex
  - Physiological
  - Psychological
- Techniques
  - Effleurage
  - Petrissage
  - Tapotement
  - Friction
  - Vibration

Principles of Heat Transfer

- Physiologic effect
- Physical principles
  - Specific heat
  - Thermal conductivity of materials
- Method of heat transfer
  - Conduction
  - Convection
  - Conversion
  - Radiation
  - Evaporation

Superficial Heat

- Purpose
- Indications
- Contraindications
- Physiologic effect
  - Hemodynamic
  - Neuromuscular
  - Nerve conduction velocity
  - Pain threshold
  - Muscular strength
  - Metabolic rate
  - Collagen extensibility
- Penetration
  - Tissue depth

- Specific agents
  - Hot packs
  - Infrared lamps
  - Whirlpool
- Normal response
- Abnormal response
- Outcome assessment
- Common conditions/diagnoses

Traction – Mechanical/Manual

- Purpose
- Indications
- Contraindications
- For each category
  - Manual techniques
  - Mechanical techniques
    - Set-up
    - Treatment parameters
      - Amount of force
      - On:off time
      - Ramps/steps
      - Duration
    - Mode
      - Progressive
      - Continuous
      - Intermittent
    - Influence of gravity
    - Patient response/tolerance
    - Safety
- Traction categories
  - Cervical traction
  - Lumbar traction

Ultrasound

- Purpose
- Indications
- Contraindications
- Physiologic effects
- Methods of application
  - Direct contact
  - Water immersion
  - Cushion contact
- Coupling agents
- Treatment parameters
  - Intensity
  - Duration
  - Frequency
  - Duty cycle
- Equipment maintenance
- Terminology
  - Effective radiating area
  - Beam nonuniformity ratio
  - Attenuation
- Outcome assessment
- Common conditions/diagnoses

Safety and Protection

Abuse

- Definition
- Types of abuse
  - Physical
  - Sexual
  - Emotional
  - Neglect
  - Abandonment
- Signs of abuse
- Sources of abuse
- Reporting abuse
- Legal requirements
- Code of Ethics
- Advocacy

Bed Mobility

- Indications
- Contraindications
- Screening
  - Strength
  - Range of motion
  - Cognitive status
  - Safety awareness
- Techniques
  - Scooting
  - Bridging
  - Log rolling
  - Segmental rolling
  - Prone prop
  - Supine-to-sit
  - Sit-to-supine
- Level of independence
- Frequency
- Potential complications
  - Surgery
  - Secondary diagnoses
  - Anatomic factors
  - Physiological factors
  - Mental status
- Considerations for specific patient populations

Body Mechanics

- Purpose
- Principles for proper posture
- Principles of body mechanics
  - Gravity
  - Friction
  - Lever arm
  - Torque
  - Center of gravity
  - Vertical gravity line
  - Base of support
  - Anterior-posterior stance
  - Medial-lateral stance
- Basic lift patterns
  - Deep squat lift
  - Diagonal squat lift
  - Half-kneel lift
  - One leg stance lift
  - Power lift
  - Traditional lift
- Pushing and pulling objects

Cardiopulmonary Resuscitation (CPR)

- Indications
- Contraindications
- For each population
  - Recognition
  - Sequence
  - Compression rate
  - Compression depth
  - Hand placement
  - Compression interruptions
  - Airway
  - Compression-to-ventilation ratio
  - Ventilations
  - Defibrillation
- Populations
  - Adult
  - Child
  - Infant
- AEDs
  - Indications
  - Sequence of operation
  - 1-rescuer versus 2-rescuer
- Termination of CPR

Emergency Care Procedures

- First aid
- Cardiopulmonary resuscitation
- For each condition
  - Signs
  - Symptoms
  - Management
- Emergent condition examples
  - Autonomic dysreflexia
  - Diabetic reaction/coma
  - Hypovolemic shock
  - Orthostatic hypotension
  - Appendicitis
  - Hemorrhage
  - Pulmonary embolism
  - Seizures

Ergonomics

- Definition
- Workstation analysis
  - Chair height
  - Seat depth
  - Arm rest height
  - Desk height
  - Monitor
  - Keyboard position
  - Lighting
- Cumulative trauma disorders
  - Definition
  - Causes
  - Risk factors
  - Signs and symptoms
  - Prevention
  - Intervention
    - Postural training
    - Stretching
    - Body mechanics
    - Proper lifting techniques
- Occupational Safety and Health Administration guidelines

Guarding Technique

- Purpose
- Positioning
  - Even ground
  - Uneven ground
  - Curbs
  - Stairs
- Level of physical assistance
  - Independent
  - Modified assistance
  - Contact guard
  - Minimal assistance
  - Moderate assistance
  - Maximum assistance
  - Dependent
- Considerations for specific patient population

Infection Control

- Definition
- Infectious disease
  - Cycle of contamination and infection
  - Methods of disease transmission
    - Direct contact
    - Droplet contact
    - Airborne transmission
    - Fecal-oral transmission
    - Vector-borne transmission
- Infection control
  - Standard precautions
    - Hand washing techniques
    - Medical asepsis
    - Surgical asepsis
  - Transmission-based precautions
    - Airborne
    - Droplet
    - Contact
- Category specific isolation precautions
  - Strict isolation
  - Contact isolation
  - Respiratory isolation
  - Tuberculosis (AFB) isolation
  - Enteric precautions
  - Drainage/secretion precautions
  - Blood/body fluid precautions
- Types and application of personal protective equipment
  - Cap

- Mask
- Gown
- Gloves
- Goggles
- Mouthpiece
- Sterile field
  - Setup and guidelines
- Resources
  - Occupational Safety and Health Administration
  - Centers for Disease Control
  - Environmental Protection Agency

Levels of Weight Bearing

- Definition
  - Non-weight bearing
  - Toe touch weight bearing
  - Partial weight bearing
  - Weight bearing as tolerated
  - Full weight bearing
- Maintaining weight bearing status
  - Patient education
  - Assistive devices
- Common conditions requiring altered weight bearing status
  - Injuries
  - Surgeries

Pressure Relief Activities

- Etiology
- Risk factors
  - Immobility
  - Decreased sensation
  - Prolonged pressure
  - Shearing forces
  - Improper positioning
  - Inadequate nutrition
- Skin inspection
- At risk areas
- Intervention
  - Proper skin care
  - Positioning
  - Weight shifting
  - Proper nutrition
  - Clothing
  - Mobility schedule
- Frequency of pressure relief activities
- Adaptive equipment for pressure relief

Transfers

- Definition
- General transfer principles
  - Screening
  - Preparation
  - Body mechanics
  - Safety
- Types of transfers
  - Sit to stand
    - Essential components
    - Patient instruction
    - Technique with assistive device
      - Cane
      - Crutches
      - Walker
  - Bed to chair/wheelchair
    - Essential components
    - Patient instruction
    - Position of chair or wheelchair
    - Use of sliding board
  - Stand-pivot technique
  - Dependent transfer
    - Dependent squat pivot
    - Two-person lift
    - Three-person lift
    - Mechanical lift (hydraulic)
- Conditions requiring special precautions during transfers

Professional Responsibilities

Accessibility Standards
- Definitions
  - Accessible
  - Adaptability
  - Alteration
- Accessibility requirements
  - Wheelchairs
    - Hallway clearance
    - Turning radius
  - Ramp
    - Rise:run ratio
    - Percent grade
    - Width
  - Doorway
  - Threshold
  - Corridor
  - Lavatory
    - Toilet
    - Sink (elevation from floor)
    - Sink depth
    - Shower
- Americans with Disabilities Act

Advanced Directives
- Purpose
- Patients' rights
- Types of advanced directives
  - Living will
  - Do not resuscitate
  - Durable power of attorney
  - Anatomical donation
- Requirements to establish advanced directives
- Modifications to existing advanced directives
- Clinical relevance

Americans with Disabilities Act (ADA)
- Purpose
- Definitions
  - Disability
  - Environmental barrier
  - Accessibility
  - Undue hardship
  - Qualified individual
  - Reasonable accommodation
- Purpose of ADA
- Important components of environmental barriers assessment
- 5 Titles of the ADA
  - Employment
  - Transportation (Public Services)
  - Public accommodations and services
  - Telecommunications
  - Miscellaneous
- Responsibility for enforcement
- Exempted parties

APTA Documents
- Standards of Practice for Physical Therapy
- Guide for Professional Conduct
- Code of Ethics for the Physical Therapist
- Guide for Conduct of the Physical Therapist Assistant
- Standards of Ethical Conduct for the Physical Therapist Assistant

Classical Conditioning
- Definition
- Unconditioned stimulus
- Neutral stimulus
- Conditioned stimulus
- Clinical relevance

Cultural Influence
- Definitions
  - Culture
  - Cultural competence
  - Cultural diversity
  - Cultural sensitivity
  - Ethnicity
  - Race

- Awareness
  - Prejudices
  - Biases
  - Beliefs
  - Values
- Understanding cultural norms

Delegation

- Definition
- Delegation of physical therapy services to PTA
  - Procedures unable to delegate
    - Initial examination
    - Reexamination
    - Diagnosis/prognosis
    - Development and modifications to plan of care
    - Development of discharge plan
    - Supervision of all care
  - Procedures able to delegate
    - Tests and measures
    - Interventions within established plan of care
    - Patient education
    - Family training
    - Tasks deemed appropriate by supervising PT
- Delegation of physical therapy services to PT aide
  - Support services directed by PT

Disablement Models

- Definition
- Purpose
- Nagi Model
  - Pathology
  - Impairment
  - Functional limitation
  - Disability
- International Classification of Functioning, Disability, and Health (ICF) Model
  - Body function
  - Body structure
  - Activity and participation
  - Environmental factors
- Utilization of disablement models in physical therapy
- Guide to Physical Therapy Practice

Documentation

- Purpose
  - Communication
  - Legal record
  - Reimbursement
- Types of documentation
  - Handwritten
  - Electronic
- Components of each section of a S.O.A.P. note
  - Subjective
    - History
  - Objective
    - Systems review
    - Tests and measures
  - Assessment
    - Evaluation
    - Diagnosis
    - Prognosis
    - Goals
  - Plan of care
    - Outcomes
- Examination
- Reassessment
- Progress reports
- Discharge summary
- Incident reports
- Role in documentation
  - Physical therapist
  - Physical therapist assistant
- Medical terminology
- Medical abbreviations
- Charting errors
- ICD codes
- CPT codes
- Confidentiality
- Patients' rights

Domains of Learning
- For each domain
  - Definition
  - Clinical relevance
- Domains
  - Cognitive
  - Affective
  - Psychomotor

Draping
- Rationale
- Explanation to patient
- Methods to ensure modesty
- Equipment
- Draping procedure by position
- Clean linen
- Disposal of soiled or used linen
- Clinical relevance

Ethical Principles
- Code of Ethics
- Autonomy
- Beneficence
- Confidentiality
- Nonmaleficence
- Justice
- Veracity
- Fidelity
- Law versus ethics
- Ethical problem solving
  - Gather relevant information
  - Identify the dilemma
  - Decide what to do
  - Complete the action
- Ethical theories
  - Teleological
  - Deontologism

Federal Legislation Affecting Children with Disabilities
- For each piece of legislation
  - Purpose
  - Inclusion criteria
  - Relevance to physical therapy
- Individuals with Disabilities Education Act
- Education for All Handicapped Children Act
- Section 504 of the Rehabilitation Act

Feedback
- Intrinsic feedback
- Extrinsic feedback
  - Knowledge of performance
  - Knowledge of results
  - Verbal instructions
  - Demonstration
  - Manual cueing
  - Visual inputs
  - Biofeedback
  - Timing of feedback
    - Immediate
    - Summary
- Role of environment
  - Open environment
  - Closed environment

Health Behavior Models
- Health Belief Model
  - Theory
    - Perceived susceptibility
    - Perceived severity
    - Perceived benefit
    - Perceived barriers
    - Cues to action
    - Self-efficacy
  - Clinical relevance
- Locus of Control
  - Theory
    - Internal locus of control
    - External locus of control
  - Clinical relevance
- Social Cognitive Theory (Social Learning Theory)
  - Theory
    - Environment
    - Situation
    - Reinforcement
    - Behavior capability

- Expectations
- Expectancies
- Self-control
- Observational learning
- Reinforcements
- Self-efficacy
- Emotional coping responses
- Reciprocal determinism
- Clinical relevance
- Transtheoretical Model (Stages of Change)
  - Theory
    - Precontemplation
    - Contemplation
    - Preparation
    - Action
    - Maintenance
  - Clinical relevance

Health Care Professions

- Job description for each health care provider
  - Level of education required
  - Scope of practice
  - Specialty areas
- Licensed health care providers
  - Physician
  - Physician assistant
  - Nurse
  - Pharmacist
  - Physical therapist
  - Physical therapist assistant
  - Occupational therapist
  - Occupational therapist assistant
  - Speech and language pathologist
  - Respiratory therapist
  - Chiropractors
  - Psychologist
- Non-licensed health care providers
  - Physical therapy aide
  - Physical therapy students

Health Insurance

- Types of health insurance
  - Managed care
    - Health Maintenance Organization
    - Preferred Provider Organization
  - Government/State programs
    - Medicare
      - Part A
      - Part B
      - Part C
      - Part D
    - Medicaid
    - Workers' compensation
  - Individual private insurance
  - Employment-based private insurance
- Reimbursement
  - Per visit
  - Per case
  - Fee for service
  - Prospective
  - Retrospective
- Terminology
  - Subscriber
  - Provider
  - Third party payer
  - Primary care physician
  - Referral
- Payment
  - Capitated
  - Per diem
  - Copayments
  - Deductibles

Individual Education Plan (IEP)

- Definition
- Purpose
- Parental rights
- Process
  - Present levels of performance
  - Meeting
  - Needs
  - Eligibility
  - Disabilities
  - Placement and services
  - Annual goals and objectives
- Medical versus educational
- Alternative school placements

- Interventions in schools

Informed Consent
- Definition
- Indication
- Purpose
  - Standards of Practice
  - Code of Ethics
- Obtaining consent
  - Role of physical therapist
  - Disclosure of information
  - Requirements of obtaining consent
  - Adult versus minor
- Documentation of informed consent

Maslow's Hierarchy of Needs
- Definition
- Purpose
- Clinical significance
- Hierarchy of needs
  - Physiological needs
  - Safety needs
  - Social needs
  - Esteem needs
  - Self-actualization
- Progression of needs
- Maximum potential
- Goal: self-actualization

Operant Conditioning
- Definition
- Stimulus-response-stimulus learning
- Reinforcement
  - Strengthen response
    - Positive
    - Negative
  - Weaken response
    - Response cost
    - Punishment
    - Extinction
  - Rules in analyzing
- Schedules of reinforcement
  - Continuous
  - Intermittent
    - Interval
      - Fixed
      - Variable
    - Ratio
      - Fixed
      - Variable

Psychological Disorders
- For each classification
  - Definition
  - Etiology
  - Clinical presentation
  - Prognosis
  - Intervention
  - Pharmacology
- Psychological disorder classification
  - Affective disorders
    - Depression
    - Mania
    - Bipolar
  - Neuroses disorders
    - Obsessive-compulsive
    - Anxiety
    - Phobia
  - Dissociative disorders
    - Multiple personality
  - Somatoform disorders
    - Conversion
    - Somatization
    - Hypochondriasis
  - Schizophrenia disorders
    - Paranoid
    - Catatonic
    - Disorganized
  - Personality disorders
    - Psychopathic personality
    - Antisocial behavior
    - Narcissistic behavior
    - Borderline behavior
  - Miscellaneous

- Attention deficit disorder
- Physical dependence

Risk Management Program

- Purpose
- Risk identification
  - Areas of concern
    - Property risks
    - Employee benefit risks
    - Liability risks
- Information obtained
  - Previous claims
  - Incident reports
  - Occurrence screening
  - Treatment records
  - Committee reports
- Analysis
  - Frequency
  - Severity
  - Effect of past occurrences
  - Likelihood of reoccurrence
  - Effect of reoccurrence
- Risk management options
  - Loss prevention
  - Loss reduction
  - Controlling exposure
  - Risk acceptance
  - Risk transfer
  - Avoidance
- Physical therapy concerns and management
  - Abuse
  - Assault
  - Harassment
  - Neglect
  - Fraud

Stages of Dying

- Definition of death
- Stages
  - Denial
  - Anger
  - Bargaining
  - Depression
  - Acceptance
- Clinical presentation within each stage
- Treatment strategies within each stage
- Clinical relevance

Teaching Methods

- Factors influencing selection of treatment methods
- Stages of learning
  - Cognitive
  - Associative
  - Autonomous
- Instruction
  - Verbal
  - Demonstration
  - Environment
  - Practice
    - Whole
    - Part
    - Serial
    - Discrete
    - Continuous
    - Blocked
    - Random
    - Mental imagery
    - Massed
    - Distributed

Team Models

- Definition
- Types of team structure
  - Multidisciplinary
  - Interdisciplinary
  - Transdisciplinary
- Clinical relevance

Research and Evidence-Based Practice

Descriptive Statistics
- Definition
- Measures of frequency
  - Frequency distribution
- Measures of central tendency
  - Mean
  - Median
  - Mode
- Measures of variability
  - Range
  - Variance
  - Standard deviation
- Measures of relative position
  - Percentiles
  - Quartiles
  - Standardized scores
- Measures of relationship
  - Coefficient of correlation
- Clinical relevance

Inferential Statistics
- Sampling concepts
  - Population
  - Sample
- Probability
- Sampling error (standard error)
- Standard error of the mean
- Confidence intervals
- Hypothesis testing
  - Null hypothesis
  - Alternate hypothesis
  - Errors in hypothesis testing
    - Type I error
    - Type II error
- Significance level
- One tailed test
- Two tailed test
- Parametric statistics
- Nonparametric statistics

Levels of Measurement
- Definition
- Purpose
- Hierarchy of levels
  - Nominal
  - Ordinal
  - Interval
  - Ratio
- Examples of variables representative of each level
- Influence on statistic selection

Normal Distribution
- Definition
- Purpose
- Proportions of the normal curve
- Standardized scores
- Clinical relevance

Qualitative Research
- Definition
- Purpose
- Assumptions
- Advantages
- Disadvantages
- Types of qualitative research
- Types of data collection
- Clinical relevance

Quantitative Research
- Definition
- Purpose
- Assumptions
- Advantages
- Disadvantages
- Types of quantitative research
- Types of data collection
- Clinical relevance

Reliability
- Definition
- Types
  - Interrater reliability

- Intrarater reliability
    - Test-retest reliability
    - Parallel-forms (alternate forms)
  - Sources of error
    - Instrument
    - Human
    - Measurement
  - Relationship to validity
  - Clinical relevance

Research Design

- Definition
- Types
  - Experimental
  - Quasi-experimental
  - Non-experimental
- Clinical relevance

Research Studies

- Purpose
- Methodology
- Hierarchy of evidence
  - Systematic reviews
  - Meta-analysis
  - Randomized controlled trials
  - Cohort studies
  - Case-control studies
  - Cross sectional surveys
  - Case reports
  - Expert opinions
  - Anecdotal

Sampling

- Definition
- Probability sampling
  - Simple random
  - Stratified random
  - Cluster
  - Systematic sampling
- Non-probability sampling
  - Convenience
  - Purposive
  - Quota
  - Snowball
- Sample size
  - Statistical power
  - Type II error
  - Components to determine sample size
- Clinical relevance

Sensitivity-Specificity

- Validity of screening tests
  - Predictive values
- Sensitivity
  - Definition
  - True positive
  - False negative
  - Examples of situations requiring screening tests with high sensitivity
- Specificity
  - Definition
  - True negative
  - False positive
  - Examples of situations requiring screening tests with high specificity
- Clinical relevance

Statistical Charts and Diagrams

- Bar graph
- Box and whisker plot
- Dot plot
- Gantt chart
- Histogram
- Line graph
- Pie chart
- Scatter plot

Validity

- Definition
- Types
  - Face

- ○ Content
- ○ Construct
- ○ Concurrent
- ○ Predictive

○ Sources of error
- ○ Instrument
- ○ Human
- ○ Measurement

○ Relationship to reliability

○ Clinical relevance

Variables

- ○ Definition
- ○ Independent variables
- ○ Dependent variable
- ○ Clinical relevance

Clinical Application Templates

On the Road to Mastery!

Clinical Application Templates allow candidates to determine if they possess talking knowledge of commonly encountered medical diagnoses.

Clinical Application Templates assist candidates to:

- Increase familiarity with a diverse group of medical diagnoses
- Improve ability to apply clinical knowledge in diverse clinical scenarios
- Establish a reinforcing loop for previously reviewed academic content
- Prioritize study time based on the relative importance of various medical diagnoses

Clinical Application Templates

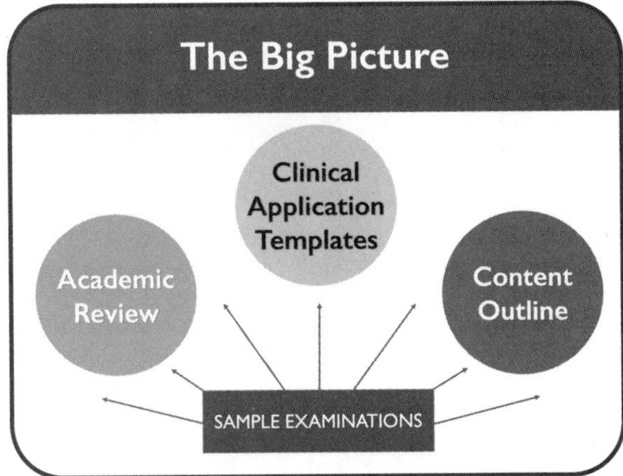
The Big Picture
Clinical Application Templates
Academic Review
Content Outline
SAMPLE EXAMINATIONS

Quiz

- Do you feel that academic knowledge alone will be adequate to pass the NPTE-PT?
- Do you feel it will be important to be familiar with the patient/client management of commonly encountered medical diagnoses on the NPTE-PT?
- Do you believe all diagnoses will be encountered with the same frequency on the NPTE-PT?

Quiz

Attempt to predict which diagnoses will be encountered on the NPTE-PT with greater frequency.

Ready, Set, Go!

Quiz

Stroke **or** Trigeminal Neuralgia

Bronchitis **or** Pulmonary Fibrosis

Diabetes Mellitus **or** Cushing's Syndrome

Cerebral Palsy **or** Post-Polio Syndrome

Anterior Compartment Syndrome **or** Rotator Cuff Tendonitis

Conclusion

Do you see the potential benefit of a classification system that attempts to prioritize diagnoses based on their hypothesized importance on the NPTE-PT?

Possible Review Strategies

- Time spent reviewing a diagnosis should be proportionate to the frequency of the diagnosis on the actual examination.
- Three level tiered approach may assist candidates to increase return on investment (ROI) since more commonly encountered diagnoses occupy a higher percentage of the study time.
- Goal is to have talking knowledge related to each of the listed diagnoses in order to reinforce academic review and improve decision making.

Gold – Main Course

- Commonly encountered
- High ROI $$$

Silver - Sides

- Occasionally encountered
- Moderate ROI $$

Bronze - Dessert

- Infrequently encountered
- Low ROI $

Clinical Application Templates (CAT)

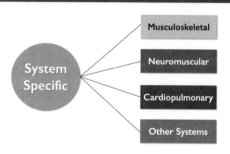

System Specific
- Musculoskeletal
- Neuromuscular
- Cardiopulmonary
- Other Systems

Clinical Application Template Masters

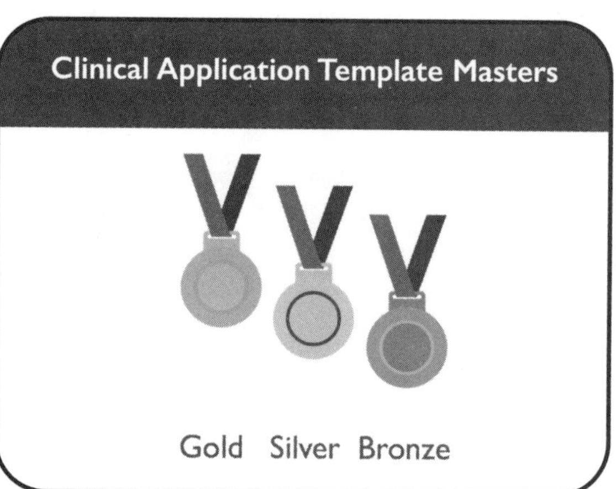
Gold
Silver
Bronze

Clinical Application Template Diagnoses
System Specific Listings

Musculoskeletal System

Gold	Silver	Bronze
Achilles Tendon Rupture	Disk Herniation	Anterior Compartment Syndrome
Adhesive Capsulitis	Glenohumeral Dislocation – Anterior	Colles' Fracture
Ankle Sprain – Lateral	Medial Epicondylitis	De Quervain's Tenosynovitis
Anterior Cruciate Ligament Sprain – Grade III	Meniscal Tear	Myositis Ossificans
Bicipital Tendonitis	Osgood-Schlatter Disease	Osteochondritis Dissecans
Lateral Epicondylitis	Piriformis Syndrome	Osteomyelitis
Medial Collateral Ligament Sprain – Grade II	Posterior Cruciate Ligament Sprain	Tarsal Tunnel Syndrome
Osteoarthritis	Spinal Stenosis – Lumbar	Ulnar Collateral Ligament Sprain – Thumb
Osteogenesis Imperfecta	Trochanteric Bursitis	
Patellofemoral Syndrome		
Plantar Fasciitis		
Rotator Cuff Tear		
Rotator Cuff Tendonitis		
Scoliosis		
Spondylolisthesis – Degenerative		
Temporomandibular Joint Dysfunction		
Torticollis – Congenital		
Total Hip Arthroplasty		
Total Knee Arthroplasty		
Total Shoulder Arthroplasty		
Transfemoral Amputation due to Osteosarcoma		
Transtibial Amputation due to Arteriosclerosis Obliterans		

Neuromuscular and Nervous Systems

Gold	Silver	Bronze
Alzheimer's Disease	Anterior Cord Syndrome	Epilepsy
Amyotrophic Lateral Sclerosis	Bell's Palsy	Polyneuropathy
Carpal Tunnel Syndrome	Cauda Equina Syndrome	Trigeminal Neuralgia
Central Cord Syndrome	Myasthenia Gravis	
Cerebral Palsy	Post-Polio Syndrome	
Cerebrovascular Accident		
Down Syndrome		
Duchenne Muscular Dystrophy		
Erb's Palsy		
Guillain-Barre Syndrome		
Huntington's Disease		
Multiple Sclerosis		
Parkinson's Disease		
Sciatica – Secondary to a Herniated Disk		
Spina Bifida – Myelomeningocele		
Spinal Cord Injury – Complete C7 Tetraplegia		
Spinal Cord Injury – Complete L3 Paraplegia		
Thoracic Outlet Syndrome		
Traumatic Brain Injury		
Vestibular Disorders		

Cardiovascular and Pulmonary Systems

Gold	Silver	Bronze
Congestive Heart Failure	Angina Pectoris	Aneurysm
Cystic Fibrosis	Coronary Artery Disease	Atelectasis
Emphysema	Hypertension	Chronic Venous Insufficiency
Myocardial Infarction		Cor Pulmonale
Peripheral Vascular Disease		Pericarditis
Restrictive Lung Disease		Pleural Effusion
		Pneumothorax
		Pulmonary Edema
		Pulmonary Embolism
		Respiratory Acidosis
		Respiratory Alkalosis
		Sarcoidosis
		Tuberculosis
		Venous Thrombosis

Other Systems

Integumentary System

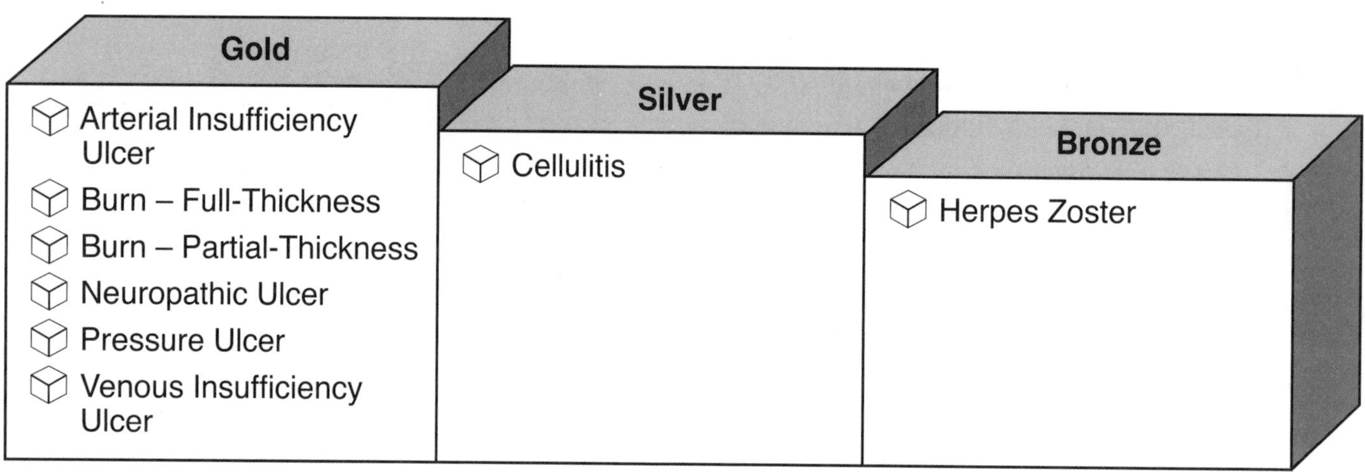
Gold
Arterial Insufficiency Ulcer
Burn – Full-Thickness
Burn – Partial-Thickness
Neuropathic Ulcer
Pressure Ulcer
Venous Insufficiency Ulcer
Silver
Cellulitis
Bronze
Herpes Zoster

Metabolic and Endocrine Systems

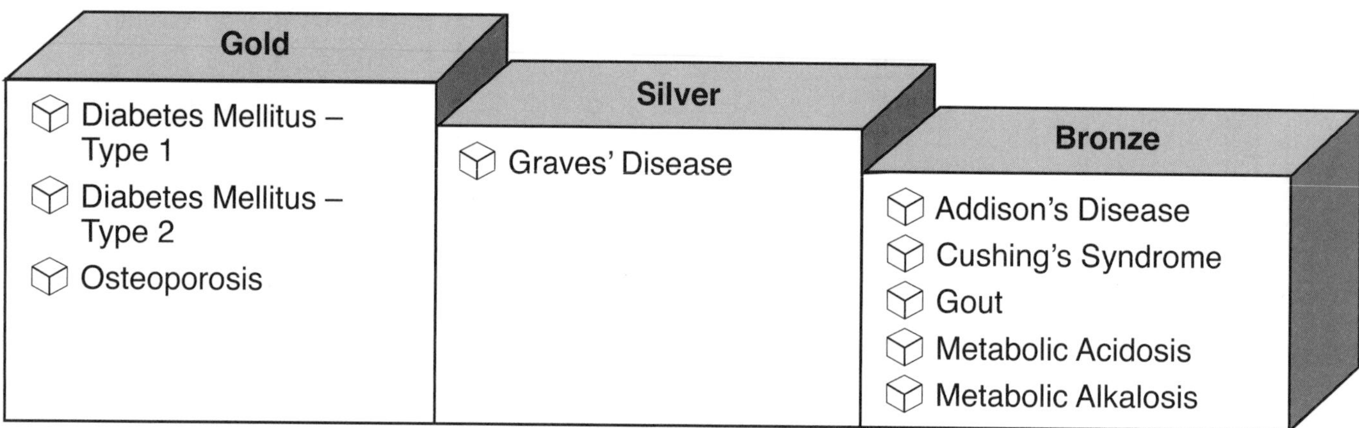
Gold
Diabetes Mellitus – Type 1
Diabetes Mellitus – Type 2
Osteoporosis
Silver
Graves' Disease
Bronze
Addison's Disease
Cushing's Syndrome
Gout
Metabolic Acidosis
Metabolic Alkalosis

Gastrointestinal System

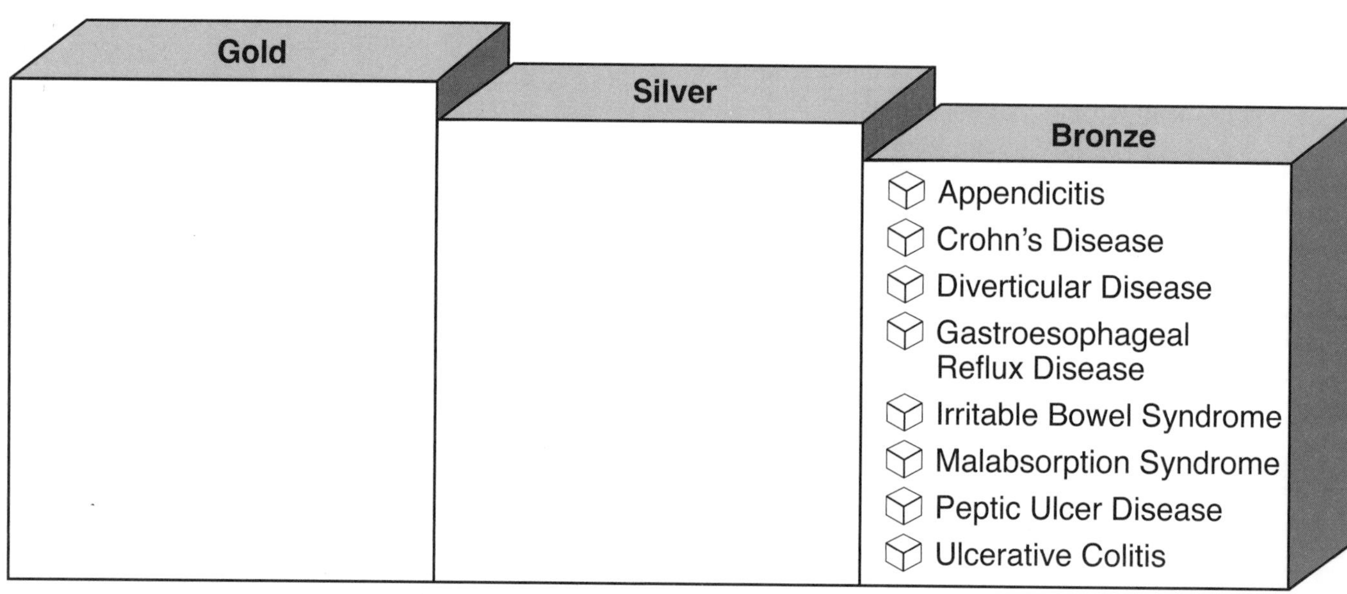
Gold
Silver
Bronze
Appendicitis
Crohn's Disease
Diverticular Disease
Gastroesophageal Reflux Disease
Irritable Bowel Syndrome
Malabsorption Syndrome
Peptic Ulcer Disease
Ulcerative Colitis

Genitourinary System

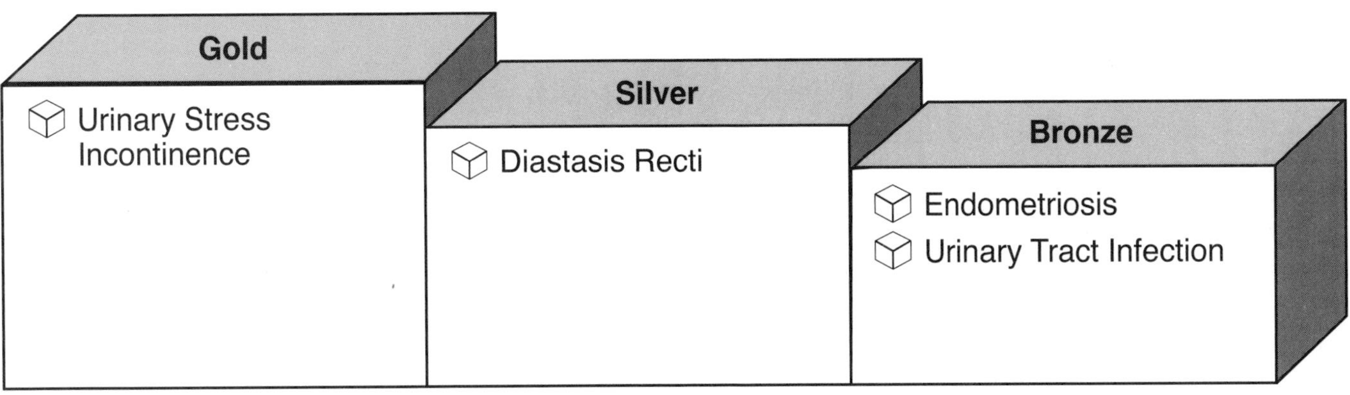

Gold
Urinary Stress Incontinence
Silver
Diastasis Recti
Bronze
Endometriosis
Urinary Tract Infection

Lymphatic System

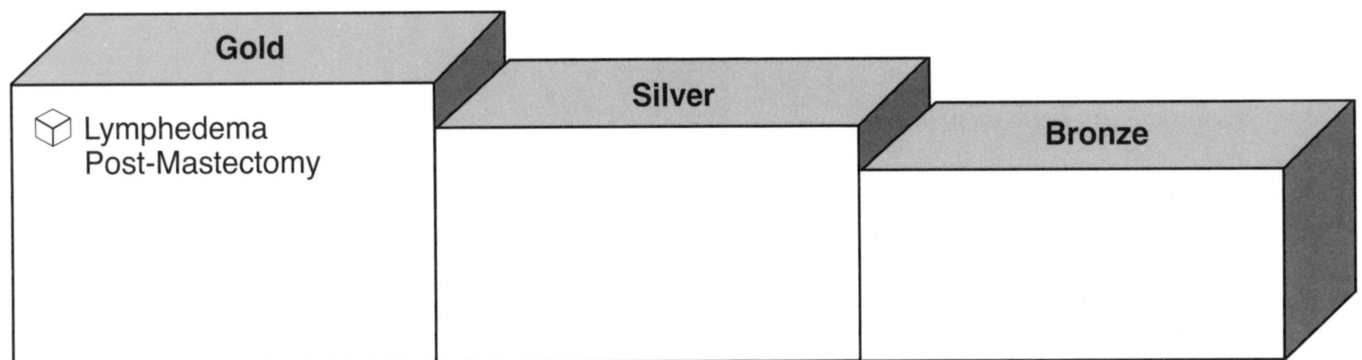

Gold
Lymphedema Post-Mastectomy
Silver
Bronze

System Interactions

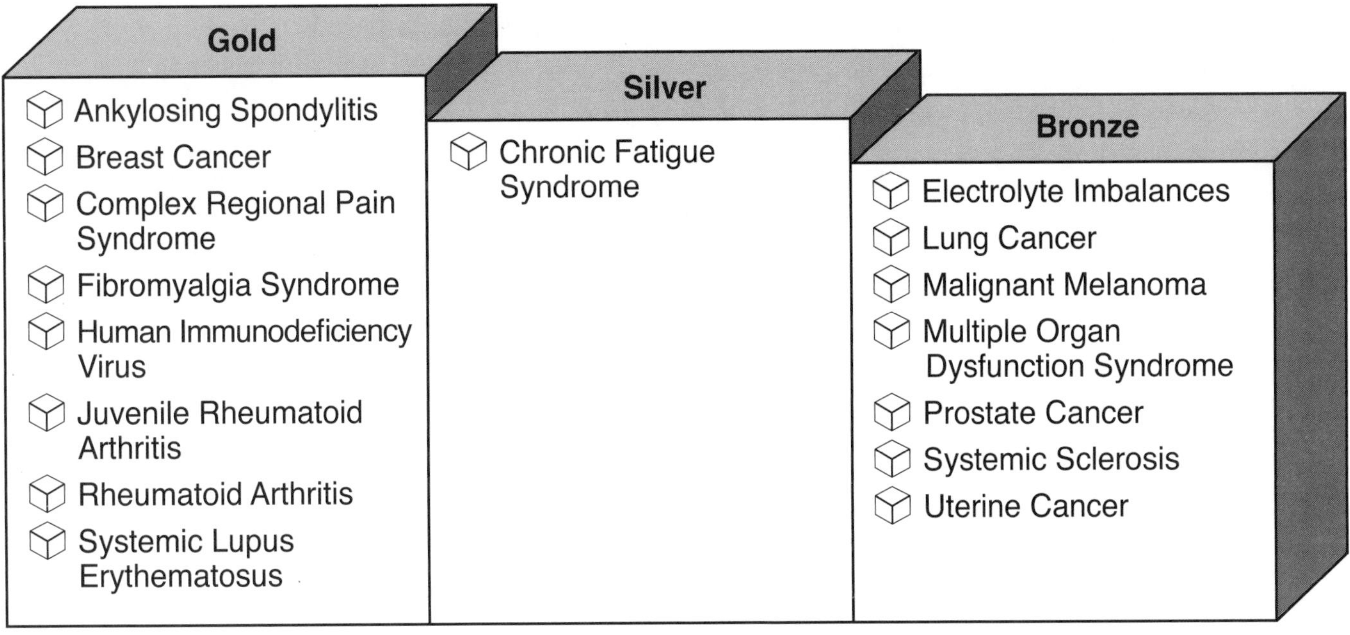

Gold
Ankylosing Spondylitis
Breast Cancer
Complex Regional Pain Syndrome
Fibromyalgia Syndrome
Human Immunodeficiency Virus
Juvenile Rheumatoid Arthritis
Rheumatoid Arthritis
Systemic Lupus Erythematosus
Silver
Chronic Fatigue Syndrome
Bronze
Electrolyte Imbalances
Lung Cancer
Malignant Melanoma
Multiple Organ Dysfunction Syndrome
Prostate Cancer
Systemic Sclerosis
Uterine Cancer

Clinical Application Template Master - Gold

Diagnosis:

What condition produces a patient's symptoms?

An injury was most likely sustained to which structure?

Inference:

What is the most likely contributing factor in the development of this condition?

Confirmation:

What is the most likely clinical presentation?

What laboratory or imaging studies would confirm the diagnosis?

What additional information should be obtained to confirm the diagnosis?

Examination:

What history should be documented?

Important areas to explore include past medical history, medications, family history, current symptoms, current health status, social history and habits, occupation, leisure activities, and social support system.

What tests/measures are most appropriate?

Aerobic capacity and endurance: assessment of vital signs at rest and with activity, perceived exertion scale, pulse oximetry, auscultation of the lungs
Anthropometric characteristics: circumferential measurements
Arousal, attention, and cognition: examine mental status, learning ability, memory and motivation, level of consciousness
Assistive and adaptive devices: analysis of components and safety of a device
Community and work integration: analysis of community, work, and leisure activities
Cranial nerve integrity: assessment of muscle innervation by the cranial nerves, dermatome assessment
Environmental, home, and work barriers: analysis of current and potential barriers or hazards
Ergonomics and body mechanics: analysis of dexterity and coordination
Gait, locomotion, and balance: static and dynamic balance in sitting and standing, safety during gait with/without an assistive device, Berg Balance Scale, Tinetti Performance Oriented Mobility Assessment, Functional Ambulation Profile, analysis of wheelchair management
Integumentary integrity: skin assessment, assessment of sensation
Joint integrity and mobility: assessment of hyper- and hypomobility of a joint, soft tissue swelling and inflammation, assessment of sprain
Motor function: equilibrium and righting reactions, motor assessment scales, coordination, posture and balance in sitting, assessment of sensorimotor integration, physical performance scales

Muscle performance: strength assessment, muscle tone assessment
Neuromotor development and sensory integration: analysis of reflex movement patterns, assessment of involuntary movements, sensory integration tests, gross and fine motor skills
Orthotic, protective, and supportive devices: analysis of components of a device, analysis of movement while wearing a device
Pain: pain perception assessment scale, visual analogue scale, assessment of muscle soreness
Posture: analysis of resting and dynamic posture
Prosthetic requirements: analysis and safety of the prosthesis, assessment of alignment, efficiency, and fit of the prosthesis, assessment of residual limb with use of the prosthesis
Range of motion: active and passive range of motion
Reflex integrity: assessment of deep tendon and pathological reflexes (e.g., Babinski, ATNR)
Self-care and home management: assessment of functional capacity, Functional Independence Measure (FIM), Barthel ADL Index, Rankin Scale
Sensory integrity: assessment of proprioception and kinesthesia
Ventilation, respiration, and circulation: assessment of cough and clearance of secretions, breathing patterns, respiratory muscle strength, accessory muscle utilization and vital capacity, perceived exertion scale, pulse oximetry, palpation of pulses, pulmonary function testing, auscultation of the lungs and heart

What additional findings are likely with this patient?

Management:

What is the most effective management of this patient?

What home care regimen should be recommended?

Outcome:

What is the likely outcome of a course in physical therapy?

What are the long-term effects of the patient's condition?

Comparison:

What are the distinguishing characteristics of a similar condition?

Clinical Scenarios:

Scenario One

Scenario Two

* Adapted from the Academy of Specialty Boards of Physical Therapy

Clinical Application Template Master - Silver

Diagnosis:

What condition produces a patient's symptoms?

An injury was most likely sustained to which structure?

Inference:

What is the most likely contributing factor in the development of this condition?

Confirmation:

What is the most likely clinical presentation?

What laboratory or imaging studies would confirm the diagnosis?

What additional information should be obtained to confirm the diagnosis?

Management:

What is the most effective management of this patient?

What home care regimen should be recommended?

Outcome:

What is the likely outcome of a course in physical therapy?

What are the long-term effects of the patient's condition?

* Adapted from the Academy of Specialty Boards of Physical Therapy

Clinical Application Template Master - Bronze

Diagnosis:

What condition produces a patient's symptoms?

An injury was most likely sustained to which structure?

Confirmation:

What is the most likely clinical presentation?

What laboratory or imaging studies would confirm the diagnosis?

What additional information should be obtained to confirm the diagnosis?

* Adapted from the Academy of Specialty Boards of Physical Therapy

GOLD

Traumatic Brain Injury

DIAGNOSIS

What condition produces a patient's symptoms?

Traumatic brain injury (TBI) occurs due to an open head injury where there is penetration through the skull or closed head injury where the brain makes contact with the skull secondary to a sudden, violent acceleration or deceleration impact. Traumatic brain injury can also occur secondary to anoxia as with cardiac arrest or near drowning.

An injury was most likely sustained to which structure?

Any structure within the brain is vulnerable to injury; however, primary damage will occur at the site of impact. Secondary damage occurs as a result of metabolic and physiologic reactions to the trauma. Brain injury may include swelling, axonal injury, hypoxia, hematoma, hemorrhage and changes in intracranial pressure (ICP).

INFERENCE

What is the most likely contributing factor in the development of this condition?

Statistics from the Centers for Disease Control indicate that falls (32.5%) and motor vehicle accidents (17.3%) are the two leading causes of TBI. Pediatric TBI occurs 50% of the time as a result of a fall. Motor vehicle accidents account for 31.8% of deaths from TBI. High risk groups include ages 0-4, 15-19, and greater than 65 years of age. Males are at greater risk in each demographic category.

CONFIRMATION

What is the most likely clinical presentation?

The incidence of head injury is close to two million individuals per year with an estimated five million individuals living with a brain injury. The clinical presentation of a TBI varies due to the type, area, extent of injury, and secondary damage within the brain. Characteristics of a TBI may include altered consciousness (coma, obtundity, delirium), cognitive and behavioral deficits, changes in personality, motor impairments, alterations in tone, and speech and swallowing issues.

What laboratory or imaging studies would confirm the diagnosis?

Diagnostic imaging such as CT scan or MRI should be performed immediately in order to rule out hemorrhage, infarction, and swelling. X-rays taken of the cervical spine can be used to rule out fracture and potential for subluxation. An electroencephalogram (EEG), positron emission tomography (PET), and cerebral blood flow mapping (CBF) may also be utilized for diagnosis and baseline data.

What additional information should be obtained to confirm the diagnosis?

A full neurological evaluation by a physician should include a mental examination, cranial nerve assessment, tonal assessment and pupillary reactivity assessment. The physician will classify the patient using the Glasgow Coma Scale and indicate severe (coma), moderate or mild brain injury. The Rancho Los Amigos Levels of Cognitive Functioning can also be used to classify injury and assist with developing an appropriate plan of care.

EXAMINATION

What history should be documented?

Important areas to explore include past medical history, medications, family history, current symptoms, level of cognitive functioning, social history and habits, occupation, leisure activities, and social support system.

What tests/measures are most appropriate?

Aerobic capacity and endurance: vital signs at rest/activity, pulse oximetry, auscultation of lungs

Arousal, attention, and cognition: using Rancho Los Amigos Levels of Cognitive Functioning

Assistive and adaptive devices: analysis of components and safety of a device

Cranial nerve integrity: muscle innervation by the cranial nerves, dermatome assessment

Environmental, home, and work barriers: analysis of current and potential barriers or hazards

Gait, locomotion, and balance: static and dynamic balance in sitting and standing, safety during gait with/without an assistive device, Berg Balance Scale, Tinetti Performance Oriented Mobility Assessment, analysis of wheelchair management

Integumentary integrity: skin and sensation assessment

Joint integrity and mobility: assessment of hypermobility and hypomobility of a joint

Motor function: equilibrium and righting reactions, motor assessment scales, coordination, posture and balance in sitting, assessment of sensorimotor integration, physical performance scales

Muscle performance: strength assessment, muscle tone assessment

Neuromotor development and sensory integration: analysis of reflex movement patterns, assessment of involuntary movements, sensory integration tests, gross and fine motor skills

Orthotic, protective, and supportive devices: analysis of components and movement while wearing a device

Pain: pain perception assessment scale, visual analogue scale, assessment of muscle soreness

Posture: analysis of resting and dynamic posture

Range of motion: active and passive range of motion

Reflex integrity: assessment of deep tendon and pathological reflexes (e.g., Babinski, ATNR)

Self-care and home management: assessment of functional capacity, Functional Independence Measure (FIM), Barthel Index, Rankin Scale, Rivermead Motor Assessment

What additional findings are likely with this patient?

There are multiple impairments that can develop secondary to TBI. Intracranial pressure must be monitored initially since it is at risk to increase or develop hemorrhage. A patient can develop heterotopic ossification, contractures, skin breakdown, seizures, and deep vein thrombosis. A patient with a severe TBI may remain in a persistent vegetative state.

MANAGEMENT

What is the most effective management of this patient?

Medical management is initiated at the site of injury or in the emergency room for life preserving measures. The initial goal is to stabilize the patient, control intracranial pressure, and prevent secondary complications. Surgical intervention may be required in attempt to regain homeostasis within the brain secondary to hemorrhage or fracture. Once a patient is medically stable, physical therapy rehabilitation is initiated. Treatment of a patient with TBI usually includes a team approach with goals based on the patient's level of injury. Pharmacological intervention may include cerebral vasoconstrictive agents, psychotropic agents, hypertensive agents, antispasticity agents, and medication to assist with cognition and attention. Physical therapy will focus on sensory stimulation and PROM for a comatose patient or pathfinding and high-level balance activities for a patient with a mild injury. Physical therapy may include functional mobility training, behavior modification, serial casting, compensatory strategies, vestibular rehabilitation, task specific activities, wheelchair seating, and pulmonary intervention.

What home care regimen should be recommended?

A home care regimen should include ongoing therapeutic activities that focus on goals associated with the patient's current Rancho Los Amigos level. Consistency is vital to the success of a home program. The patient may also participate in a community re-entry based program for the TBI population if warranted by their level of current function.

OUTCOME

What is the likely outcome of a course in physical therapy?

A patient diagnosed with TBI does not have a specific projected outcome. Outcome is based on the degree of primary and secondary damage and the extent of cognitive and behavioral impairments. Physical therapy should continue in all settings until the patient has attained all realistic goals.

What are the long-term effects of the patient's condition?

TBI affects approximately 1.7 million Americans each year. Approximately 52,000 individuals die each year as a result of TBI. Long-term effects are determined by the extent of injury and impairments resulting from the TBI. Many patients experience life long deficits that do not allow them to return to their pre-injury lifestyle.

COMPARISON

What are the distinguishing characteristics of a similar condition?

Meningitis is a bacterial or viral infection that spreads through the cerebrospinal fluid to the brain. The meninges of the brain become inflamed as well as the meningeal membranes. The patient will have a headache and may complain of stiffness in the neck. The patient may also show symptoms of confusion, fatigue, and irritability. As the virus progresses the patient may experience seizures and may progress into a coma. Medical treatment varies based on the causative strain of the virus/bacteria. Mortality ranges from 5-25% and approximately 30% have some degree of permanent neurological impairment.

CLINICAL SCENARIOS

Scenario One

A 22-year-old male with TBI is admitted to an inpatient rehabilitation hospital. The patient is presently classified as Rancho Los Amigos Level IV. The patient required surgical decompression after the TBI. The patient's parents are with the patient almost constantly.

Scenario Two

A 42-year-old female sustained a severe TBI in a motor vehicle accident and is presently classified as Rancho Los Amigos Level II. The accident was two weeks ago. Prior to admission the patient was healthy and worked full-time. She has a supportive husband.

SILVER

Cauda Equina Syndrome

DIAGNOSIS

What condition produces a patient's symptoms?

Cauda equina syndrome (CES) is considered to be a peripheral nerve injury and results from damage and loss of function involving two or more nerves of the cauda equina. CES is associated with numerous mechanisms of injury and typically presents as a complex of symptoms.

An injury was most likely sustained to which structure?

The spinal cord typically extends to L1, terminating with the conus medullaris. Paired lower lumbar, sacral, and coccygeal nerve roots extend beyond the conus medullaris and are termed the cauda equina. The cauda equina provides sensory innervation to the "saddle area" of the lower extremities, lower extremity motor innervation, parasympathetic innervation to the bowel and bladder, and voluntary control over the associated sphincters. The nerves of the cauda equina are more susceptible to damage than most other nerve root pairs due to a poorly developed protective epineurium and the tendency to form edema even with mild injury.

INFERENCE

What is the most likely contributing factor in the development of this condition?

CES may result from any source of compression on the cauda equina nerve roots, including spinal structure pathology (e.g., ruptured disk, fracture, stenosis), trauma (e.g., fall, gunshot wound), infectious conditions (e.g., abscess or tuberculosis), tumor or iatrogenic factors.

CONFIRMATION

What is the most likely clinical presentation?

CES may develop slowly or rapidly depending on the underlying pathology. For patients with gradual onset, diagnosis may be difficult since early symptoms may be poorly defined or mimic other conditions. Altered reflexes, pain, and decreased strength and sensation are common symptoms. Other symptoms can include severe back pain, functional impairment, diminished sensation in the saddle distribution, bowel and bladder dysfunction (e.g., retention or incontinence), and sexual dysfunction. The incidence of CES is higher in adults, however, children with spinal birth defects may also be at an increased risk.

What laboratory or imaging studies would confirm the diagnosis?

MRI studies are able to identify the widest range of potential etiologies as they are able to best delineate soft tissue structures and pathology (e.g., tumor, abscess). Compression due to bony abnormalities, such as narrowed disk spaces, altered bony alignment or arthritic changes are more readily identified with x-ray imaging or a CT scan.

What additional information should be obtained to confirm the diagnosis?

A thorough medical history should be obtained and a physical examination performed if CES is suspected. The physical examination should include an assessment of lower extremity muscle strength, sensation, and deep tendon reflexes. Perineal sensation, reflexes, and rectal tone should also be assessed.

MANAGEMENT

What is the most effective management of this patient?

Surgical and medical interventions are typically directed toward nerve root decompression. Though CES is not fatal, it can signal a surgical emergency since delayed intervention may limit long-term outcomes. Medical management may include radiation therapy or chemotherapeutic agents for tumor-related compression. Other pharmaceutical agents may also be used for compression (e.g., anti-inflammatory, antibiotic agents). Physical therapy interventions should emphasize maximal functional return and accommodation for residual deficits. Therapeutic exercise, functional mobility training, coordination activities, sensory stimulation, orthotics, and adaptive equipment training are typical components of the plan of care. Physical therapists may also provide education related to bowel and bladder retraining. Modalities such as biofeedback and neuromuscular electrical stimulation may assist in targeted muscle retraining.

What home care regimen should be recommended?

A home care regimen should be consistent with physical therapy interventions, including therapeutic exercise and activities that emphasize functional independence with adaptive equipment.

OUTCOME

What is the likely outcome of a course of physical therapy?

A patient with CES does not have a specific projected outcome. Outcomes are based on the degree of primary and secondary damage and the extent of motor and sensory impairments. Physical therapy should continue until the patient has attained realistic goals.

What are the long-term effects of the patient's condition?

Long-term effects are determined by the extent of injury and the resulting impairments. CES is a self-limiting condition, however, the longer a patient is symptomatic prior to intervention, the less likely the patient is to achieve a complete recovery. Morbidity is typically associated with long-term effects including weakness and bowel or bladder dysfunction. Other complications may include the development of decubitus ulcers or thrombus formation.

Crohn's Disease

BRONZE

DIAGNOSIS

What condition produces a patient's symptoms?

Crohn's disease is a specific form of inflammatory bowel disease in which the lining of the gastrointestinal (GI) tract becomes abnormally inflamed. Symptoms can involve any aspect of the GI tract, however, typically present in lower structures (e.g., small bowel, colon). Symptom complaints are typically associated with an exacerbation of the inflammatory process or complications such as fibrosis or obstruction.

An injury was most likely sustained to which structure?

The etiology of Crohn's disease is idiopathic, but likely the result of an imbalance between anti-inflammatory and pro-inflammatory mediators within the GI tract. Structural injury typically begins with ulceration, hyperemia, and edema of the GI tract's superficial mucosal lining. The inflammatory process may cause adhesions, fibrosis, thickening, and may also spread to deeper mucosal layers forming granulomas or abscesses.

CONFIRMATION

What is the most likely clinical presentation?

The typical signs and symptoms range from mild to significantly debilitating to life-threatening. Symptoms may develop gradually or rapidly and typically include abdominal pain, cramping, and diarrhea. Other symptoms may include blood in the stool, GI tract ulcers, diminished appetite, and weight loss. Over time, some patients may develop complications including anal fissures, intestinal fistula, malnutrition, and bowel obstruction. The chronic inflammatory process may also precipitate symptoms such as gallstones, kidney stones, arthritis, and osteoporosis. Children with Crohn's disease typically experience delays in normal growth and development.

What laboratory or imaging studies would confirm the diagnosis?

Blood tests may be utilized to determine the presence of infection, anemia or abnormal antibodies and also typically include a fecal occult blood test. Invasive imaging procedures such as colonoscopy and sigmoidoscopy allow for lower GI visualization and the collection of tissue samples. X-ray, MRI, and CT scan may be visually enhanced using barium to assist in the identification of affected intestinal segments.

What additional information should be obtained to confirm the diagnosis?

A medical history should be completed to rule out similar diagnoses such as colon cancer, irritable bowel syndrome, and diverticulitis. Patients with a family history of Crohn's disease, who smoke, or who maintain a diet high in fat are at greater risk for developing the condition.

Cushing's Syndrome

BRONZE

DIAGNOSIS

What condition produces a patient's symptoms?

Cortisol is a glucocorticoid hormone produced by the adrenal cortex which assists in the regulation of cardiovascular function, metabolism, and the body's response to stress. Cushing's syndrome is a condition resulting from abnormally high levels of cortisol due to endogenous overproduction of cortisol or excessive exogenous use of corticosteroids.

An injury was most likely sustained to which structure?

The most common endogenous etiology of hypercortisolism is a pituitary or adrenal gland tumor. Pituitary tumors are typically benign and linked to increased production of the adrenocorticotropic hormone (ACTH) which stimulates cortisol overproduction. This condition is termed Cushing's syndrome. A benign adrenal cortex tumor may also cause cortisol overproduction independent of ACTH influence. Less common endogenous etiologies include genetics and malignancy. Exogenous etiologies are linked to high doses of corticosteroids typically used for inflammatory conditions.

CONFIRMATION

What is the most likely clinical presentation?

Patients with Cushing's syndrome typically present with hallmark physical signs including weight gain, purple striae, and a ruddy complexion. Weight gain is accompanied by increased adipose tissue distribution in the face (e.g., "moon face"), upper back (e.g., "buffalo hump"), torso (e.g., central obesity), and supraclavicular region. Other symptoms include fatigue, depression, emotional lability, excessive hair growth, bruising, and proximal muscle weakness. Systemically, Cushing's syndrome may contribute to conditions such as hypertension, diabetes mellitus, peptic ulcer disease, osteopenia, and immune system impairment. There is a significantly greater prevalence among women with the onset of symptoms between 25 and 40 years of age.

What laboratory or imaging studies would confirm the diagnosis?

Cushing's syndrome may be diagnosed by laboratory analysis of cortisol levels in urine, saliva or blood. Laboratory studies detailing the body's response to a low dose of dexamethasone, alone or in combination with ACTH stimulation, are also considered to be diagnostically valid.

What additional information should be obtained to confirm the diagnosis?

A thorough medical history and physical examination should be completed to rule out similar diagnoses and identify characteristics commonly associated with the condition.

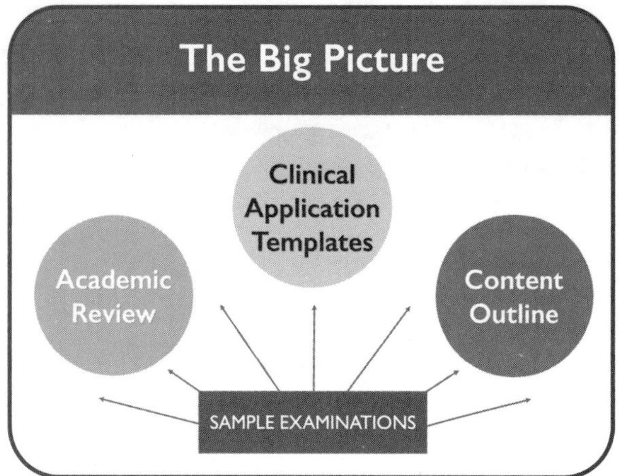
The Big Picture
Clinical Application Templates
Academic Review
Content Outline
SAMPLE EXAMINATIONS

NPTE Practice Analysis

The purpose of the practice analysis is to ensure that the NPTE-PT covers important, current, entry-level PT work requirements.

Implementation Date: January 2024

NPTE-PT Content Outline Weighting*

Category	Midrange (%)	Range
Physical Therapy Examination	44 (24.4%)	38-50
Foundations for Evaluation, Differential Diagnosis, and Prognosis	58.5 (32.5%)	51-66
Interventions	52.5 (29.2%)	47-58
Equipment, Devices, and Technologies; Therapeutic Modalities	10.5 (5.8%)	9-12
Safety and Protection; Professional Responsibilities; Research and EBP	14.5 (8.1%)	12-17

NPTE-PT System Specific Weighting*

Category	Midrange (%)	Range
Musculoskeletal System	49 (27.2%)	44-54
Neuromuscular and Nervous Systems	43.5 (24.2%)	39-48
Cardiovascular and Pulmonary Systems	24.5 (13.6%)	22-27
Other Systems	37 (20.6%)	29-45
Integumentary	9.5 (5.3%)	8-11
Metabolic and Endocrine	5 (2.8%)	4-6
Gastrointestinal	4.5 (2.5%)	3-6
Genitourinary	3.5 (1.9%)	2-5
Lymphatic	5.5 (3.1%)	4-7
System Interactions	9 (5%)	8-10
Non-Systems	25 (13.9%)	21-29

*NPTE-PT Test Content Outline, Federation of State Boards of Physical Therapy, www.fsbpt.org

Activity 3
Content Outline

Physical Therapy Examination
Midrange: 44 Questions (24.4%) Range: 38-50 Questions

○ Correct
● Incorrect
☒ Academic
☐ Decision Making
☐ Test Taking

Level 1

1. A physical therapist completes a portion of a cranial nerve assessment by examining the facial nerve. Which of the following tests would be the **MOST** useful when assessing this particular nerve?

   ○ 1. Close the eyes tightly
   ○ 2. Listen to a watch ticking
   ○ 3. Say "Ahhh"
   ● 4. Assess face sensation

○ Correct
● Incorrect
☒ Academic
☐ Decision Making
☐ Test Taking

Level 1

2. A physical therapist measures the angle of torsion of the femur on an adult male with leg pain of unknown etiology. Which of the following measurements would be the **MOST** indicative of a normal measurement?

   ○ 1. 4 degrees anteversion
   ○ 2. 11 degrees anteversion
   ● 3. 6 degrees retroversion
   ○ 4. 12 degrees retroversion

● Correct
○ Incorrect
☐ Academic
☐ Decision Making
☐ Test Taking

Level 2

3. A physical therapist performs a special test on a patient diagnosed with carpal tunnel syndrome by asking the patient to maximally flex their wrists and hold the position by pushing the wrists together for 60 seconds. Which finding would be **MOST** indicative of a positive test?

   ○ 1. Pain in an area innervated by the ulnar nerve
   ○ 2. Pain in an area innervated by the median nerve
   ● 3. Tingling into the thumb, index finger, middle finger, and lateral half of the ring finger
   ○ 4. Tingling into the palmar aspect of the hand

4. A physical therapist assesses the respiration of a patient prior to initiating a physical therapy session. The patient has a lengthy medical history including chronic obstructive pulmonary disease. Which ratio **BEST** represents the anticipated duration of the patient's inspiratory phase to the expiratory phase?

1. 1:2
2. 1:3
3. 2:1
4. 3:1

5. A physical therapist completes a sensory assessment of the hand. The therapist notes that the patient is unable to detect the stimulus shown in the image. Which nerve would **MOST** likely be associated with this impairment?

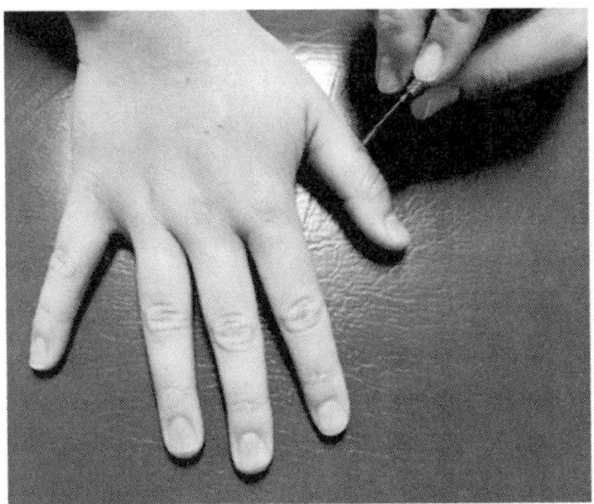

1. Median
2. Musculocutaneous
3. Radial
4. Ulnar

6. A patient with burns over their anterior right upper extremity, genital region, and the anterior portions of the right and left lower extremities is examined in physical therapy. What percentage of the patient's body is burned using the rule of nines?

1. 19.0%
2. 23.5%
3. 28.0%
4. 38.5%

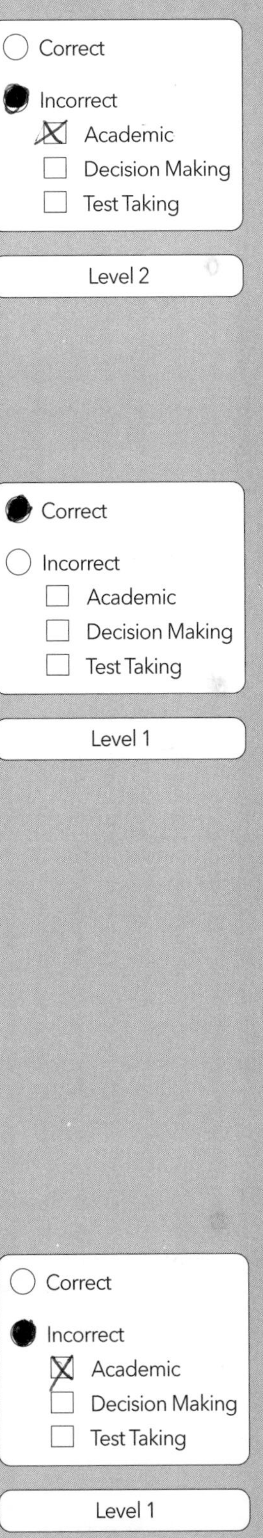

Correct
Incorrect
Academic
Decision Making
Test Taking
Level 2
Correct
Incorrect
Academic
Decision Making
Test Taking
Level 1
Correct
Incorrect
Academic
Decision Making
Test Taking
Level 1

Foundations for Evaluation, Differential Diagnosis, and Prognosis

Midrange: 58.5 Questions (32.5%) Range: 51-66 Questions

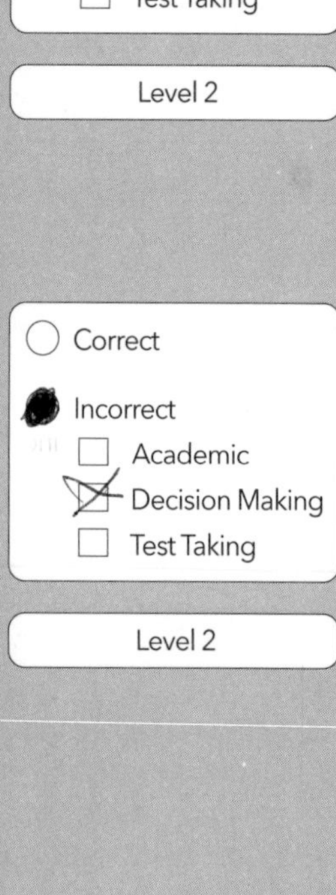

Correct
Incorrect
Academic
Decision Making
Test Taking
Level 2
Correct
Incorrect
Academic
Decision Making
Test Taking
Level 2

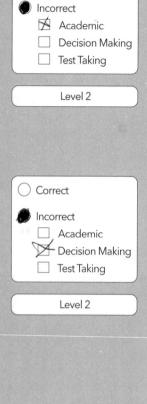

7. A physical therapist treats a two-year-old child with behavioral and social problems secondary to intellectual disability. Which condition would **MOST** likely be associated with the described clinical scenario?

○ 1. Mitochondrial disorder
○ 2. Phenylketonuria
○ 3. Osteogenesis imperfecta
○ 4. Wilson's disease

8. A water polo player reports diffuse pain in their right shoulder that begins 10-15 minutes after the onset of activity. Examination reveals subjective reports of pain at 90 degrees of passive and active abduction. Medial and lateral rotation range of motion are within normal limits. Resistive isometrics are strong and painful for flexion and abduction. Which medical condition is **MOST** likely associated with the described clinical presentation?

○ 1. Adhesive capsulitis
○ 2. Rotator cuff tear
○ 3. Impingement syndrome
○ 4. Upper trapezius strain

Correct
Incorrect
Academic
Decision Making
Test Taking

Level 1

9. A physical therapist performs an examination on a patient status post stroke. Which perceptual deficit is **MOST** characteristic with a lesion in the right hemisphere?

○ 1. Motor apraxia
○ 2. Sequencing deficits
○ 3. Impaired body image
○ 4. Difficulty initiating tasks

10. A patient with a long-standing history of recurrent back pain is examined in physical therapy. The patient reports having difficulty with lifting activities and as a result has been unable to return to their job as a machinist. The medical history indicates that the patient has tried a variety of treatment alternatives including chiropractic, polarity therapy, and massage, however, has not had any success. Which physical therapy goal would be the **MOST** desirable?

1. Promote function
2. Control pain
3. Diminish nerve root compression
4. Control inflammation

Correct
Incorrect
Academic
Decision Making
Test Taking

Level 3

11. A physical therapist providing patient coverage for a colleague on vacation reviews the examination of a patient who has post-polio syndrome. Which of the following complications would be **MOST** likely expected given the patient's diagnosis?

1. Bronchiectasis
2. Lower extremity spasticity
3. Osteoporosis
4. Heat intolerance

Correct
Incorrect
Academic
Decision Making
Test Taking

Level 2

12. A physical therapist reviews the medical record of a male child diagnosed with Duchenne muscular dystrophy. Which of the following is required in order for a male child to present with this condition?

1. The dominant trait is received from the father.
2. The recessive trait is received from both parents.
3. The dominant trait is received from the mother.
4. The recessive trait is received from the mother.

Correct
Incorrect
Academic
Decision Making
Test Taking

Level 1

3, 1
1, 2

Interventions

Midrange: 52.5 Questions (29.2%) Range: 47-58 Questions

Correct
Incorrect
Academic
Decision Making
Test Taking

Level 3

13. A patient that has been on extended bed rest is positioned on a tilt table. After slightly elevating the head of the tilt table, the patient begins to experience mild dizziness. The patient's systolic blood pressure is measured as 10 mm Hg less than the value recorded at the beginning of the treatment session. What is the **MOST** appropriate physical therapist action?

   1. Reassure the patient that the response is not unusual
   2. Contact the director of rehabilitation for assistance
   3. Document the incident in the patient's chart
   4. Lower the tilt table

Correct
Incorrect
Academic
Decision Making
Test Taking

Level 3

14. A patient diagnosed with adhesive capsulitis informs a physical therapist that their shoulder has been quite sore since the last treatment session. During the previous treatment session the therapist performed grade III and IV mobilizations followed by progressive resistive exercises. What is the **MOST** appropriate activity for the current treatment session?

   1. Active stretching activities and resistance exercises using elastic tubing
   2. Passive range of motion and superficial heat
   3. Grade I and II mobilizations and palliative modalities
   4. Proprioceptive neuromuscular facilitation upper extremity diagonals and cryotherapy

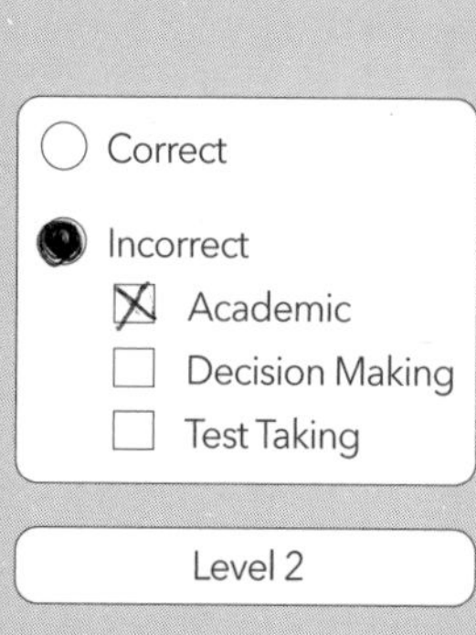
Correct
Incorrect
Academic
Decision Making
Test Taking

Level 2

15. A five-month-old infant is referred to physical therapy for a developmental assessment. During the examination the physical therapist observes the infant roll from prone to supine. Integration of which primitive reflex is often associated with completion of this milestone?

   1. Asymmetrical tonic neck reflex
   2. Symmetrical tonic neck reflex
   3. Galant reflex
   4. Moro reflex

16. A patient diagnosed with left patellofemoral pain is referred to physical therapy. The patient reports the onset of pain in the left knee when they run for more than two miles. Physical examination of the left knee reveals mild edema along the medial joint line, diminished patella medial glide, and mild vastus medialis atrophy. Which treatment option would be the **MOST** appropriate?

- ○ 1. Medial patella glides and squats to 90 degrees knee flexion with hip adduction
- ○ 2. Open chain knee extension in short sitting
- ● 3. Squats to 30 degrees knee flexion and medial patella glides
- ○ 4. Phonophoresis and retro-walking on a treadmill

● Correct
○ Incorrect
- ☐ Academic
- ☐ Decision Making
- ☐ Test Taking

Level 3

17. A male physical therapist examines a female patient with chronic obstructive pulmonary disease. The therapist would like to incorporate bronchial drainage techniques into the plan of care, but is concerned about applying pressure around the woman's breasts. Which lung segment(s) would require the therapist to direct force closest to the breast area?

- ● 1. Right middle lobe
- ○ 2. Posterior segments of the upper lobes
- ○ 3. Lateral basal segments of the lower lobes
- ○ 4. Apical segments of the upper lobes

● Correct
○ Incorrect
- ☐ Academic
- ☐ Decision Making
- ☐ Test Taking

Level 1

18. An infant diagnosed with congenital torticollis has been under the care of a physical therapist for four months. During a reexamination, the therapist notes full passive cervical range of motion is present. However, the patient is unable to independently maintain a neutral head position. Based on these findings, which therapist action would be the **MOST** appropriate?

- ○ 1. Continue to emphasize stretching and massage to maintain range of motion
- ● 2. Suggest home activity options that regularly facilitate active range of motion
- ○ 3. Incorporate specific progressive resistance exercises into the plan of care
- ○ 4. Refer the patient to a pediatric orthopedic surgeon for consultation

● Correct
○ Incorrect
- ☐ Academic
- ☐ Decision Making
- ☐ Test Taking

Level 3

Equipment, Devices, and Technologies; Therapeutic Modalities

Midrange: 10.5 Questions (5.8%) Range: 9-12 Questions

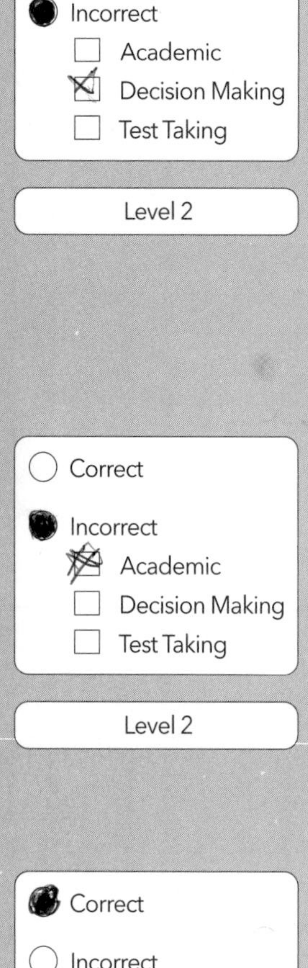

Correct
Incorrect
Academic
Decision Making
Test Taking
Level 2
Correct
Incorrect
Academic
Decision Making
Test Taking
Level 2

19. A physical therapist instructs a patient rehabilitating from anterior cruciate ligament reconstruction surgery how to perform a three-point gait pattern. Which of the following instructions would **MOST** likely be included in patient education regarding an unrecoverable backward loss of balance?

    1. Grip your crutches tightly
    2. Reach backward with your arms
    3. Move your chin toward your chest
    4. Lock your knees

20. A child with cerebral palsy is assessed in an orthotic clinic. This patient is prescribed a floor reaction ankle-foot orthosis to assist with gait. What is the **PRIMARY** indication for this type of orthosis?

    1. Inability to passively extend the knee in standing
    2. Inability to maintain knee extension during stance
    3. Inability to perform knee flexion during toe off
    4. Inability to plantar flex the ankle during late stance

Correct
Incorrect
Academic
Decision Making
Test Taking
Level 1

21. A physical therapist positions a patient diagnosed with lateral spinal stenosis in supine on a traction table. The patient is 6 feet 2 inches tall and weighs approximately 220 pounds. Assuming low friction from the traction table, what is the **MINIMUM** amount of force necessary for mechanical separation of the vertebrae in the lumbar spine?

    1. 55 lbs
    2. 110 lbs
    3. 165 lbs
    4. 200 lbs

22. A patient with an acute low back injury is examined in an outpatient physical therapy clinic. The patient complains of severe pain and stiffness in the spine following any period of inactivity. Physical examination reveals muscle spasm throughout the lumbar spine and reduced lumbar range of motion in all directions. Which intervention would be the **MOST** appropriate for the initial treatment session?

- ● 1. Transcutaneous electrical nerve stimulation and postural awareness exercises
- ○ 2. Biofeedback and orientation to appropriate lifting techniques
- ○ 3. Passive range of motion and pelvic stabilization exercises
- ○ 4. Continuous ultrasound and hot packs

● Correct
○ Incorrect
☐ Academic
☐ Decision Making
☐ Test Taking

Level 3

23. A physical therapist has ultrasound orders for a patient with medial epicondylitis. The injury occurred three weeks ago while playing golf. Which parameters would be the **MOST** appropriate when treating the patient?

- ○ 1. 1 W/cm^2, 1 MHz, 12 minutes
- ○ 2. 1 W/cm^2, 1 MHz, 5 minutes
- ● 3. 1 W/cm^2, 3 MHz, 5 minutes
- ○ 4. 1 W/cm^2, 3 MHz, 12 minutes

● Correct
○ Incorrect
☐ Academic
☐ Decision Making
☐ Test Taking

Level 2

24. A physical therapist prepares to use iontophoresis with a dosage of 40 mA-min to treat a patient with lateral epicondylitis. What is the expected duration of treatment if the therapist elects to use a current amplitude of 2.5 mA?

- ○ 1. 12 minutes
- ✓ 2. 16 minutes
- ○ 3. 20 minutes
- ● 4. 24 minutes

○ Correct
● Incorrect
☒ Academic
☐ Decision Making
☐ Test Taking

Level 1

Safety and Protection; Professional Responsibilities; Research and Evidence-Based Practice

Midrange: 14.5 Questions (8.1%) Range: 12-17 Questions

● Correct
○ Incorrect
☐ Academic
☐ Decision Making
☐ Test Taking

Level 2

25. A physical therapist suspects that a geriatric patient with unilateral hearing loss often has difficulty hearing verbal instructions. Which accommodation would be the **MOST** appropriate when communicating with the patient?

○ 1. Speak loudly and slowly
● 2. Speak to the patient's uninvolved side
○ 3. Speak with varying vocal pitch
○ 4. Speak directly to the patient

● Correct
○ Incorrect
☐ Academic
☐ Decision Making
☐ Test Taking

Level 1

26. A physical therapist reviews the available research in an attempt to determine the reliability and validity of the Berg Balance Test. One of the articles the therapist reviews indicates that the test has high internal consistency. Which interpretation is **MOST** consistent with the research findings?

○ 1. The test has high external validity.
○ 2. The test items were assembled from existing reliable and valid survey instruments.
● 3. The test items appear to measure the same underlying construct.
○ 4. The test has been reliable under test-retest situations.

● Correct
○ Incorrect
☐ Academic
☐ Decision Making
☐ Test Taking

Level 1

27. A physical therapist serves as an accessibility consultant for a local business designing a new office complex. What is the **MINIMUM** recommended width necessary to safely propel a wheelchair in a corridor?

○ 1. 28 inches
○ 2. 32 inches
● 3. 36 inches
○ 4. 40 inches

28. A physical therapist completing documentation at a workstation observes a patient enter the gym and begin to use the weight machines. When approached by the therapist, the patient indicates they are ten minutes early for a scheduled appointment, however, states that they often begin exercising before formal contact with the therapist. What would be the **MOST** appropriate action for the therapist to take?

- 1. Monitor the patient while they initiate the exercise program
- 2. Ask the patient to return to the waiting area
- 3. Review the patient's medical record
- 4. Allow the patient to exercise independently

Correct
Incorrect
Academic
Decision Making
Test Taking

Level 3

29. The National Health Survey reports that women's heights are normally distributed with a mean of 65 inches and a standard deviation of 2.5 inches. What percent of women are between 62.5 inches and 67.5 inches tall?

- 1. Approximately 34%
- 2. Approximately 68%
- 3. Approximately 95%
- 4. Approximately 99%

Correct
Incorrect
Academic
Decision Making
Test Taking

Level 2

30. A physical therapist participates in a research study that requires monitoring of a select group of patients. During the study the therapist hypothesizes that two of the patients experienced a positive change simply due to participation in the study and in response to being observed. Which theory **BEST** supports this phenomenon?

- 1. Bystander effect
- 2. Hawthorne effect
- 3. Halo effect
- 4. Placebo effect

Correct
Incorrect
Academic
Decision Making
Test Taking

Level 1

PERFORMANCE ANALYSIS

Content Outline

30 Questions
Time (30:00)

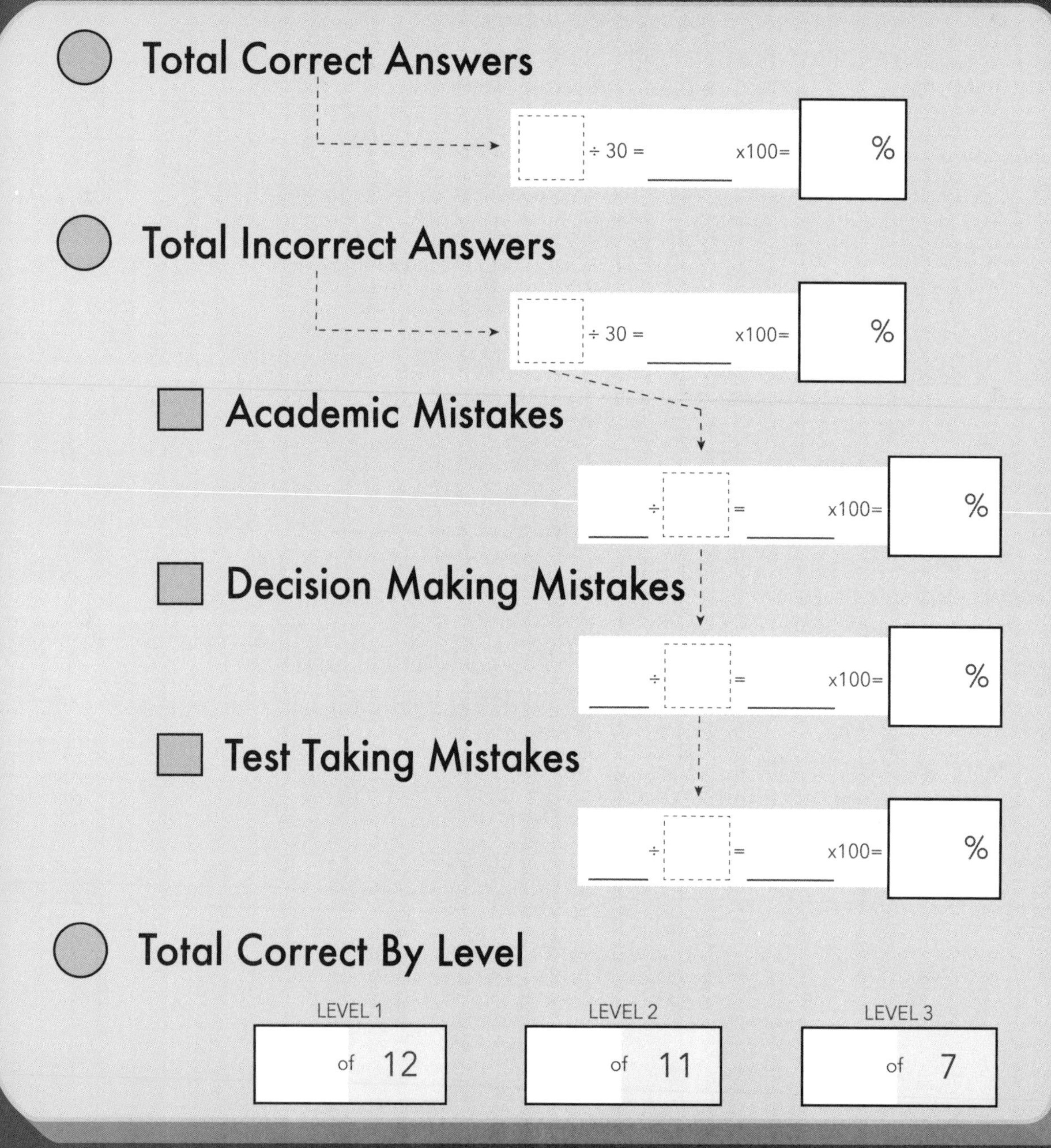
Total Correct Answers
÷ 30 =
x100=
%
Total Incorrect Answers
÷ 30 =
x100=
%
Academic Mistakes
÷
=
x100=
%
Decision Making Mistakes
÷
=
x100=
%
Test Taking Mistakes
÷
=
x100=
%
Total Correct By Level
LEVEL 1
of 12
LEVEL 2
of 11
LEVEL 3
of 7

"There are no shortcuts to any place worth going."

— Anonymous

NPTE-PT Practice Analysis

Developing the Practice Analysis

Work Activities (WAs)

The WA survey includes a list of statements describing tasks sometimes performed by entry-level practitioners.

Knowledge and Skill Requirements (KSRs)

The KSR survey includes statements describing knowledge or skills sometimes needed by entry-level practitioners on the job.

Work Activity Examples

- Screening of the neuromuscular system (e.g., gross coordination, motor function, balance, locomotion, gross sensory function)
- Application of topical agents (e.g., cleansers, creams, moisturizers, ointments, sealants) and dressings (e.g., hydrogels, wound coverings)
- Assess barriers (e.g., social, economic, physical, psychological, environmental, work conditions and activities) to home, community, work, or school integration/reintegration

Knowledge and Skill Requirement Examples

- Anatomy and physiology of the cardiovascular/pulmonary system as related to physical therapy interventions, daily activities, and environmental factors
- Gastrointestinal system diseases/conditions and their pathophysiology to establish and carry out plan of care, including prognosis
- Active listening - Giving full attention to what other people are saying, taking time to understand the points being made, asking questions as appropriate, and not interrupting at inappropriate times

System Summary

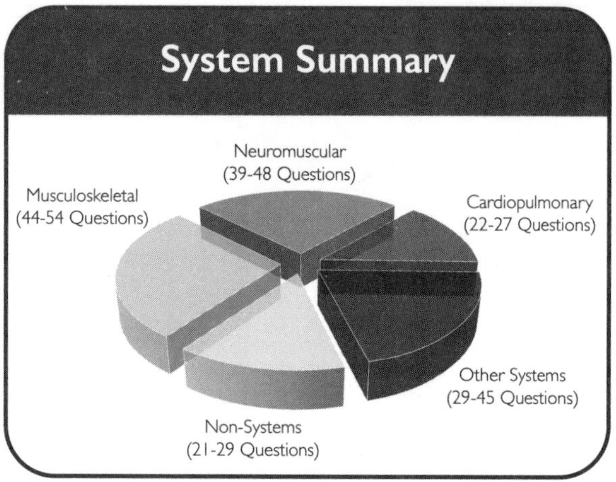

Neuromuscular (39-48 Questions)
Musculoskeletal (44-54 Questions)
Cardiopulmonary (22-27 Questions)
Other Systems (29-45 Questions)
Non-Systems (21-29 Questions)

System Summary

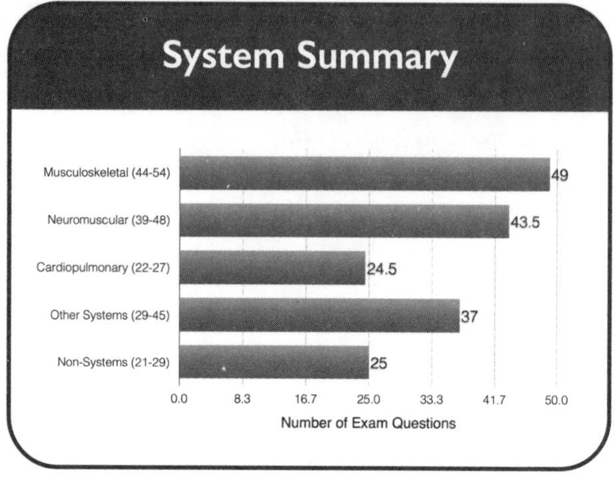

Musculoskeletal (44-54) 49
Neuromuscular (39-48) 43.5
Cardiopulmonary (22-27) 24.5
Other Systems (29-45) 37
Non-Systems (21-29) 25
0.0 8.3 16.7 25.0 33.3 41.7 50.0
Number of Exam Questions

Content Outline Summary

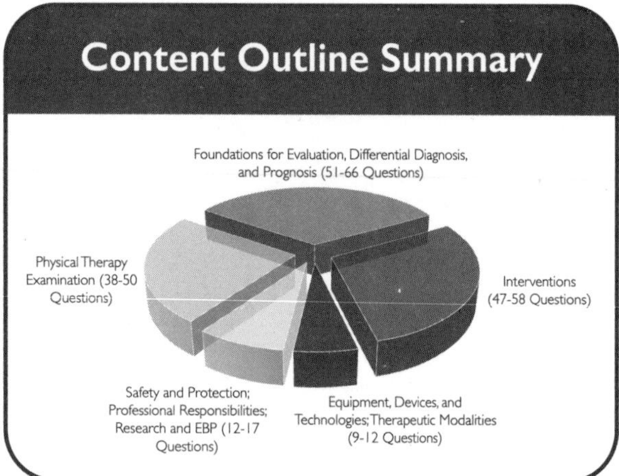

Foundations for Evaluation, Differential Diagnosis, and Prognosis (51-66 Questions)
Physical Therapy Examination (38-50 Questions)
Interventions (47-58 Questions)
Safety and Protection; Professional Responsibilities; Research and EBP (12-17 Questions)
Equipment, Devices, and Technologies; Therapeutic Modalities (9-12 Questions)

Content Outline Summary

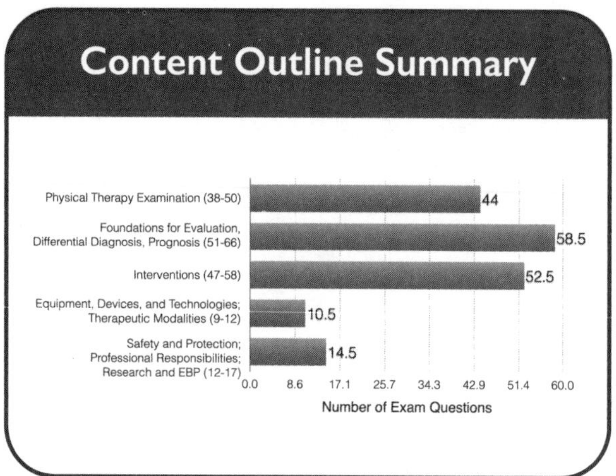

Physical Therapy Examination (38-50) 44
Foundations for Evaluation, Differential Diagnosis, Prognosis (51-66) 58.5
Interventions (47-58) 52.5
Equipment, Devices, and Technologies; Therapeutic Modalities (9-12) 10.5
Safety and Protection; Professional Responsibilities; Research and EBP (12-17) 14.5
0.0 8.6 17.1 25.7 34.3 42.9 51.4 60.0
Number of Exam Questions

Item Categorization

A physical therapist examines a patient's subtalar range of motion. When goniometrically assessing subtalar range of motion, where should the moving arm of the goniometer be positioned?

1. Posterior midline of the calcaneus
2. Anterior aspect of the ankle midway between the malleoli
3. Over the posterior aspect of the ankle between the malleoli
4. Anterior midline of the second metatarsal

Content Outline: Physical Therapy Examination
System: Musculoskeletal System

System Summary

	% Correct
Musculoskeletal System	
Neuromuscular and Nervous Systems	
Cardiovascular and Pulmonary Systems	
Other Systems	
Non-Systems	

Content Outline Summary

	% Correct
Physical Therapy Examination	
Foundations for Evaluation, Differential Diagnosis, and Prognosis	
Interventions	
Equipment, Devices, and Technologies; Therapeutic Modalities	
Safety and Protection; Professional Responsibilities; Research and EBP	

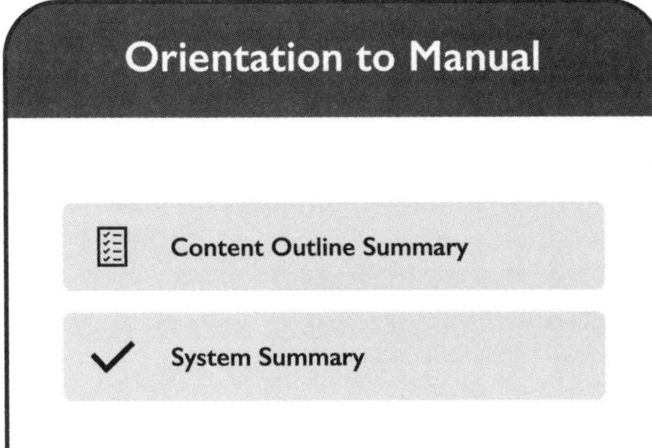

Orientation to Manual
Content Outline Summary
System Summary

Work Activity Statements

- Work activities tend to be more objective than knowledge statements
- Review of work activities late in the study plan ensures emphasis of "Big Ticket" items
- Goal: Talking Knowledge

Content Outline Summary

PHYSICAL THERAPY EXAMINATION
Midrange: 44 Questions (24.4%) Range: 38-50 Questions

This category refers to knowledge of the types and applications of specific system tests/measures, including outcome measures, according to current best evidence, and their relevance to information collected from the history and systems review. The category includes the reaction of the specific system to tests/measures. Information covered in these areas supports appropriate and effective patient/client management for rehabilitation, health promotion, and performance across the lifespan.

Sample Content

- System tests/measures, including outcome measures, and their applications according to current best evidence
- Anatomy and physiology of a specific system as related to tests/measures
- Movement analysis as related to a specific system

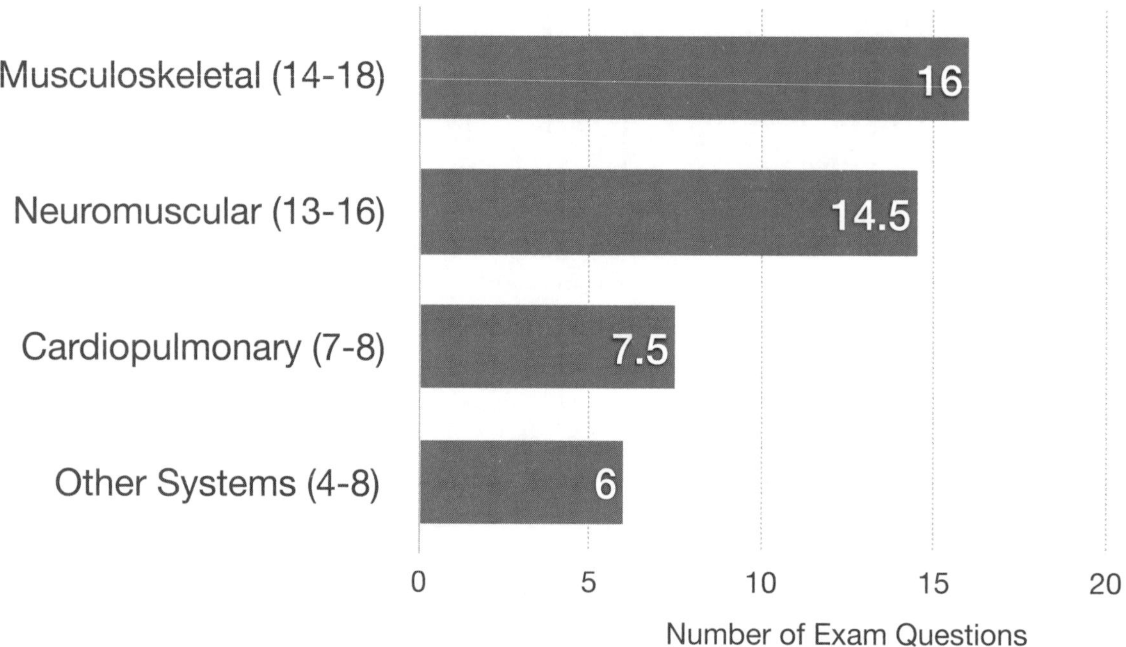

Musculoskeletal (14-18)
16
Neuromuscular (13-16)
14.5
Cardiopulmonary (7-8)
7.5
Other Systems (4-8)
6
0
5
10
15
20
Number of Exam Questions

Adapted from the NPTE-PT Test Content Outline, Federation of State Boards of Physical Therapy, www.fsbpt.org

FOUNDATIONS FOR EVALUATION, DIFFERENTIAL DIAGNOSIS, & PROGNOSIS
Midrange: 58.5 Questions (32.5%) Range: 51-66 Questions

This category refers to the interpretation of knowledge about diseases/conditions impacting a specific system, according to current best evidence, in order to support appropriate and effective patient/client treatment and management decisions for rehabilitation, health promotion, and performance across the lifespan.

Sample Content

- Differential diagnoses related to diseases/conditions
- Diseases/conditions and their pathophysiology to establish and carry out a plan of care, including prognosis
- The impact of pharmacology used to treat a specific system on physical therapy management
- Nonpharmacological medical management (e.g., diagnostic imaging, laboratory test values, other medical tests, surgical procedures)

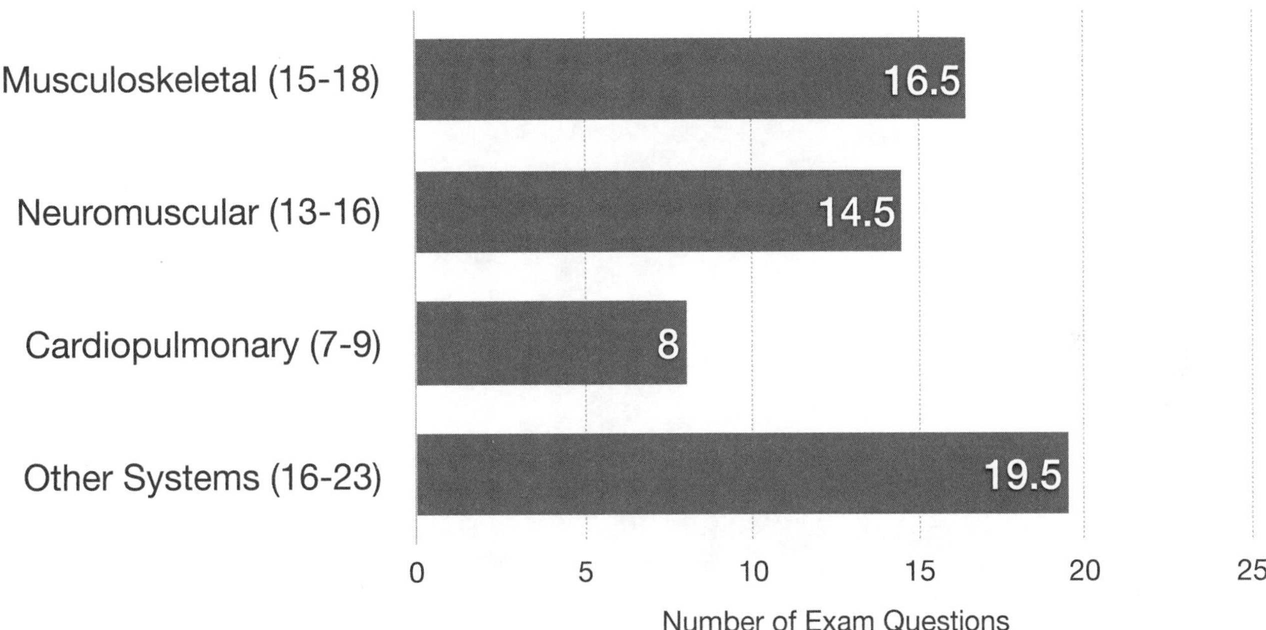

Musculoskeletal (15-18)
16.5
Neuromuscular (13-16)
14.5
Cardiopulmonary (7-9)
8
Other Systems (16-23)
19.5
0
5
10
15
20
25
Number of Exam Questions

Adapted from the NPTE-PT Test Content Outline, Federation of State Boards of Physical Therapy, www.fsbpt.org

INTERVENTIONS

Midrange: 52.5 Questions (29.2%) Range: 47-58 Questions

This category refers to specific system interventions (including types, applications, responses, and potential complications), according to current best evidence, as well as the impact on the specific system of interventions performed on other systems in order to support patient/client management for rehabilitation, health promotion, and performance across the lifespan.

Sample Content

- System specific physical therapy interventions and their applications for rehabilitation, health promotion, and performance according to current best evidence
- Anatomy and physiology as related to physical therapy interventions, daily activities, and environmental factors
- Adverse effects or complications from physical therapy and medical interventions on a specific system
- Adverse effects or complications on a specific system from physical therapy and medical interventions used on other systems

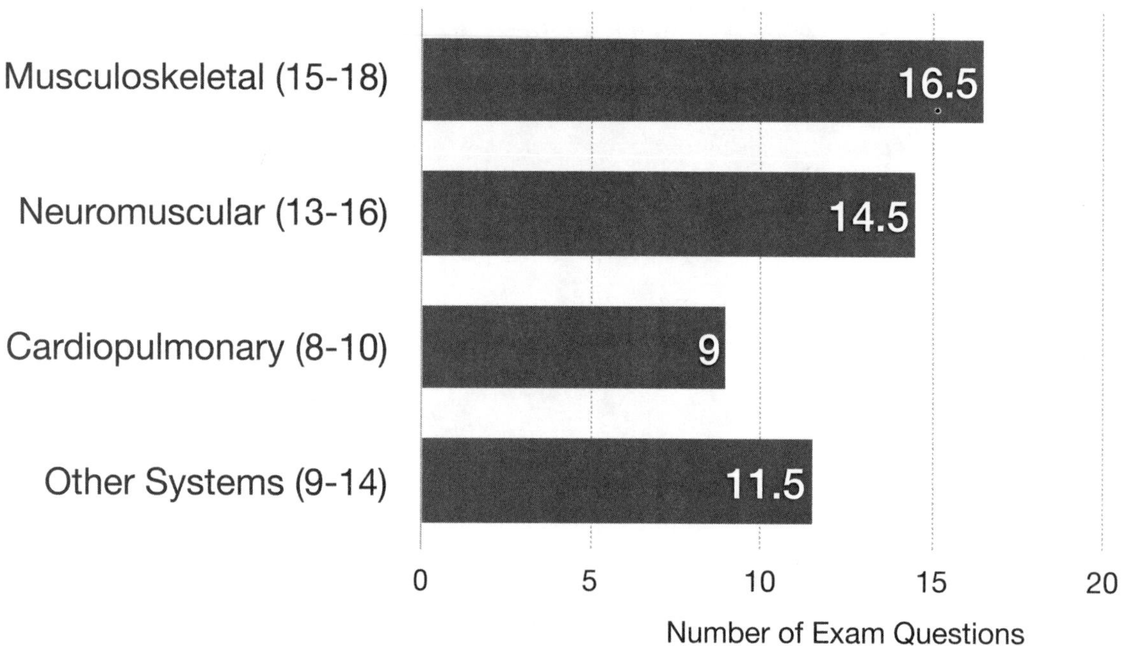
Musculoskeletal (15-18)
16.5
Neuromuscular (13-16)
14.5
Cardiopulmonary (8-10)
9
Other Systems (9-14)
11.5
0
5
10
15
20
Number of Exam Questions

Adapted from the NPTE-PT Test Content Outline, Federation of State Boards of Physical Therapy, www.fsbpt.org

EQUIPMENT, DEVICES, AND TECHNOLOGIES

Midrange: 5.5 Questions (3.1%) Range: 5-6 Questions

This category refers to the different types of equipment, devices, and technologies use requirements, and/or contextual determinants, as well as any other influencing factors involved in the selection and application of equipment, devices, and technologies, including consideration of current best evidence, in order to support patient/client management for rehabilitation, health promotion, and performance across the lifespan.

- Assistive and adaptive devices/technologies (e.g., walkers, wheelchairs, adaptive seating systems and positioning devices, mechanical lifts)
- Prosthetic devices/technologies (e.g., lower extremity and upper extremity prostheses, microprocessor-controlled prosthetic devices)
- Protective, supportive, and orthotic devices/technologies(e.g., braces, helmets, taping, compression garments, serial casts, shoe inserts, splints)

THERAPEUTIC MODALITIES

Midrange: 5 Questions (2.8%) Range: 4-6 Questions

This category refers to the underlying principles for the use of therapeutic modalities as well as the justification for the selection and use of various types of therapeutic modalities, including consideration of current best evidence, in order to support patient/client management for rehabilitation, health promotion, and performance across the lifespan.

- Thermal modalities
- Iontophoresis
- Electrotherapy modalities, (e.g., neuromuscular electrical stimulation (NMES), transcutaneous electrical nerve stimulation (TENS), functional electrical stimulation (FES), interferential therapy, high-voltage pulsed current)
- Ultrasound modalities, excluding phonophoresis
- Mechanical modalities (e.g., mechanical motion devices, traction devices)
- Biofeedback
- Intermittent compression

Adapted from the NPTE-PT Test Content Outline, Federation of State Boards of Physical Therapy, www.fsbpt.org

SAFETY AND PROTECTION
Midrange: 6 Questions (3.3%) Range: 5-7 Questions

This category refers to the critical issues involved in patient/client safety and protection and the responsibilities of health care providers to ensure that patient/client management and health care decisions take place in a secure environment.

- Factors influencing safety and injury prevention (e.g., safe patient handling, fall prevention, equipment maintenance, environmental safety)
- Function, implications, and related precautions of lines, tubes, catheters, monitoring devices, and mechanical ventilators/oxygen delivery devices
- Emergency preparedness (e.g., CPR, first aid, disaster response)
- Infection control procedures (e.g., standard/universal precautions, isolation techniques, sterile technique)
- Signs/symptoms of physical, sexual, and psychological abuse and neglect

PROFESSIONAL RESPONSIBILITIES
Midrange: 4.5 Questions (2.5%) Range: 4-5 Questions

This category refers to the responsibilities of health care providers to ensure that patient/client management and health-care decisions take place in a trustworthy environment.

- Standards of documentation
- Patient/client rights (e.g., ADA, IDEA, HIPAA, patient bill of rights)
- Human resource legal issues (e.g., OSHA, sexual harassment)
- Roles and responsibilities of the physical therapist, physical therapist assistant, other health care professionals, and support staff
- Standards of professional ethics
- Standards of billing, coding, and reimbursement
- Obligations for reporting illegal, unethical, or unprofessional behaviors (e.g., fraud, abuse, neglect)
- State and federal laws, rules, regulations, and industry standards set by state and accrediting bodies (e.g., state licensing entities, Joint Commission, CARF, CMS)
- Risk management and quality assurance (e.g., policies and procedures, incident reports, peer chart review)
- Cultural factors and/or characteristics that affect patient/client management (e.g., language differences, disability, ethnicity, customs, demographics, religion)
- Socioeconomic factors that affect patient/client management
- Applications and utilization of health information technology (e.g., electronic medical records)
- The provision and utilization of telehealth (i.e., the use of telecommunication technologies to provide health care information and services)

Adapted from the NPTE-PT Test Content Outline, Federation of State Boards of Physical Therapy, www.fsbpt.org

RESEARCH AND EVIDENCE-BASED PRACTICE
Midrange: 4 Questions (2.2%) Range: 3-5 Questions

This category refers to the application of measurement principles and research methods to make reasoned and appropriate assessment and to the interpretation of information sources and practice research to support patient/client management decisions fundamental to evidence-based practice.

- Research methodology and interpretation (e.g., qualitative, quantitative, levels of evidence)
- Data collection techniques (e.g., surveys, direct observation)
- Measurement science (e.g., reliability, validity)
- Techniques for assessing evidence (e.g., peer-reviewed publications, scientific proceedings, guidelines, clinical prediction rules)
- Statistics (e.g., t-test, chi-square, correlation coefficient, ANOVA, likelihood ratio, effect size, confidence interval)

Adapted from the NPTE-PT Test Content Outline, Federation of State Boards of Physical Therapy, www.fsbpt.org

System Summary

Musculoskeletal System	
Category	**# Items**
Examination	16 (14-18)
Foundations	16.5 (15-18)
Interventions	16.5 (15-18)
Total	49 (44-54)

Neuromuscular System	
Category	**# Items**
Examination	14.5 (13-16)
Foundations	14.5 (13-16)
Interventions	14.5 (13-16)
Total	43.5 (39-48)

Cardiopulmonary System	
Category	**# Items**
Examination	7.5 (7-8)
Foundations	8 (7-9)
Interventions	9 (8-10)
Total	24.5 (22-27)

Integumentary System	
Category	**# Items**
Examination	2.5 (2-3)
Foundations	3.5 (3-4)
Interventions	3.5 (3-4)
Total	9.5 (8-11)

Metabolic and Endocrine Systems	
Category	**# Items**
Examination	0 (0)
Foundations	2.5 (2-3)
Interventions	2.5 (2-3)
Total	5 (4-6)

Gastrointestinal System	
Category	**# Items**
Examination	1.5 (1-2)
Foundations	1.5 (1-2)
Interventions	1.5 (1-2)
Total	4.5 (3-6)

Genitourinary System	
Category	**# Items**
Examination	0.5 (0-1)
Foundations	1.5 (1-2)
Interventions	1.5 (1-2)
Total	3.5 (2-5)

Lymphatic System	
Category	**# Items**
Examination	1.5 (1-2)
Foundations	1.5 (1-2)
Interventions	2.5 (2-3)
Total	5.5 (4-7)

System Interactions	
Category	**# Items**
Examination	0 (0)
Foundations	9 (8-10)
Interventions	0 (0)
Total	9 (8-10)

Critical Work Activities

On the Road to Mastery!

Critical Work Activities allow candidates to determine if they possess talking knowledge related to the critical work activities of the NPTE-PT.

Critical Work Activities assist candidates to:

- Improve ability to anticipate academic content likely to be on the actual exam
- Discover potentially relevant academic content not previously reviewed
- Expand breadth and depth of content knowledge related to each work activity
- Utilize a final reinforcing loop for previously reviewed academic content

NPTE-PT Critical Work Activities

PATIENT/CLIENT ASSESSMENT

Information Gathering and Synthesis

Interview patients/clients, caregivers, and family to obtain patient/client history and current information (e.g., medical, surgical, medications, social, cultural, language preference, economic) to:

- ○ establish prior and current level of function/activity
- ○ establish general health status
- ○ identify red flags (e.g., unexplained weight change, fever, or malaise) and contraindications
- ○ identify risk factors and needs for preventative measures
- ○ identify patient/client's, family/caregiver's goals, values, and preferences
- ○ determine if patient/client is appropriate for PT
- ○ determine insurance and financial resources and issues (e.g., co-pays, deductibles, insurance limitations)
- ○ determine impact of medications on plan of care (e.g., medication reconciliation, timing of intervention delivery, adherence)

○ Administer standardized questionnaires (e.g., pain inventory, fall risk assessment)

○ Review medical records (e.g., lab values, diagnostic tests, imaging, specialty reports, narrative, consults)

○ Gather information/discuss patient/client's current health status with interprofessional/interdisciplinary team members

○ Identify signs/symptoms of change in patient/client's health status that require intervention by interprofessional/interdisciplinary team members

Systems Review

Perform screen of the:

- ○ patient/client's current affect, cognition, communication, and learning preferences (e.g., ability to convey needs, consciousness, orientation, expected emotional/behavioral responses)
- ○ patient/client's quality of speech, hearing, and vision (e.g., dysarthria, pitch/tone, use of corrective lenses, use of hearing aids)
- ○ vestibular system (e.g., dizziness, vertigo)
- ○ gastrointestinal system (e.g., difficulty swallowing, nausea, change in appetite/diet, change in bowel function)
- ○ genitourinary system (e.g., changes in bladder function, catheter complications)
- ○ reproductive system (e.g., sexual dysfunction, menstrual dysfunction, menopause/andropause status)
- ○ cardiovascular/pulmonary system (e.g., blood pressure, heart rate, respiration rate)

- ○ lymphatic system (e.g., primary or secondary lymphedema)
- ○ integumentary system (e.g., presence of scar formation, skin integrity, discoloration)
- ○ musculoskeletal system (e.g., gross symmetry, strength, range of motion)
- ○ neuromuscular system (e.g., gross coordination, motor function, balance, locomotion, gross sensory function)

TESTS AND MEASURES

Cardiovascular/Pulmonary

Select and perform tests and measures of:

- ○ cardiovascular function (e.g., blood pressure, heart rate, heart sounds)
- ○ pulmonary function (e.g., respiratory rate, breathing patterns, breath sounds, chest excursion)
- ○ perfusion and gas exchange (e.g., oxygen saturation)
- ○ peripheral circulation (e.g., capillary refill, blood pressure in upper versus lower extremities)
- ○ critical limb ischemia (e.g., peripheral pulses, skin perfusion pressure)
- ○ physiological responses to position change (e.g., orthostatic hypotension, skin color, blood pressure, heart rate)
- ○ aerobic capacity under maximal and submaximal conditions (e.g., endurance, exercise tolerance, metabolic equivalents, perceived exertion)

Anthropometric

Select and perform tests and measures of:

- ○ body composition (e.g., percent body fat, lean muscle mass, body mass index (BMI))
- ○ body dimensions (e.g., height, weight, girth, limb length, head circumference/shape)
- ○ edema (e.g., pitting, volume, circumference)

Arousal, Attention, and Cognition

Select and perform tests and measures of:

- ○ arousal and orientation (e.g., level of consciousness, time, person, place, situation)
- ○ attention and cognition (e.g., ability to process commands, delirium, confusion)
- ○ communication (e.g., expressive and receptive skills, following instructions)
- ○ recall (including memory and retention)

Nerve Integrity

Select and perform tests and measures of:

- ○ cranial nerve integrity (e.g., facial asymmetry, oculomotor function, hearing)
- ○ spinal nerve integrity (e.g., dermatome, myotome)
- ○ peripheral nerve integrity (e.g., sensation, strength)
- ○ neural provocation (e.g., tapping, tension, stretch)

Environmental and Community Integration/Reintegration (Home, Work, Job, School, Play, and Leisure)

- ○ Assess activities of daily living (ADL) (e.g., bed mobility, transfers, household mobility, dressing, self-care, toileting, sexual relations)

- ○ Assess instrumental activities of daily living (IADL) (e.g., household chores, hobbies)
- ○ Assess ability to perform skills needed for integration or reintegration into the community, work, or school
- ○ Assess barriers (e.g., social, economic, physical, psychological, environmental, work conditions and activities) to home, community, work, or school integration/reintegration
- ○ Assess safety in home, community, work, or school environments
- ○ Assess ability to participate in activities with or without the use of devices, equipment, or technologies

Ergonomics and Body Mechanics

Select and perform tests and measures of:

- ○ ergonomics and body mechanics during functional activities
- ○ postural alignment and position (static and dynamic)
- ○ specific work conditions or activities
- ○ tools, devices, equipment, and workstations related to work actions, tasks, or activities

Functional Mobility, Balance, and Vestibular

Select and perform tests and measures of:

- ○ balance (dynamic and static) with or without the use of specialized equipment
- ○ gait and locomotion (e.g., ambulation, wheelchair mobility) with or without the use of specialized equipment
- ○ mobility during functional activities and transitional movements (e.g., transfers, bed mobility)
- ○ vestibular function (e.g., peripheral dysfunction, central dysfunction)

Integumentary Integrity

- ○ Assess skin characteristics (e.g., continuity of skin color, sensation, temperature, texture, turgor)
- ○ Assess wound characteristics (e.g., tissue involvement, depth, tunneling, burn degree, ulcer/injury classification)
- ○ Assess scar tissue characteristics (e.g., banding, pliability, sensation, and texture)
- ○ Assess activities, positioning, and postures that may produce or relieve trauma to the skin
- ○ Assess devices and equipment that may produce or relieve trauma to the skin

Joint Integrity and Range of Motion

Select and perform tests and measures of:

- ○ spinal and peripheral joint stability (e.g., ligamentous integrity, joint structure)
- ○ spinal and peripheral joint mobility (e.g., glide, end feel)
- ○ range of motion (e.g., passive, active, functional)
- ○ flexibility (e.g., muscle length, soft tissue extensibility)

Motor Function

Select and perform tests and measures of:

- ○ muscle tone (e.g., hypertonicity, hypotonicity, dystonia)

- ○ dexterity, coordination, and agility (e.g., rapid alternating movement, finger to nose)
- ○ ability to initiate, modify and control movement patterns and postures (e.g., catching a ball, gait)
- ○ ability to change movement performance with practice (e.g., motor learning)
- ○ movement quality (e.g., purpose, precision, efficiency, biomechanics, kinematics, compensatory strategies)

Muscle Performance

Select and perform tests and measures of:

- ○ muscle strength, power, and endurance without specialized equipment (e.g., manual muscle test, functional strength testing)
- ○ muscle strength, power, and endurance with specialized equipment (e.g., isokinetic testing, dynamometry)

Neuromotor Development and Sensory Integration

Select and perform tests and measures of:

- ○ acquisition and evolution of motor skills throughout the lifespan
- ○ sensorimotor integration
- ○ developmental reflexes and reactions (e.g., asymmetrical tonic neck reflex, righting reactions)

Reflex Integrity

Select and perform tests and measures of:

- ○ deep tendon/muscle stretch reflexes (e.g., quadriceps, biceps)
- ○ upper motor neuron integrity (e.g., Babinski reflex, Hoffman sign)
- ○ superficial reflexes and reactions (e.g., plantar reflex, abdominal reflexes)

Pain and Sensory Integrity

Select and perform tests and measures of:

- ○ pain (e.g., location, intensity, frequency, central, peripheral, psychogenic)
- ○ deep sensation (e.g., proprioception, kinesthesia, pressure)
- ○ superficial sensation (e.g., touch, temperature discrimination)
- ○ visceral organ sensitivity and integrity (e.g., palpation, auscultation)

Evaluation and Diagnosis

Interpret each of the following types of data to determine the need for intervention or the response to intervention:

- ○ cardiovascular/pulmonary system
- ○ lymphatic system
- ○ arousal, attention, cognition, and communication
- ○ neuromuscular system
- ○ functional mobility, balance, and vestibular
- ○ musculoskeletal system
- ○ integumentary system
- ○ anthropometric

- ○ gastrointestinal system
- ○ genitourinary system
- ○ need for or use of assistive and adaptive devices/technologies
- ○ need for or use of orthotic, protective, and supportive devices/technologies
- ○ need for or use of prosthetic devices/technologies
- ○ barriers to home, community, work, or school integration/reintegration
- ○ ergonomics and body mechanics
- ○ pain and sensory integrity
- ○ ADLs/IADLs and home management
- ○ imaging, lab values, and medications
- ○ electrodiagnostic test results (e.g., electromyography, nerve conduction velocity)

○ Evaluate the patient/client's ability to assume or resume home, community, work, school, and/or leisure activities

○ Develop physical therapy diagnosis by integrating system and non-system data

Development of Prognosis, Plan of Care, and Goals

- ○ Establish PT prognosis based on information gathered during the examination process
- ○ Develop plan of care based on data gathered during the examination process, incorporating information from the patient/client, caregiver, family members, and other professionals
- ○ Revise treatment intervention plan based on treatment outcomes, change in patient/client's health status, and ongoing evaluation
- ○ Develop objective and measurable goals based on information gathered during the examination process, in collaboration with the patient/client, caregiver, family members, and/or other professionals
- ○ Select interventions based on information gathered during the examination process, incorporating information from the patient/client, caregiver, family members, and other professionals
- ○ Modify plan of care based on patient/client's resources (e.g., financial, transportation, time, insurance benefits, available technologies)

INTERVENTIONS

Procedural Interventions

Therapeutic Exercise/Therapeutic Activities

Perform and/or train patient/client/caregiver in:

- ○ aerobic capacity/endurance conditioning
- ○ balance, coordination, and agility activities
- ○ body mechanics and postural stabilization techniques
- ○ flexibility techniques
- ○ neuromotor techniques (e.g., movement pattern training, neuromuscular education or reeducation)
- ○ relaxation techniques
- ○ strength, power, and endurance exercises

- ○ genitourinary management (e.g., pelvic floor exercises, bladder strategies)
- ○ gastrointestinal management (e.g., bowel strategies, positioning to avoid reflux)
- ○ manual/mechanical airway clearance techniques (e.g., assistive devices, assistive cough, incentive spirometer, flutter valve, percussion, vibration)
- ○ techniques to maximize ventilation and perfusion (e.g., positioning, active cycle breathing, autogenic drainage, paced breathing, pursed lip breathing)
- ○ mechanical repositioning for vestibular dysfunction
- ○ habituation/adaptation exercises for vestibular dysfunction
- ○ postural drainage

Functional Training

Recommend:

- ○ barrier accommodations or modifications (e.g., ramps, grab bars, raised toilet, environmental control units)

Perform and/or train patient/client in:

- ○ the use of environmental modifications (e.g., ramps, grab bars, raised toilet, environmental control units)
- ○ activities of daily living (ADL) (e.g., bed mobility, transfers, household mobility, dressing, self-care, toileting, sexual relations)
- ○ community and leisure integration or reintegration (e.g., work/school/play)
- ○ instrumental activities of daily living (IADL) (e.g., household chores, hobbies)
- ○ mobility techniques
- ○ gross motor developmental progression
- ○ fall prevention and fall recovery strategies
- ○ behavior modification and strategies that enhance functioning (e.g., energy conservation, pacing, pre-activity planning, reminder schedules)

Manual Therapy Techniques

Perform:

- ○ manual lymphatic drainage
- ○ spinal and peripheral manual traction
- ○ train patient/client/caregiver in soft tissue mobilization (e.g., connective tissue massage, therapeutic massage, foam rolling)
- ○ instrument-assisted soft tissue mobilization
- ○ peripheral joint range of motion
- ○ peripheral mobilization/manipulation (thrust)
- ○ peripheral mobilization/manipulation (non-thrust)
- ○ spinal mobilization/manipulation (non-thrust)
- ○ cervical spinal mobilization/manipulation (thrust)
- ○ thoracic and lumbar spinal mobilization/manipulation (thrust)

Apply taping for:

- ○ neuromuscular reeducation
- ○ edema management
- ○ pain management

Equipment and Devices

Fabricate, apply, and/or adjust:

- ○ adaptive devices (e.g., utensils, seating and positioning devices, steering wheel devices)
- ○ protective devices (e.g., braces, cushions, helmets, protective taping)
- ○ supportive devices (e.g., compression garments, corsets, elastic wraps, neck collars, serial casts, short-stretch bandages)
- ○ orthotic devices (e.g., braces, shoe inserts, splints)

Apply and/or adjust:

- ○ assistive devices/technologies (e.g., canes, crutches, walkers, wheelchairs, tilt tables, standing frames)
- ○ prosthetic devices/technologies (e.g., lower extremity and upper extremity protheses, microprocessor-controlled prosthetic devices)
- ○ mechanical neuromuscular re-education devices/technologies (e.g., weighted vests, therapeutic suits, body weight supported treadmill)
- ○ prescribed oxygen during interventions

Train patient/client/caregiver in the use of:

- ○ adaptive devices (e.g., seating and positioning devices, steering wheel devices)
- ○ assistive devices/technologies (e.g., canes, crutches, walkers, wheelchairs, tilt tables, standing frames)
- ○ orthotic devices (e.g., braces, shoe inserts, splints)
- ○ prosthetic devices/technologies (e.g., lower extremity and upper extremity prostheses, microprocessor-controlled prosthetic devices)
- ○ protective devices (e.g., braces, cushions, helmets, protective taping)
- ○ supportive devices (e.g., compression garments, corsets, elastic wraps, neck collars, serial casts, short-stretch bandages)
- ○ mechanical neuromuscular re-education devices/technologies (e.g., weighted vests, therapeutic suits, body weight supported treadmill)

Integumentary Repair and Protection Techniques

Perform and/or train patient/client/caregiver in:

- ○ nonselective debridement (e.g., removal of nonselective areas of devitalized tissue)
- ○ selective enzymatic or autolytic debridement (e.g., removal of specific areas of devitalized tissue)
- ○ negative pressure wound therapy (e.g., vacuum-assisted wound closure)
- ○ application of topical agents (e.g., cleansers, creams, moisturizers, ointments, sealants) and dressings (e.g., hydrogels, wound coverings)
- ○ desensitization techniques (e.g., brushing, tapping, use of textures)

○ Perform sharp debridement (e.g., removal of specific areas of devitalized tissue)

○ Recommend topical agents (e.g., pharmacological to physician, over-the-counter to patient) and advanced wound dressings (e.g., negative pressure wound therapy, wound coverings)

Therapeutic Modalities

Perform and/or train patient/client/caregiver in:

- ○ biofeedback therapy (e.g., relaxation techniques, muscle reeducation, EMG)
- ○ iontophoresis
- ○ electrotherapy modalities, excluding iontophoresis (e.g., neuromuscular electrical stimulation (NMES), transcutaneous electrical nerve stimulation (TENS), functional electrical stimulation (FES), interferential therapy, high-voltage pulsed current)
- ○ cryotherapy (e.g., cold pack, ice massage, vapocoolant spray)
- ○ hydrotherapy (e.g., aquatic exercise, underwater treadmill)
- ○ ultrasound procedures
- ○ hot pack thermotherapy

Mechanical Modalities

Apply and/or train patient/client/caregiver in:

- ○ intermittent pneumatic compression
- ○ assisted movement devices (e.g., continuous passive motion devices, dynamic splint)
- ○ mechanical spinal traction

Non-Procedural Interventions

Communication

Discuss physical therapy evaluation findings, interventions, goals, prognosis, discharge planning, and plan of care with:

- ○ physical therapists, physical therapist assistants, and/or support staff
- ○ interprofessional/interdisciplinary team members
- ○ patient/client and caregiver

Provide:

- ○ written, oral, and electronic information to the patient/client and/or caregiver

Documentation

Document:

- ○ examination results
- ○ evaluation to include diagnosis, goals, and prognosis
- ○ intervention(s) and patient/client response(s) to intervention
- ○ patient/client/caregiver education
- ○ outcomes (e.g., discharge summary, reassessments)
- ○ communication with the interdisciplinary/interprofessional team related to the patient/client's care
- ○ rationale for billing and reimbursement
- ○ disclosure and consent (e.g., disclosure of medical information, consent for treatment)
- ○ letter of medical necessity (e.g., wheelchair, assistive equipment, disability parking placard)
- ○ intervention/plan of care for specialized services and settings (e.g., individual education plan, individual family service plan, vocational transition plan)

- Assign billing codes for physical therapy evaluation and treatment provided

Education

Educate patient/client and/or caregiver about:

- patient/client's current condition and health status (e.g., nature of the condition, prognosis, potential benefits of physical therapy interventions, potential treatment outcomes)
- role of the physical therapist and/or physical therapist assistant in patient/client management
- lifestyle and behavioral changes to promote wellness (e.g., nutrition, physical activity, tobacco cessation)
- the role of physical therapy in transitional planning (e.g., hospice, palliative care, setting changes)

Educate the health care team about:

- the role of the physical therapist and/or physical therapist assistant in patient/client management
- safe patient handling (e.g., injury prevention, ergonomics, use of equipment)

Educate community groups on:

- lifestyle and behavioral changes to promote wellness (e.g., nutrition, physical activity, tobacco cessation)

Participate in:

- clinical education of students

Patient/Client and Staff Safety

Emergency Procedures

- Implement emergency procedures (e.g., CPR, AED, calling a code)
- Perform first aid
- Implement disaster response procedures

Environmental Safety

- Perform risk assessment of the physical environment (e.g., barrier-free environment, outlets, windows, floors, lighting)
- Prepare and maintain a safe working environment for performing interventions (e.g., unobstructed walkways, equipment availability)
- Perform regular equipment inspections and/or maintenance (e.g., modalities, assistive devices)

Infection Control

- Perform and/or train patient/client and/or caregiver on appropriate infection control practices (e.g., universal precautions, hand hygiene, isolation, airborne precautions, equipment cleaning)

Research and Evidence-Based Practice

- Search the literature for current best evidence
- Evaluate the quality of published data

- ○ Integrate current best evidence, clinical experience, and patient values in clinical practice (e.g., clinical prediction rules, patient preference, clinical practice guidelines)
- ○ Design, direct, and/or participate in research activities
- ○ Compare intervention outcomes with normative data

Professional Responsibilities

- ○ Supervise physical therapist assistant(s) and support personnel (licensed/unlicensed)
- ○ Assign tasks to other personnel (licensed/unlicensed) to assist with patient/client care
- ○ Discuss ongoing patient care with the interprofessional/interdisciplinary team members
- ○ Refer patient/client to specialists or other health care providers when necessary
- ○ Disclose financial interest in recommended products or services to the patient/client
- ○ Provide notice and information about alternative care when the physical therapist terminates provider relationship with the patient/client
- ○ Document transfer of patient/client care to another physical therapist (therapist of record)
- ○ Report health care providers that are suspected to not perform their professional responsibilities with reasonable skill and safety to the appropriate authorities
- ○ Report suspected cases of abuse to the appropriate authority
- ○ Report suspected illegal or unethical acts performed by health care professionals to the relevant authority
- ○ Advocate for public access to physical therapy and other health care services
- ○ Determine own need for professional development
- ○ Participate in learning and/or development activities (e.g., journal clubs, self-directed reading, continuing competence activities) to maintain the currency of knowledge, skills, and abilities
- ○ Practice within the federal and jurisdiction regulations and professional standards
- ○ Participate in professional organizations
- ○ Perform community-based screenings (e.g., fall risk, posture, musculoskeletal, flexibility, sports-specific)
- ○ Participate in performance improvement and quality reporting activities (e.g., Physician Quality Reporting System, standardized outcomes measurement, application of health informatics)

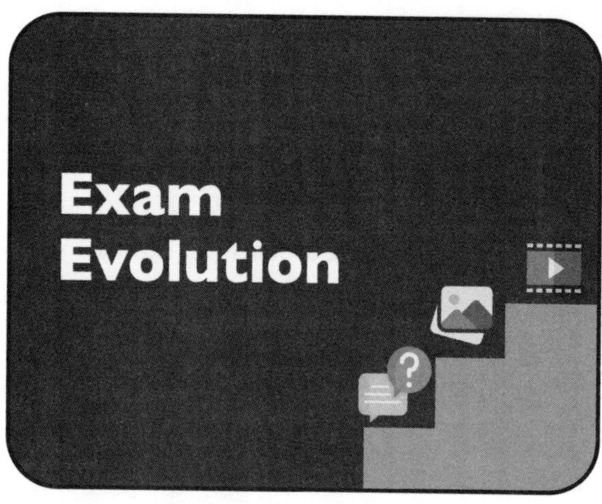
Exam
Evolution

Types of Questions

- Standard
- Graphic
- Video
- Scenario

Standard Questions

An athlete sustained a grade III lateral ankle sprain while playing basketball and plans to return to full participation in athletic activities. Which component of the rehabilitation process is **MOST** important to address the concern of chronic functional instability?

1. Use of ice and compression to rapidly reduce the inflammation and swelling
2. High-voltage pulsed current to promote tissue healing
3. Single-leg support proprioception exercises with dynamic strengthening
4. Isometric stabilization exercises and isokinetic ankle strengthening exercises

Graphic Questions

A physical therapist assesses a patient's passive and active range of motion following total knee arthroplasty. The therapist is able to fully extend the patient's knee passively. However, when the patient extends the knee actively, they lack 20 degrees of extension. Which term **BEST** describes what is occurring?

1. Extension lag
2. Disuse atrophy
3. Flexion contracture
4. Inhibition by pain

Video Questions

A physical therapist assigns a grade of fair after performing a manual muscle test for a patient with shoulder pain. Which muscle would **MOST** likely be associated with the depicted testing procedure?

1. Pectoralis major
2. Anterior deltoid
3. Latissimus dorsi
4. Lower trapezius

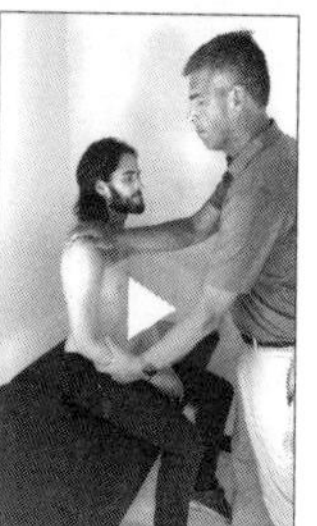

Video Question Functionality

 Play

 Pause

 Forward frame by frame progression

 Backward frame by frame progression

 Looping button

 Variable speed playback

Scenario Questions

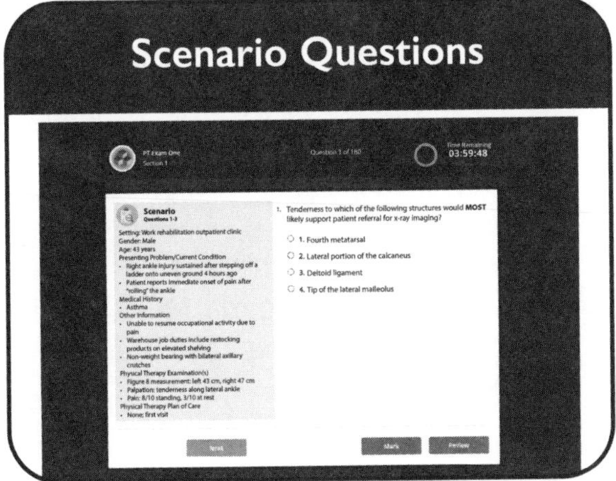

Activity 4

5 Video Questions

15 Scenario Questions

Instruction – Video Questions

Group

Select the best response to the five video questions. The questions will be discussed after all five questions have been answered.

Instruction – Scenario Questions

Individual

Select the best response to the five scenario sets (15 questions).

More Alternate Exam Items

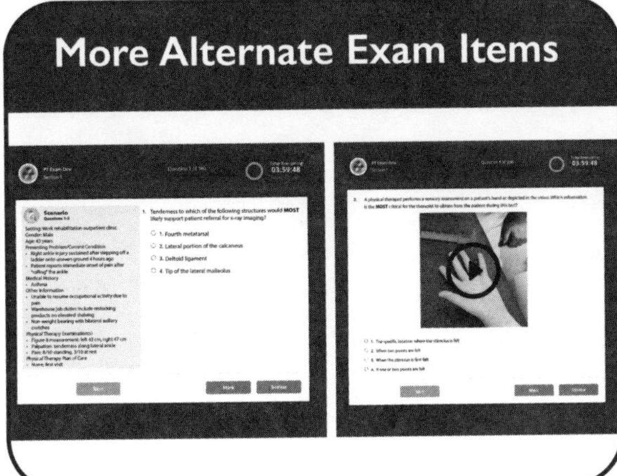

We Got You!

insight
STUDENT VERSION
ONLINE ADVANTAGE
SCOREBUILDERS

Activity 4
Alternate Exam Items

Video Questions

● Correct
○ Incorrect
☐ Academic
☐ Decision Making
☐ Test Taking

Level 1

1. A physical therapist performs a sensory assessment on a patient's hand as depicted in the video. Which information is the **MOST** critical for the therapist to obtain from the patient during this test?

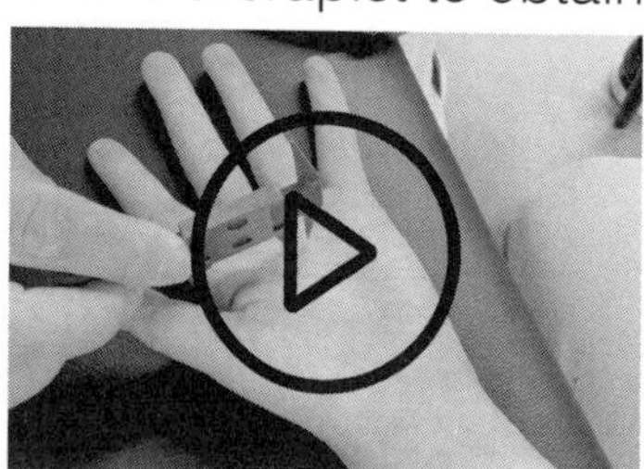

○ 1. The specific location where the stimulus is felt
○ 2. When two points are felt
○ 3. When the stimulus is first felt
● 4. If one or two points are felt

● Correct
○ Incorrect
☐ Academic
☐ Decision Making
☐ Test Taking

Level 2

2. A physical therapist asks a patient to use their upper extremity in the manner depicted in the video to indicate that they feel a Semmes-Weinstein monofilament contacting their skin. Which situation would **BEST** support this type of modification to the typical testing procedure?

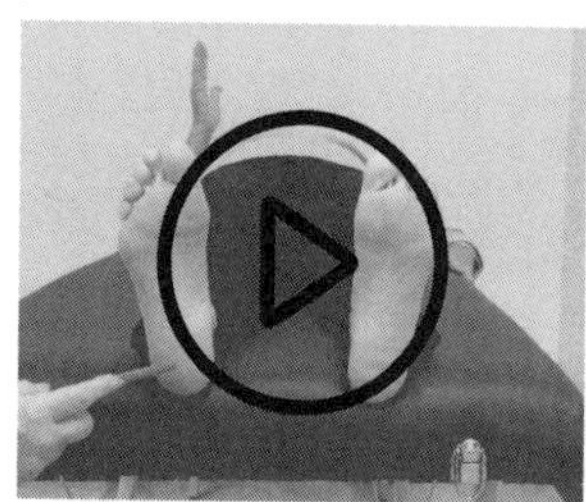

○ 1. The patient does not speak English
○ 2. The patient has ideomotor apraxia
○ 3. The patient has diabetes mellitus
● 4. The patient has Broca's aphasia

3. A physical therapist takes a measurement as depicted in the video and records it as 10 inches. Given that measurement, what would be the **MOST** appropriate value for the associated wheelchair dimension?

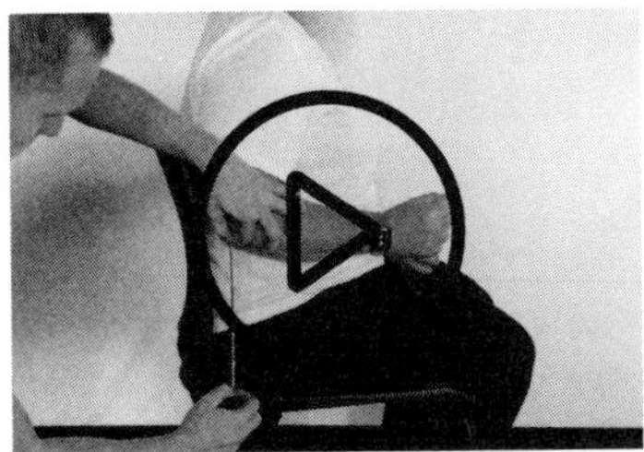

- ○ 1. 9 inches
- ● 2. 10 inches
- ○ 3. 11 inches
- ○ 4. 12 inches

4. A physical therapist attempts to assess a primitive reflex as shown in the video. What minimum age would the therapist anticipate this reflex being integrated?

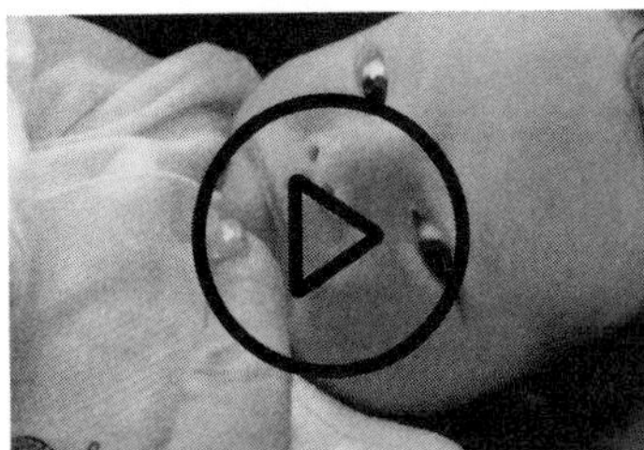

- ○ 1. One month
- ○ 2. Four months
- ● 3. Seven months
- ○ 4. Ten months

5. A physical therapist observes a patient apply a finger splint as shown in the video. The patient's physician instructed them to wear the splint only at night for four weeks. Which condition would **MOST** likely be associated with this scenario?

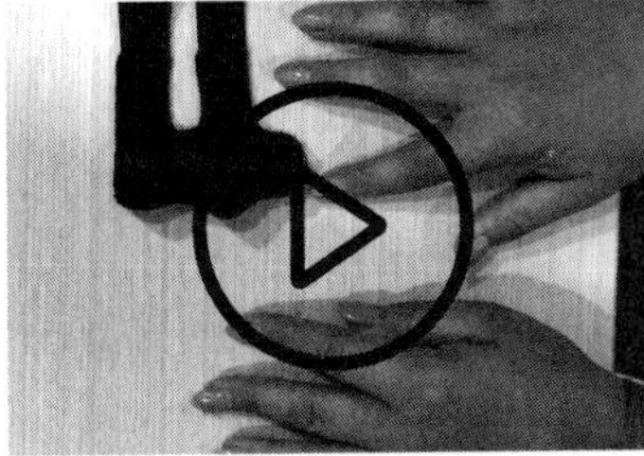

- ○ 1. Dupuytren's contracture
- ○ 2. Mallet finger
- ○ 3. Swan neck deformity
- ● 4. Trigger finger

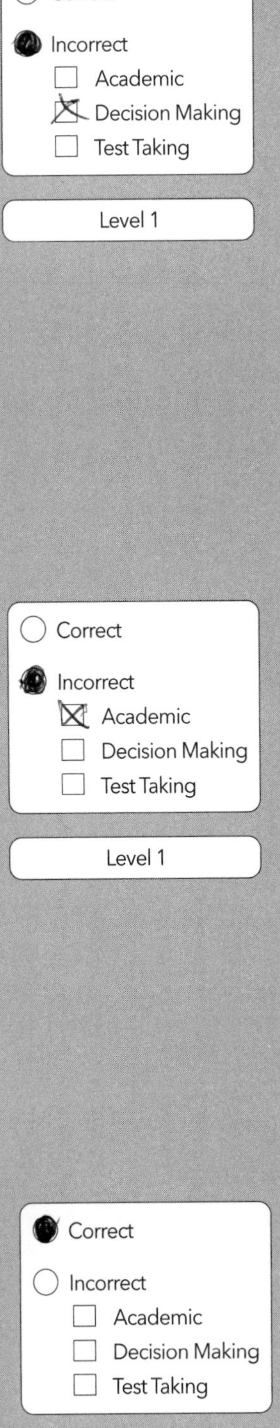

Correct
Incorrect
Academic
Decision Making
Test Taking
Level 1
Correct
Incorrect
Academic
Decision Making
Test Taking
Level 1
Correct
Incorrect
Academic
Decision Making
Test Taking
Level 2

Scenario 1
Questions 6-8

Setting: School-based therapy services
Gender: Male
Age: 6 years
Presenting Problem/Current Condition
- Down syndrome

Medical History
- Patent ductus arteriosus with surgical repair in infancy

Other Information
- Single parent with three younger children

Physical Therapy Examination(s)
- Tonal abnormalities
- Child prefers to lie on floor or "W" sit instead of traditional sitting
- Minimal assist with cross legged sitting
- Minimal assist with floor to stand transition
- Unable to keep up with peers when walking at school

Physical Therapy Plan of Care
- Mobility training
- Activities emphasizing core stability
- Introduce and reinforce learning strategies
- Family and caregiver education

● Correct
○ Incorrect
☐ Academic
☐ Decision Making
☐ Test Taking

Level 2

6. Which of the following techniques would be the **MOST** beneficial when treating the patient's tonal abnormalities?

● 1. Quick stretch
○ 2. Deep pressure
○ 3. Prolonged icing
○ 4. Neutral warmth

○ Correct
● Incorrect
☒ Academic
☐ Decision Making
☐ Test Taking

Level 1

7. The physical therapist designs interventions to focus on long-term goals of increasing functional activities, including cross legged sitting on the floor, transitions from the floor to standing, and improved mobility within the school building, as part of the child's Individualized Educational Plan. Which of the following timeframes is the **MOST** appropriate to attain these goals?

○ 1. One month
● 2. Four months
○ 3. Six months
✓ 4. One year

● Correct
○ Incorrect
☐ Academic
☐ Decision Making
☐ Test Taking

Level 3

8. The child's preference for "W" sitting is **MOST** likely a result of which of the following impairments?

○ 1. Hypotonicity
○ 2. Hypertonicity
● 3. Decreased core strength
○ 4. Fatigue

Scenario 2
Questions 9-11

Setting: Work rehabilitation outpatient clinic
Gender: Male
Age: 43 years
Presenting Problem/Current Condition
- Right ankle injury sustained after stepping off a ladder onto uneven ground 4 hours ago
- Patient reports immediate onset of pain after "rolling" the ankle

Medical History
- Asthma

Other Information
- Unable to resume occupational activity due to pain
- Warehouse job duties include restocking products on elevated shelving using a ladder and lifting up to 75 pounds
- Non-weight bearing right lower extremity with bilateral axillary crutches

Physical Therapy Examination(s)
- Figure 8 measurement: left 43 cm, right 47 cm
- Palpation: tenderness along lateral ankle
- Pain: 8/10 standing, 3/10 at rest

Physical Therapy Plan of Care
- None; first visit

- [x] Correct
- [ ] Incorrect
  - [ ] Academic
  - [ ] Decision Making
  - [ ] Test Taking

Level 2

9. Tenderness to which of the following structures would **MOST** likely support patient referral for x-ray imaging?

- [ ] 1. Fourth metatarsal
- [ ] 2. Lateral portion of the calcaneus
- [ ] 3. Deltoid ligament
- [x] 4. Tip of the lateral malleolus

- [x] Correct
- [ ] Incorrect
  - [ ] Academic
  - [ ] Decision Making
  - [ ] Test Taking

Level 3

10. A physical therapist prepares to write a functional goal to determine when the patient is ready to return to work. Which of the following goals is the **BEST** indicator that the patient can return to work?

- [ ] 1. Ability to push 75 pounds for 30 feet
- [x] 2. Ability to ascend and descend 12 ladder rungs
- [ ] 3. Ability to lift 25 pounds overhead five times
- [ ] 4. Ability to perform ten repetitions of sit to stand

- [ ] Correct
- [x] Incorrect
  - [ ] Academic
  - [x] Decision Making
  - [ ] Test Taking

Level 2

11. Based on the patient's current status and assuming an x-ray was negative for a fracture, which piece of medical equipment would be **MOST** beneficial during the acute phase of this injury?

- [ ] 1. Walking boot ✓
- [ ] 2. Heel cup
- [x] 3. Lace up brace
- [ ] 4. Rigid orthoses

Scenario 3
Questions 12-14

Setting: Inpatient cardiac rehabilitation
Gender: Female
Age: 65 years

Presenting Problem/Current Condition
- Status post coronary artery bypass graft 4 days ago

Medical History
- Myocardial infarction secondary to occlusion of circumflex artery

Other Information
- Standard sternal precautions

Physical Therapy Examination(s)
Resting values:
- Heart rate: 95 beats/minute
- Blood pressure: 132/85 mm Hg
- Respiratory rate: 17 breaths/minute

Physical Therapy Plan of Care
- None; first session

● Correct
○ Incorrect
☐ Academic
☐ Decision Making
☐ Test Taking

Level 2

12. Based on the patient's surgical procedure, which pharmacological agent would **MOST** likely have been prescribed post-operatively?

○ 1. ACE inhibitor agents
○ 2. Alpha adrenergic antagonist agents
● 3. Anticoagulant agents
○ 4. Antihyperlipidemia agents

● Correct
○ Incorrect
☐ Academic
☐ Decision Making
☐ Test Taking

Level 1

13. Which of the patient's objective measurements would be considered abnormal?

○ 1. Heart rate and systolic blood pressure
● 2. Systolic and diastolic blood pressures
○ 3. Heart rate and respiratory rate
○ 4. Diastolic blood pressure and respiratory rate

● Correct
○ Incorrect
☐ Academic
☐ Decision Making
☐ Test Taking

Level 1

14. A physical therapist monitors the patient's vital signs and electrocardiogram while walking on a treadmill during the first day of an inpatient cardiac rehabilitation program. Which of the following criteria would **MOST** warrant the therapist terminating the exercise session?

○ 1. PR interval = 0.18 seconds
○ 2. QRS complex = 0.08 seconds
○ 3. Diastolic blood pressure = 88 mm Hg
● 4. Heart rate = 140 beats/minute

Scenario 4
Questions 15-17

Setting: Outpatient clinic
Gender: Male
Age: 5 years

Presenting Problem/Current Condition
- Duchenne muscular dystrophy

Medical History
- Elevated creatine kinase (CK-MM) blood level

Other Information
- Child's mother is the primary caregiver for her parents

Physical Therapy Examination(s)
- Exaggerated lumbar lordosis and genu recurvatum
- Lower extremity weakness
- Difficulty rising from the floor to stand, ascending stairs, and keeping up with peers on the playground

Physical Therapy Plan of Care
- Family and caregiver education
- Postural training
- Mobility skills

● Correct
○ Incorrect
☐ Academic
☐ Decision Making
☐ Test Taking

Level 2

15. Assuming a normal progression of the disease process, which of the following impairments would have **MOST** likely been present at the initial onset of the patient's condition?

○ 1. Distal muscle weakness
● 2. Proximal muscle weakness
○ 3. Impaired respiratory function
○ 4. Diminished sensation to light touch

● Correct
○ Incorrect
☐ Academic
☐ Decision Making
☐ Test Taking

Level 2

16. What other finding is the physical therapist **MOST** likely to identify?

○ 1. Impaired hearing
○ 2. Dystonia
● 3. Gowers' sign
○ 4. Lower extremity muscle contractures

● Correct
○ Incorrect
☐ Academic
☐ Decision Making
☐ Test Taking

Level 2

17. Which muscle group is **MOST** likely to be weak given the identified postural deformity?

○ 1. Trunk extensors
○ 2. Ankle plantar flexors
● 3. Hip extensors
○ 4. Knee flexors

Scenario 5
Questions 18-20

Setting: Outpatient clinic
Gender: Female
Age: 42 years

Presenting Problem/Current Condition
- Plantar fasciitis

Medical History
- Patellofemoral syndrome
- Iliotibial band syndrome
- Medial tibial stress syndrome

Other Information
- Medications: Aleve (naproxen)
- Severe pain in the plantar aspect of the foot with first morning steps
- Intermittent cramping in the plantar aspect of the foot

Physical Therapy Examination(s)
- Observation: pes planus, flattened medial longitudinal arch
- Palpation: tenderness on medial calcaneal tubercle
- Ankle AROM: 5 degrees dorsiflexion, 40 degrees plantar flexion

Physical Therapy Plan of Care
- Stretching, strengthening, taping
- Self-care management skills
- Home exercise program

● Correct
○ Incorrect
☐ Academic
☐ Decision Making
☐ Test Taking

Level 1

18. Which of the following muscles should be strengthened to accommodate for the identified foot structural abnormality?

○ 1. Gastrocnemius, soleus, and plantaris
○ 2. Fibularis (peroneus) longus and brevis
○ 3. Tibialis anterior and extensor hallucis longus
● 4. Tibialis posterior and flexor digitorum longus

● Correct
○ Incorrect
☐ Academic
☐ Decision Making
☐ Test Taking

Level 2

19. Which of the following interventions is **MOST** likely to reduce the symptoms experienced when first standing in the morning?

○ 1. Heel cup
○ 2. Rigid orthoses
○ 3. Low dye taping
● 4. Dorsiflexion night splint

● Correct
○ Incorrect
☐ Academic
☐ Decision Making
☐ Test Taking

Level 1

20. What type of equipment would be the **MOST** appropriate for the physical therapist to incorporate into a home exercise program if the goal was to address the patient's reported cramping?

○ 1. Elastic band
● 2. Tennis ball
○ 3. Towel
○ 4. Foot rocker

PERFORMANCE ANALYSIS

Alternate Exam Items

20 Questions
Time (Videos - Group, Scenarios 15:00)

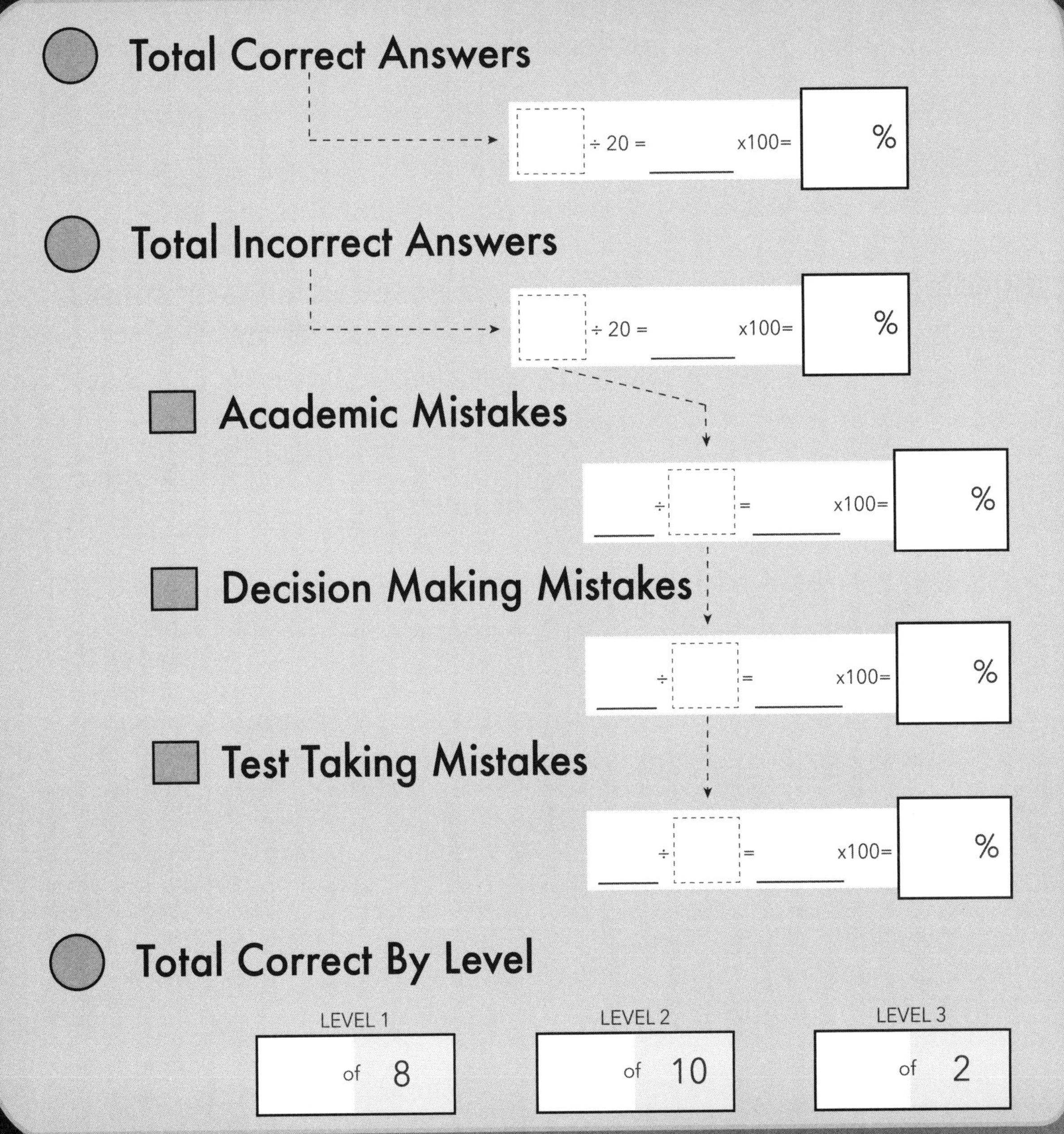

Total Correct Answers
÷ 20 =
x100=
%
Total Incorrect Answers
÷ 20 =
x100=
%
Academic Mistakes
÷
=
x100=
%
Decision Making Mistakes
÷
=
x100=
%
Test Taking Mistakes
÷
=
x100=
%
Total Correct By Level
LEVEL 1
of 8
LEVEL 2
of 10
LEVEL 3
of 2

"Pressure is a privilege - it only comes to those who have earned it."

— Billie Jean King

Building A Study Plan

Build it and they will come!

Building a Study Plan provides a candidate with a customized roadmap to prepare for the NPTE-PT. Use of the study plan increases the efficiency of study sessions and enhances mastery.

Building a Study Plan allows candidates to:

- Design an individualized study plan based on learning style preferences and current strengths/weaknesses
- Allocate study time in a manner that is consistent with the relative weighting of the NPTE-PT
- Utilize active and passive strategies to enhance mastery of essential academic information
- Assess mastery through the use of active study tools and sample examinations

Building a Study Plan

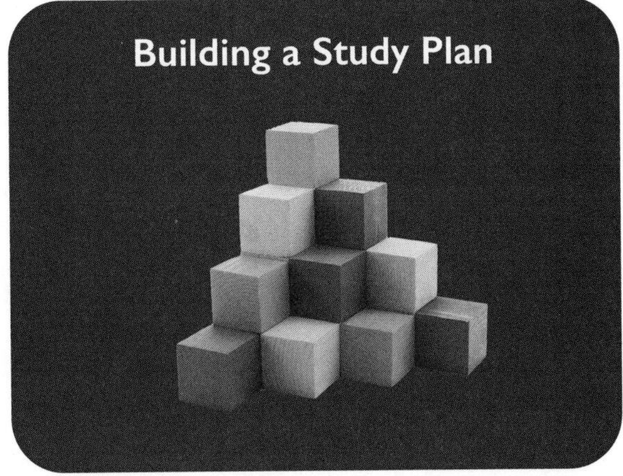
Building a Study Plan

Study Plan Pearls

- Studying for the exam is not a time dependent phenomenon (e.g., 6 weeks, 8 weeks, 12 weeks)
- There is no such thing as a perfect study plan
- A study plan must have a definitive starting and ending point
- The quality and quantity of your studying will determine your rate of progress
- Self-assessment is a critical component
- Specific strategies must be adopted to address identified deficiencies (e.g., decision making)

Necessary Supplies

- Review Books
  - Academic Review
  - Sample Exams
- Applied Materials
- Textbooks
- Class Notes
- Classmates

Meet The Cast

Academic Review

The process of retrieving what you once knew pretty well plus some bonus material.

p. 26

Basecamp

BASECAMP

A super fun academic content review tool. Use your access code to start your journey!

p. 32

NPTE-PT

NPTE-PT

The Big Kahuna or stated differently, 225 little things that will greatly influence your future.

p. 111

Rest

zZZ

The relaxing period of time you used to experience before entering a PT program.

Meet The Cast

Review Book

PTEXAM
SCOREBUILDERS

Your soon-to-be good friend! Academic content review and three full-length sample exams.

p. 23

Study Tool 1- Content Prompts

Study Tool 1

An academic trail guide using mastery cubes and strength/weakness circles.

p. 34

Study Tool 2- Clinical Application Templates (CATS)

Study Tool 2

A valuable opportunity to explore commonly encountered medical conditions.

p. 94

Study Tool 3- Critical Work Activities (CWA)

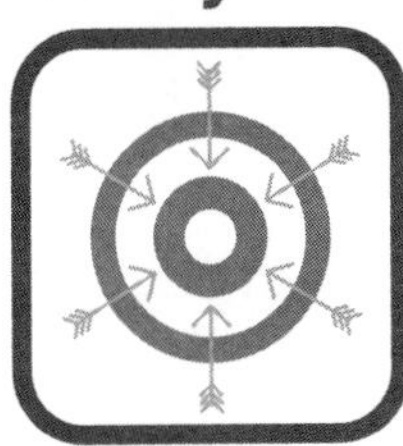

Study Tool 3

A perfect late review designed to ensure familiarity with essential exam information.

p. 133

Study Plan Flow Overview

Initial Content Review

Review Book

Basecamp

Exams

1-2

Intensive Content Review

Content Prompts

CATS

Review Book

Basecamp

Exams

3-5

Coming Home

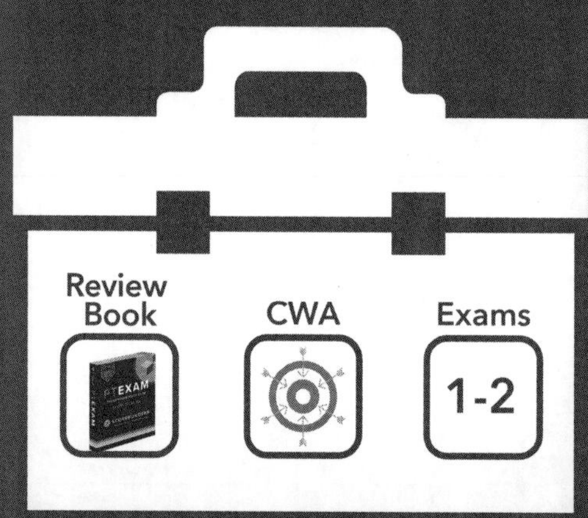
Review Book
CWA
Exams
1-2

TRUTH!

Hope is <u>not</u> a strategy!

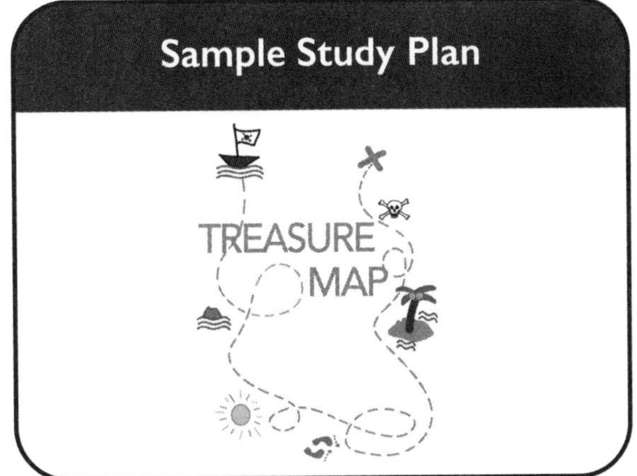
Sample Study Plan
TREASURE
MAP

Sample Study Plan Key

M — Musculoskeletal

N — Neuromuscular

C — Cardiopulmonary

OS — Other Systems

NS — Non-Systems

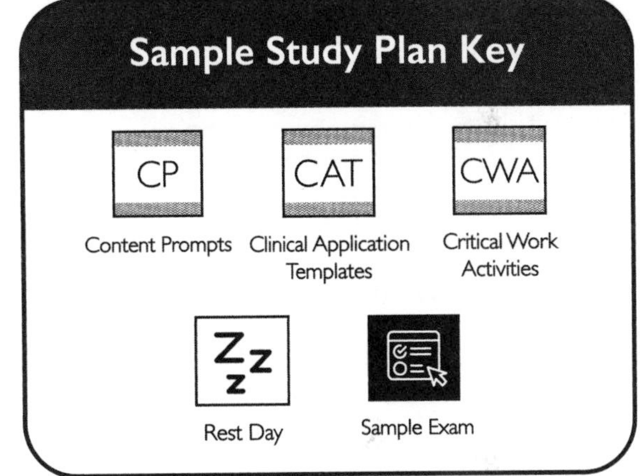
Sample Study Plan Key
CP
Content Prompts
CAT
Clinical Application Templates
CWA
Critical Work Activities
Rest Day
Sample Exam

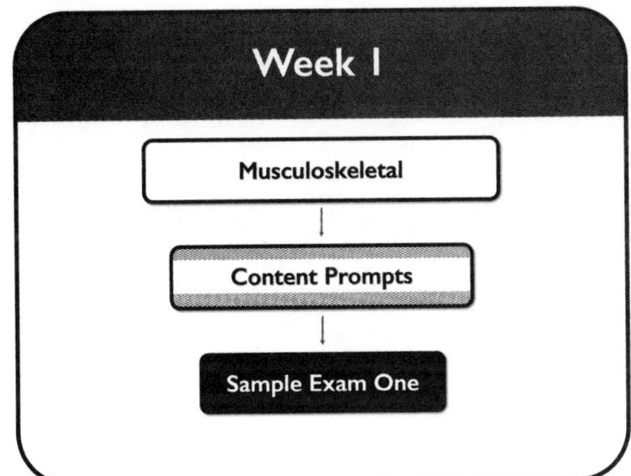
Week 1
Musculoskeletal
Content Prompts
Sample Exam One

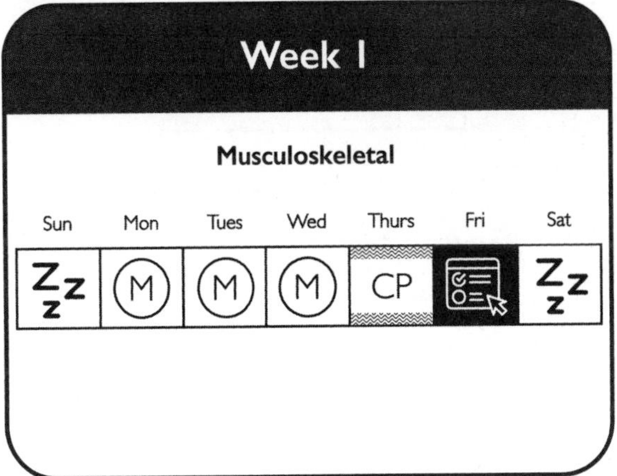
Week 1
Musculoskeletal
Sun
Mon
Tues
Wed
Thurs
Fri
Sat
M
M
M
CP

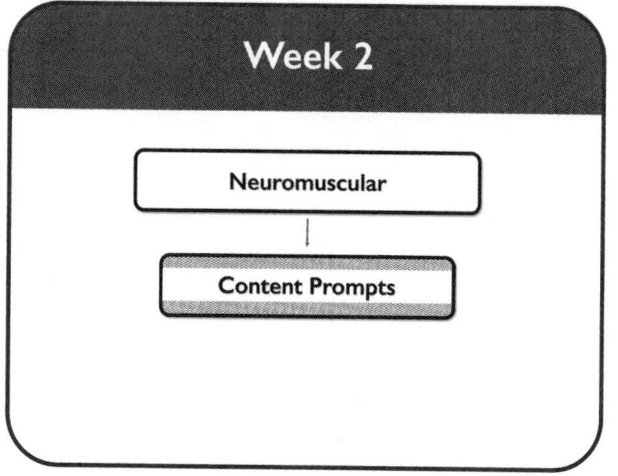
Week 2
Neuromuscular
Content Prompts

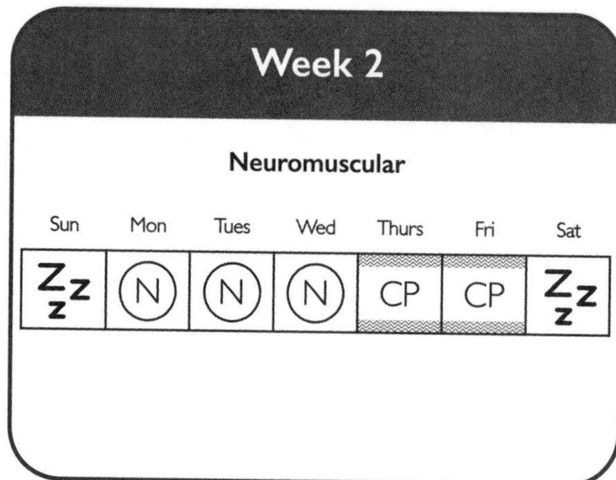
Week 2
Neuromuscular
Sun
Mon
Tues
Wed
Thurs
Fri
Sat
N
N
N
CP
CP

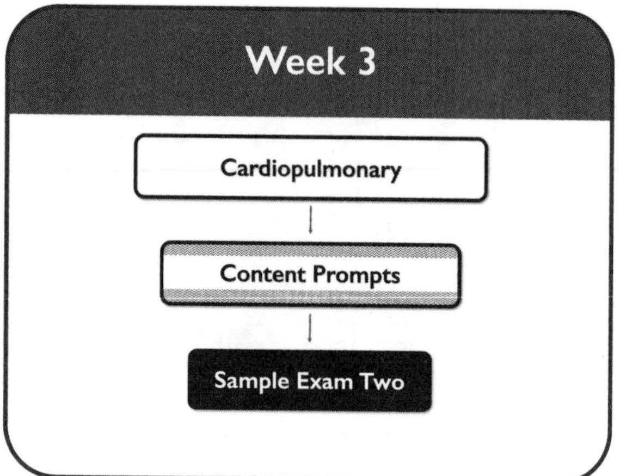
Week 3
Cardiopulmonary
Content Prompts
Sample Exam Two

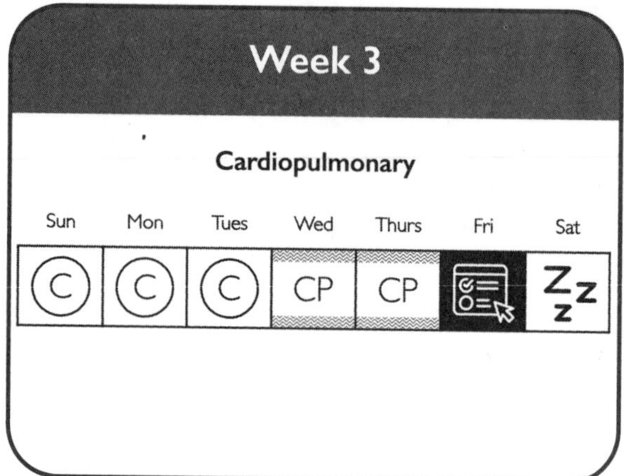
Week 3
Cardiopulmonary
Sun
Mon
Tues
Wed
Thurs
Fri
Sat
C
C
C
CP
CP

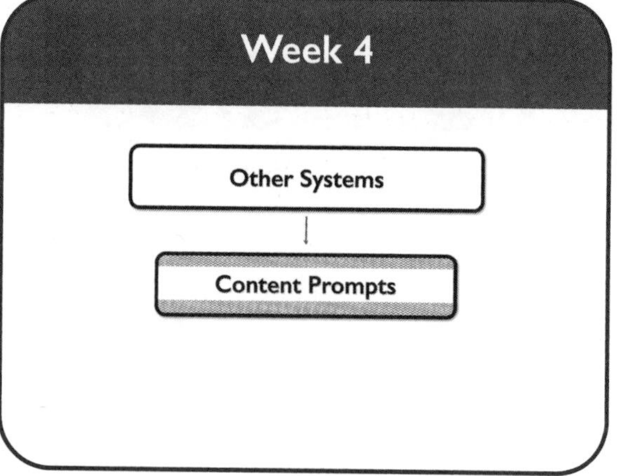
Week 4
Other Systems
Content Prompts

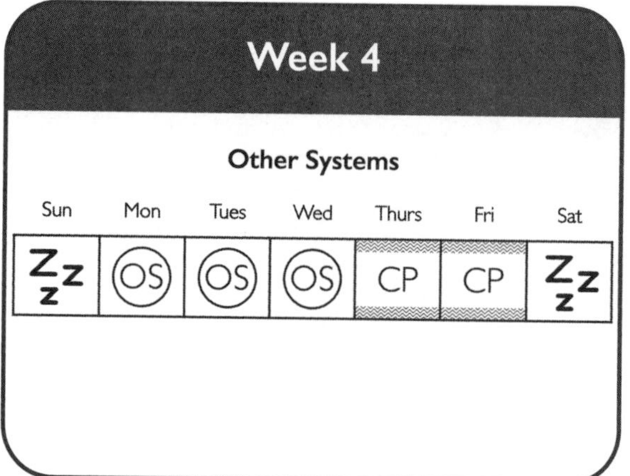
Week 4
Other Systems
Sun
Mon
Tues
Wed
Thurs
Fri
Sat
OS
OS
OS
CP
CP

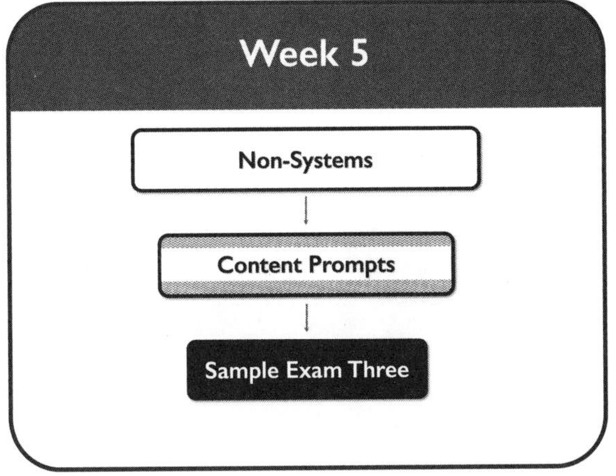
Week 5
Non-Systems
Content Prompts
Sample Exam Three

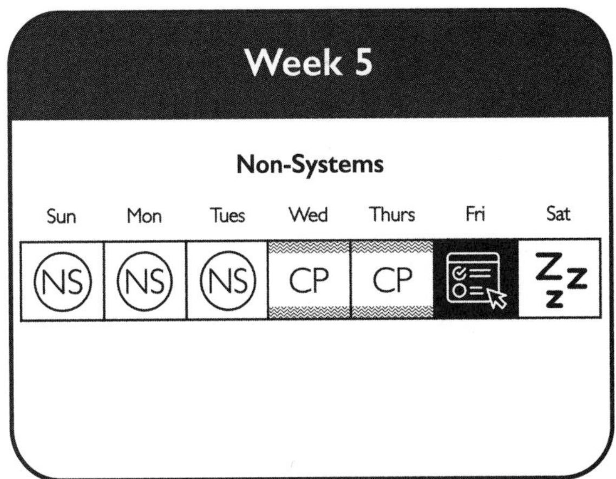
Week 5
Non-Systems
Sun Mon Tues Wed Thurs Fri Sat
NS NS NS CP CP

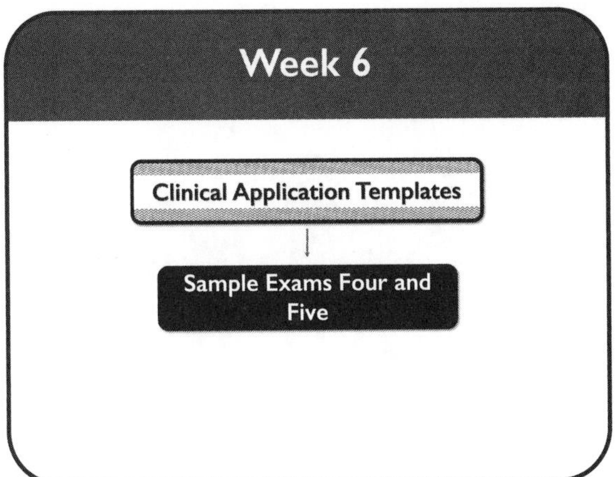
Week 6
Clinical Application Templates
Sample Exams Four and Five

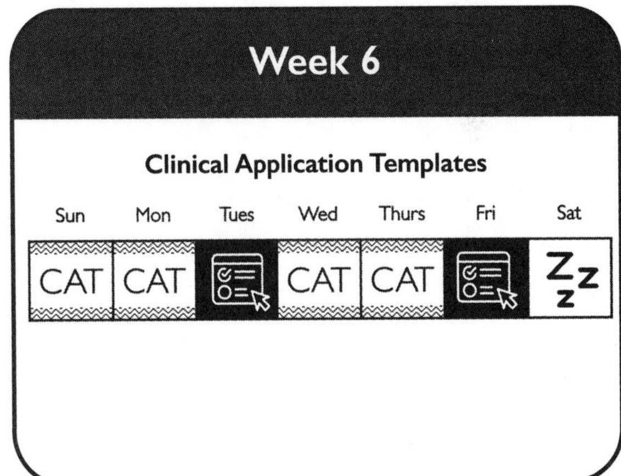
Week 6
Clinical Application Templates
Sun Mon Tues Wed Thurs Fri Sat
CAT CAT CAT CAT

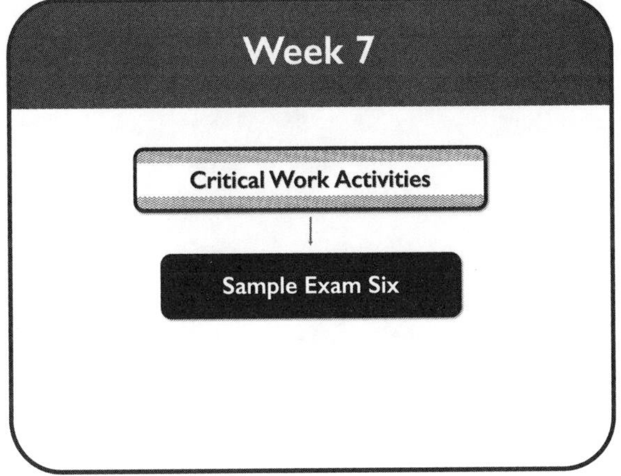
Week 7
Critical Work Activities
Sample Exam Six

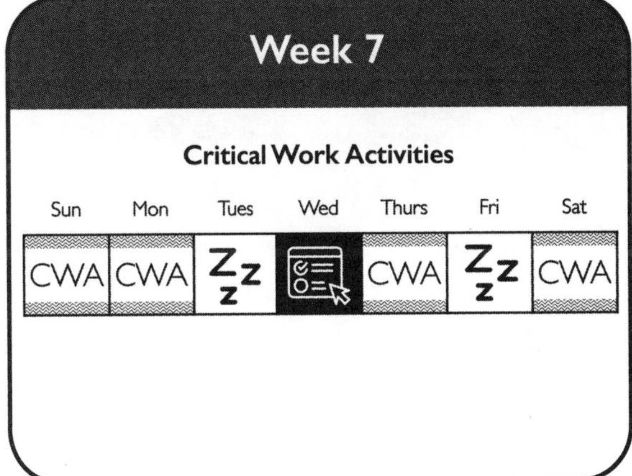
Week 7
Critical Work Activities
Sun Mon Tues Wed Thurs Fri Sat
CWA CWA CWA CWA

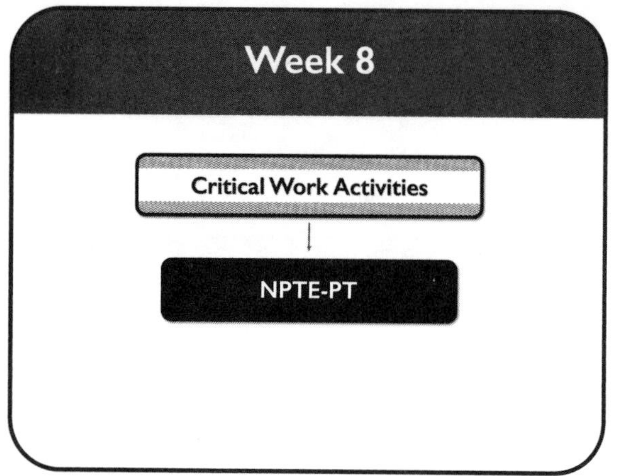
Week 8
Critical Work Activities
NPTE-PT

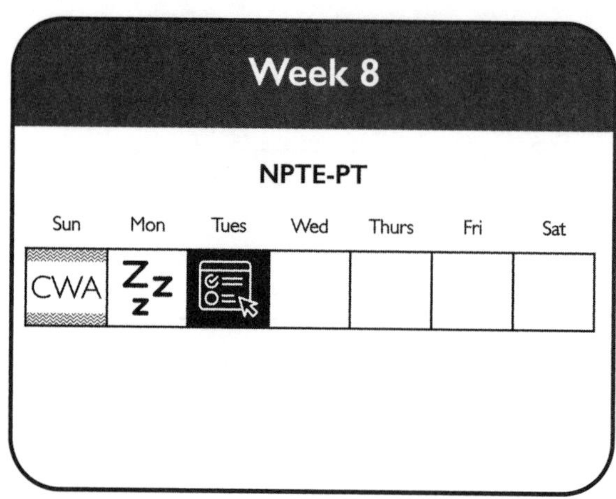
Week 8
NPTE-PT
Sun
Mon
Tues
Wed
Thurs
Fri
Sat
CWA
Zzz

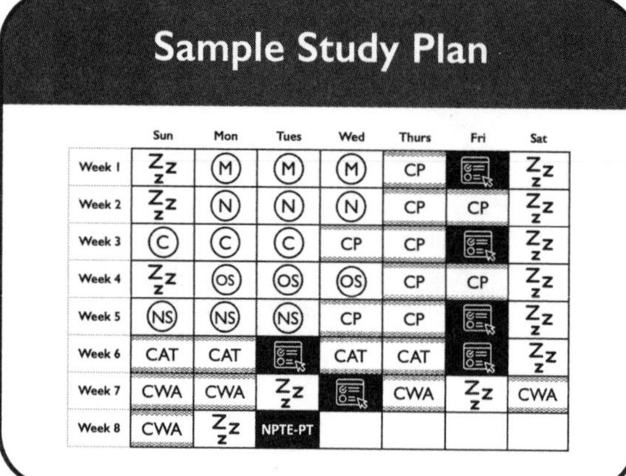
Sample Study Plan

	Sun	Mon	Tues	Wed	Thurs	Fri	Sat
Week 1	Zzz	M	M	M	CP		Zzz
Week 2	Zzz	N	N	N	CP	CP	Zzz
Week 3	C	C	C	CP	CP		Zzz
Week 4	Zzz	OS	OS	OS	CP	CP	Zzz
Week 5	NS	NS	NS	CP	CP		Zzz
Week 6	CAT	CAT		CAT	CAT		Zzz
Week 7	CWA	CWA	Zzz		CWA	Zzz	CWA
Week 8	CWA	Zzz	NPTE-PT				

Designing the Perfect Study Plan
The Possibilities are Endless!

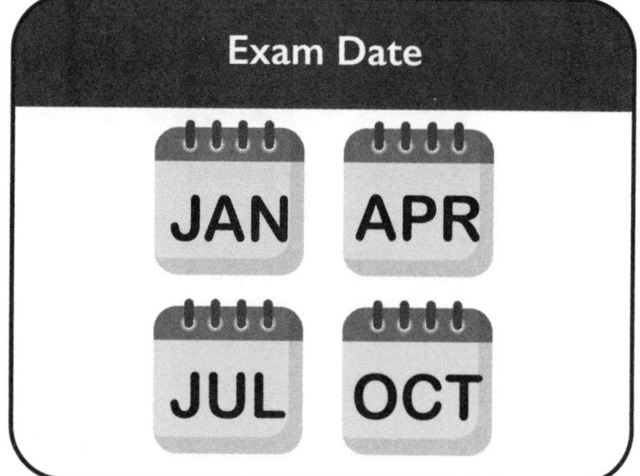
Exam Date
JAN
APR
JUL
OCT

Academic Mastery

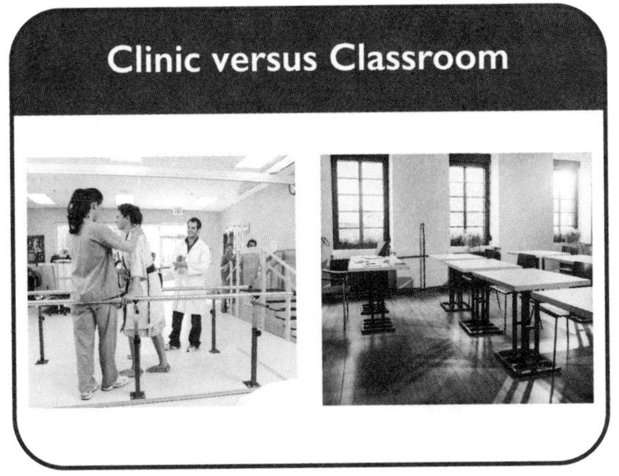
Clinic versus Classroom

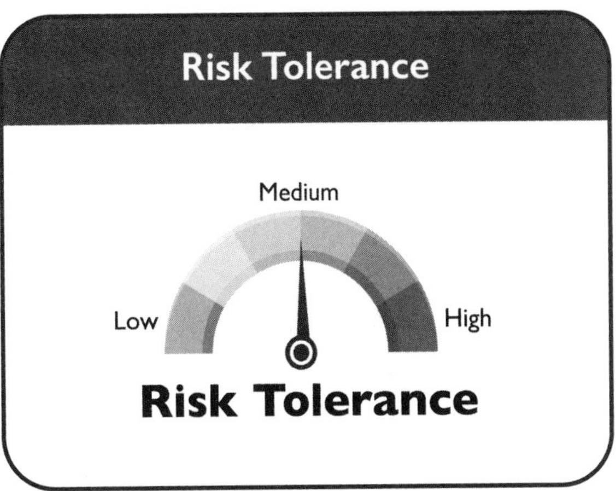
Risk Tolerance
Medium
Low
High
Risk Tolerance

Designing an Individualized Study Plan

The ideal study plan for each candidate depends on a number of critical values including the relative level of academic mastery, perceived strengths and weaknesses, composition of the portfolio, learning style, and scheduled date of the NPTE-PT.

All study plans should include formal academic content review based on the actual weighting of the NPTE-PT. Candidates should integrate active and passive study tools and have intermittent opportunities to assess their performance. As the date of the NPTE-PT approaches, candidates should return to the most fundamental concepts likely to be encountered on the NPTE-PT. Candidates should avoid initially being too prescriptive on the duration of study sessions and instead allow their relative progress to dictate this variable.

Three sample study plans are presented for candidates to consider. These study plans serve only as examples of the infinite number of plans that could be developed. A brief description of the circumstances that could potentially warrant each study plan are provided.

Sample Study Plan 1
This study plan is a very condensed plan consisting of a good mix of active and passive study strategies. A candidate selecting this type of plan is typically a strong student with exceptional mastery of academic content.

Sample Study Plan 2
This study plan is a 12 week plan that provides more extensive opportunities for in-depth content review. The plan is fairly intense and includes study sessions averaging five days a week. The plan utilizes active and passive study tools throughout the duration of the plan.

Sample Study Plan 3
This study plan is a 16 week plan that also provides extensive opportunities for in-depth content review. The plan, however, permits students to engage in a more leisurely initial pass through core academic content before integrating active study tools. As the plan progresses, active study tools are introduced and the intensity and frequency of study sessions is increased.

Sample Study Plan 1

	Sun	Mon	Tues	Wed	Thurs	Fri	Sat
Week 1		M	M	M	CP	Sample Exam	
Week 2		N	N	N	CP	CP	
Week 3	C	C	C	CP	CP	Sample Exam	
Week 4		OS	OS	OS	CP	CP	
Week 5	NS	NS	NS	CP	CP	Sample Exam	
Week 6	CAT	CAT	Sample Exam	CAT	CAT	Sample Exam	
Week 7	CWA	CWA		Sample Exam	CWA		CWA
Week 8	CWA		NPTE-PT				

CP — Content Prompts

CAT — Clinical Application Templates

CWA — Critical Work Activities

Sample Exams

Rest Day

Week 1 Musculoskeletal

Week 2 Neuromuscular

Week 3 Cardiopulmonary

Week 4 Other Systems

Week 5 Non-Systems

Week 6 Clinical Application Templates

Week 7 Critical Work Activities

Week 8 NPTE-PT

Sample Study Plan 2

	Sun	Mon	Tues	Wed	Thurs	Fri	Sat
Week 1		M	M	M	M	M	
Week 2		M	M	CP	CP		
Week 3		N	N	N	N	N	
Week 4		N	N	CP	CP		
Week 5		C	C	C	C	C	
Week 6		CP	CP		OS	OS	
Week 7		OS	OS	OS	CP	CP	
Week 8		NS	NS	NS	CP		
Week 9		CAT	CAT	CAT	CAT		
Week 10		CAT		CAT	CAT		
Week 11	CWA	CWA			CWA		CWA
Week 12	CWA		NPTE-PT				

Week 1 Musculoskeletal
Week 2 Musculoskeletal
Week 3 Neuromuscular
Week 4 Neuromuscular
Week 5 Cardiopulmonary
Week 6 Other Systems
Week 7 Other Systems
Week 8 Non-Systems
Week 9 Clinical Application Templates
Week 10 Clinical Application Templates
Week 11 Critical Work Activities
Week 12 NPTE-PT

Sample Study Plan 3

	Sun	Mon	Tues	Wed	Thurs	Fri	Sat
Week 1			M		M		
Week 2			M		M		
Week 3		M		M		M	
Week 4			N		N		
Week 5			N		N		
Week 6		N		N		N	
Week 7		C		C		C	
Week 8		OS		OS		OS	
Week 9		NS		NS		NS	
Week 10		M	M	M	CP		
Week 11		N	N	N	CP		
Week 12		C	C	CP	OS	OS	
Week 13	OS	CP	NS	NS	CP		
Week 14	CAT	CAT		CAT	CAT		
Week 15	CWA	CWA			CWA		CWA
Week 16	CWA		NPTE-PT				

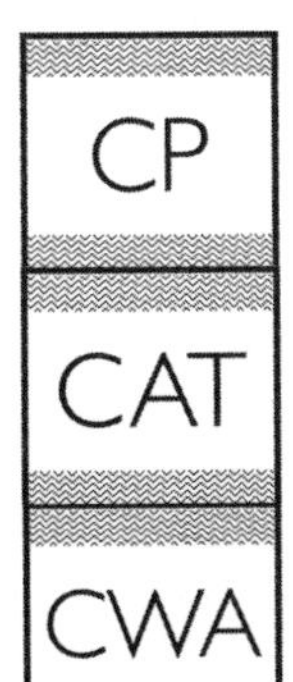
CP
CAT
CWA

Content Prompts

Clinical Application Templates

Critical Work Activities

Sample Exams

Rest Day

Week 1	Musculoskeletal
Week 2	Musculoskeletal
Week 3	Musculoskeletal
Week 4	Neuromuscular
Week 5	Neuromuscular
Week 6	Neuromuscular
Week 7	Cardiopulmonary
Week 8	Other Systems
Week 9	Non-Systems
Week 10	Musculoskeletal
Week 11	Neuromuscular
Week 12	Cardiopulmonary and Other
Week 13	Other and Non-Systems
Week 14	Clinical Application Templates
Week 15	Critical Work Activities
Week 16	NPTE-PT

MONTH: Dec

LET THE PLANNING BEGIN!

WEEK							
WEEK							
WEEK							
WEEK							
WEEK							

MONTH: Jan

WEEK							
WEEK							
WEEK							
WEEK							
WEEK							

MONTH: Feb

WEEK							
WEEK							
WEEK							
WEEK							
WEEK							

MONTH: Mar

LET THE PLANNING BEGIN!

WEEK							
WEEK							
WEEK							
WEEK							
WEEK							

MONTH: April

WEEK		1	2	3	4	5	6
WEEK	7	8	9	10	11	12	13
WEEK	14	15	16	17	18	19	20
WEEK	21	22	23	24 NPTE	25 NPTE	26	27
WEEK	28	29	30				

MONTH:

WEEK							
WEEK							
WEEK							
WEEK							
WEEK							

Which Sample Exam Progression Is Right For Me?

Consider these variables when selecting an exam progression:

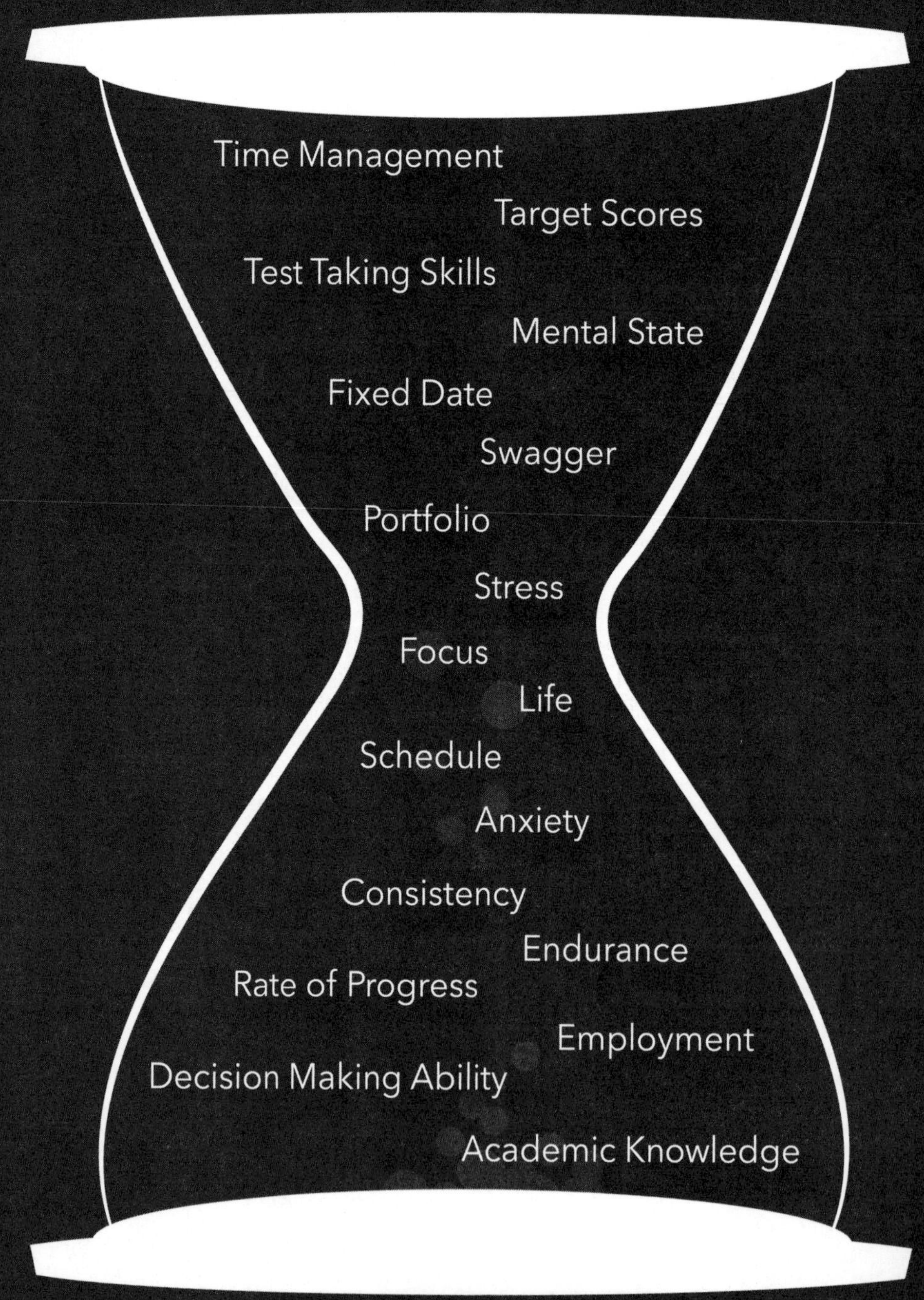

Time Management
Target Scores
Test Taking Skills
Mental State
Fixed Date
Swagger
Portfolio
Stress
Focus
Life
Schedule
Anxiety
Consistency
Endurance
Rate of Progress
Employment
Decision Making Ability
Academic Knowledge

Remember, you are constantly evolving!

Sample Exam Progression Options

Review Course + Five Exams

Review Course

Exam 1

Exam 2

OA Student 1

Exam 3

OA Student 2

Review Course + Six Exams

Review Course

Exam 1

Exam 2

OA Student 1

PEAT
PEAT 1

OA Student 2

PEAT
PEAT 2

Review Course + Seven Exams

Review Course

Exam 1

Exam 2

OA Student 1

PEAT
PEAT 1

Exam 3

OA Student 2

PEAT
PEAT 2

Target Score and Portfolio Analysis

Date	Time	Exam	Score	Target Score	(+/-)

Target Score and Portfolio Analysis

Incorrect Items	Academic (%)	Decision Making (%)	Test Taking (%)

Challenges and Solutions

Challenges and Solutions

1. My exam scores are consistently above the target scores across multiple sources.

Take the Exam!

Challenges and Solutions

2. My exam scores are consistently below the target scores across multiple sources.

The answer is never to take the exam when exam scores are consistently below target scores.

Challenges and Solutions

3. The vast majority of my mistakes are academic.

Activities need to focus on improving academic knowledge in system and non-system areas requiring remediation. Sources used to improve academic knowledge include:

- **Textbooks**
- **Class notes**
- **Review books**
- **Flash cards**
- **New technology**
- **Content prompts**

Challenges and Solutions

4. Decision making mistakes represent a large portion of my portfolio.
   - **Carefully analyze the reason for answering a question incorrectly.**
   - **Attempt to identify recurring themes and avoid making the same mistake.**
   - **Increase the frequency of exams.**

Challenges and Solutions

5. I am making an average of 10 test taking mistakes on each exam.
   - **Increase the frequency of exams.**
   - **Adopt a consistent and regimented approach (i.e., task approach) to answer each question.**
   - **Attempt to identify if external variables such as the time of day the exam was taken or environment (e.g., testing location) influence the number of test taking mistakes.**

Challenges and Solutions

6. I have difficulty maintaining concentration throughout the entire exam.
   - **Increase the frequency of exams.**
   - **Adopt a consistent and regimented approach (i.e., task approach) to answer each question.**
   - **Take exams in a formal setting that closely approximates the Prometric setting and minimizes the possibility of distractions.**
   - **Remind yourself of the relative importance of the NPTE-PT.**

Challenges and Solutions

7. I am constantly second guessing myself and changing answers.
   - **By limiting the number of marked and incomplete questions candidates will be less likely to revisit a large number of questions.**
   - **Imagine having to convince a vast majority of your class that another answer is better than your original answer. If you are not sure you could do this, avoid changing your original answer.**

Challenges and Solutions

8. I can comfortably reach the target scores with a given source, but not with another source.
   - **Utilize an additional source of exams since each source functions as an independent judge.**
   - **Attempt to determine why a given source of exams is more problematic than another.**

Challenges and Solutions

9. I am honestly not sure of my readiness for the exam. My exam scores are approaching the target scores, however, I would like to have a higher degree of confidence in my likelihood of passing the exam.

Candidates should strive to be intolerant of any unnecessary risk. Focus on improving exam scores by assessing relevant performance data and implementing appropriate remedial activities. Do not take the exam until you are virtually certain of the outcome.

Challenges and Solutions

10. I am having great difficulty with a given system and non-system area, however, I have successfully achieved the target scores across multiple sources.

The composition of the portfolio becomes relatively unimportant once a candidate consistently achieves the target scores across multiple sources.

System and Non-System Exploration

Let Us Ask You A Hundred Questions Before They Do!

Sample Examinations are active assessment activities designed to determine the relative mastery of a candidate using multiple-choice questions.

- **Musculoskeletal System**
- **Neuromuscular and Nervous Systems**
- **Cardiovascular and Pulmonary Systems**
- **Other Systems**
- **Equipment, Devices, and Technologies; Therapeutic Modalities**
- **Safety and Protection; Professional Responsibilities; Research and Evidence-Based Practice**

Activity 5
Musculoskeletal System

1. A patient diagnosed with bicipital tendonitis is approved for 24 physical therapy visits over a 90-day period by the patient's third party payer. After 16 visits the patient has made little objective progress and has failed to achieve any of the established long-term goals. Which action by the physical therapist would be the **MOST** appropriate?

   - ○ 1. Develop a series of short-term goals that are attainable for the patient
   - ● 2. Reassess the patient and develop a new plan of care
   - ○ 3. Reduce the frequency of the patient's physical therapy visits
   - ○ 4. Contact the referring physician to discuss the patient's progress

○ Correct
● Incorrect
☐ Academic
☒ Decision Making
☐ Test Taking

Level 3

2. A physical therapist prepares to utilize mechanical spinal traction to the cervical spine of an adult patient with radiating pain into their right arm. The therapist would like to select a patient position for the session that will reduce the lordotic curve of the patient's cervical spine. Which position would be the **MOST** appropriate to meet the therapist's objective?

   - ○ 1. Prone
   - ○ 2. Sitting
   - ● 3. Supine
   - ○ 4. Sidelying

● Correct
○ Incorrect
☐ Academic
☐ Decision Making
☐ Test Taking

Level 2

3. A patient four months following rotator cuff repair surgery reports an inability to reach behind their back to tuck in a shirt and difficulty with reaching across their body. Which intervention would be **MOST** appropriate for this patient given the reported limitations?

   - ○ 1. Glenohumeral joint distraction mobilizations
   - ○ 2. 20% pulsed ultrasound to the shoulder to control pain and inflammation
   - ● 3. Stretching of the posterior capsule of the shoulder
   - ○ 4. Shoulder medial and lateral rotation with resistance

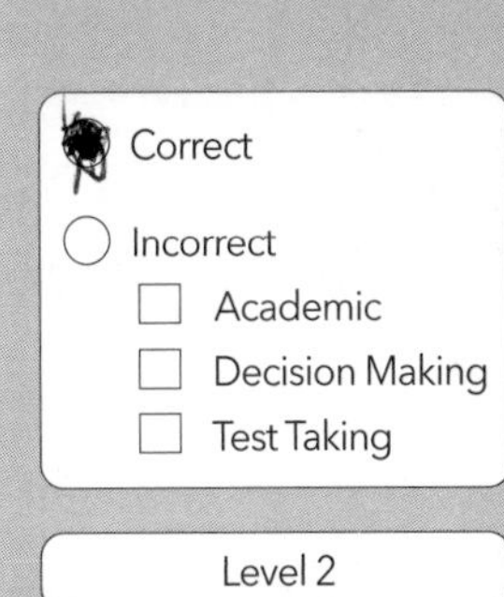
Correct
Incorrect
Academic
Decision Making
Test Taking

Level 2

Correct

Incorrect
- Academic
- Decision Making
- Test Taking

Level 2

4. A patient with unilateral lower extremity weakness is referred to physical therapy. When testing the right hip abductors with the patient positioned in left sidelying, the patient is able to maintain the test position. Further testing reveals the patient is unable to maintain the test position when even slight pressure is added. What is the **MOST** appropriate grade for this muscle?

   1. Fair minus
   2. Fair
   3. Fair plus
   4. Good minus

Correct

Incorrect
- Academic
- Decision Making
- Test Taking

Level 1

5. A physical therapist examines a patient diagnosed with a meniscal lesion. Which meniscal injury would be the **MOST** likely to heal without surgical intervention?

   1. A tear involving the inner third of the lateral meniscus.
   2. A tear involving the middle third of the lateral meniscus.
   3. A tear involving the inner third of the medial meniscus.
   4. A tear involving the outer third of the medial meniscus.

Correct

Incorrect
- Academic
- Decision Making
- Test Taking

Level 2

6. A physical therapist prepares to administer Speed's test to a patient with an upper extremity injury. Where should the therapist's hands be positioned when administering this special test?

   1. Dorsal surface of the forearm and the bicipital groove of the humerus
   2. Volar surface of the forearm and the bicipital groove of the humerus
   3. Dorsal surface of the humerus and distal biceps tendon in the antecubital fossa
   4. Volar surface of the humerus and distal biceps tendon in the antecubital fossa

Correct

Incorrect
- Academic
- Decision Making
- Test Taking

Level 1

7. A patient is referred to physical therapy after undergoing shoulder surgery as a result of recurrent anterior glenohumeral dislocations. The operative report states that a Hill-Sachs fracture was identified during the procedure. Which bony structure is characteristically involved in this type of fracture?

   1. Posterior superior humeral head
   2. Anterior medial humeral head
   3. Inferior glenoid rim
   4. Greater tuberosity of the humerus

8. A physical therapist prepares to perform grade I and II joint mobilizations to the wrist of a patient rehabilitating from a work-related injury. The therapist begins by placing the radiocarpal joint in the loose packed position. Which description is **MOST** consistent with this position?

1. The wrist in neutral with slight ulnar deviation
2. The wrist in neutral with slight radial deviation
3. The wrist in flexion with ulnar deviation
4. The wrist in extension with radial deviation

Correct
Incorrect
Academic
Decision Making
Test Taking

Level 1

9. A physical therapist participates in a scoliosis screening program at a local school. The therapist completes the screening by having the participants complete the forward bend test. Which age range would be the **MOST** appropriate when administering this type of screening?

1. 4-7 years
2. 8-10 years
3. 11-14 years
4. 15-18 years

Correct
Incorrect
Academic
Decision Making
Test Taking

Level 1

10. A physical therapist performs joint mobilizations to increase wrist flexion at the radiocarpal joint on a patient eight weeks status post fracture. Which mobilization technique would be the **MOST** appropriate to increase wrist flexion?

1. Ventral glides of the carpals
2. Dorsal glides of the carpals
3. Ulnar glides of the carpals
4. Radial glides of the carpals

Correct
Incorrect
Academic
Decision Making
Test Taking

Level 2

11. A physical therapist instructs a patient with a transfemoral amputation in active stretching techniques. Which of the following motions would be **MOST** important to emphasize in the stretching program?

1. Hip flexion and abduction
2. Hip extension and abduction
3. Hip flexion and adduction
4. Hip extension and adduction

Correct
Incorrect
Academic
Decision Making
Test Taking

Level 2

Correct
Incorrect
Academic
Decision Making
Test Taking

Level 3

12. A physical therapist observes a patient with a transtibial amputation ambulating in the physical therapy gym. The therapist notices that the patient cannot maintain full knee extension during the loading response on the prosthetic side. What is the **MOST** likely rationale for this observation?

1. Weakness of the hip flexors
2. Alignment of the foot into excessive dorsiflexion
3. Pistoning of the residual limb within the prosthesis
4. Excessive softness of the SACH (solid ankle cushion heel) foot

Correct
Incorrect
Academic
Decision Making
Test Taking

Level 2

13. A physical therapist reviews the medical record of a patient rehabilitating from a total knee arthroplasty. One of the entries in the medical record indicates the presence of a 15 degree extension lag at the knee. Which of the following goniometric readings would be **MOST** consistent with this condition?

1. 15-100 degrees active range of motion; 0-100 degrees passive range of motion
2. 15-100 degrees passive range of motion; 0-100 degrees active range of motion
3. 15-120 degrees passive range of motion; 15-135 degrees active range of motion
4. 15-135 degrees active range of motion; 15-135 degrees passive range of motion

Correct
Incorrect
Academic
Decision Making
Test Taking

Level 2

14. A patient with a unilateral transfemoral prosthesis places the prosthetic foot either medially or laterally during the initial contact (heel strike) phase of gait. The patient reports it is difficult to control where they place their foot. What exercise is the **MOST** appropriate to improve the control of the prosthesis?

1. Standing on the prosthesis and tapping the contralateral foot on a step
2. Side stepping to the side of the prosthesis with a resistance band
3. Controlled tapping of the prosthesis on a colored circle while standing
4. Repeated sit to stand transfers from a normal height chair

15. A physical therapist designs an inservice on the ligamentous stability of the knee. As part of the inservice, the therapist describes the effect of rotation of the tibia on the collateral and cruciate ligaments. Which of the following statements is **MOST** accurate with medial rotation of the tibia?

1. The collateral ligaments become more relaxed and the cruciate ligaments become tighter.
2. The collateral ligaments become tighter and the cruciate ligaments become more relaxed.
3. The collateral ligaments and the cruciate ligaments become more relaxed.
4. The collateral ligaments and the cruciate ligaments become tighter.

Correct
Incorrect
- Academic
- Decision Making
- Test Taking

Level 1

16. A patient with a left transtibial amputation receives outpatient physical therapy for gait training with a prosthesis. The patient cannot flex their left knee beyond 40 degrees. During which phase of gait would the described knee range of motion deficit be **MOST** problematic?

1. Left initial swing phase
2. Left midswing phase
3. Left terminal swing phase
4. Left terminal stance phase

Correct
Incorrect
- Academic
- Decision Making
- Test Taking

Level 2

17. A patient is referred to physical therapy following a lengthy inpatient hospitalization. The physician referral indicates "general deconditioning." During the examination the patient indicates that their shoulder is often stiff and expresses concern that they may be losing strength and range of motion. Which activity would be the **MOST** appropriate to incorporate into the plan of care to maintain upper extremity range of motion?

1. Grade II oscillations
2. Grade III distractions
3. Passive range of motion exercises
4. Active range of motion exercises

Correct
Incorrect
- Academic
- Decision Making
- Test Taking

Level 3

Correct

Incorrect

- [ ] Academic
- [ ] Decision Making
- [ ] Test Taking

Level 2

18. A physical therapist works with a patient ambulating with a right transtibial prosthesis. The therapist notes that the socket is positioned with an excessive anterior tilt. Which deviation would **MOST** likely occur with this type of malalignment?

1. Right lateral trunk lean
2. Insufficient knee flexion
3. Circumduction
4. Excessive knee flexion

Correct

Incorrect

- [ ] Academic
- [x] Decision Making
- [ ] Test Taking

Level 2

19. A patient is instructed in extension activities in an attempt to reduce a moderate disk protrusion in the lumbar spine. Which of the following activities would be the **MOST** appropriate to initiate the exercise program?

1. Have the patient perform a prone press-up
2. Have the patient position themselves in prone on elbows
3. Have the patient lie in prone on a firm surface
4. Have the patient perform extension exercises in standing

Correct

Incorrect

- [ ] Academic
- [ ] Decision Making
- [x] Test Taking

Level 1

20. A physical therapist performs a muscle test of the shoulder medial rotators using a handheld dynamometer. Where should the dynamometer be positioned during the testing procedure?

1. Over the anterior aspect of the distal humerus just proximal to the elbow
2. Over the posterior aspect of the distal humerus just proximal to the elbow
3. Over the anterior aspect of the distal forearm just proximal to the wrist
4. Over the posterior aspect of the distal forearm just proximal to the wrist

Correct

Incorrect

- [ ] Academic
- [ ] Decision Making
- [ ] Test Taking

Level 1

21. A physical therapist treats an infant diagnosed with myelomeningocele. A component of the established treatment plan includes mobilization and stretching of contracted muscles around the foot due to talipes equinovarus deformity. Which description is **MOST** consistent with this type of foot deformity?

1. Ankle dorsiflexion, hindfoot varus, forefoot adduction
2. Ankle dorsiflexion, hindfoot valgus, forefoot abduction
3. Ankle plantar flexion, hindfoot varus, forefoot adduction
4. Ankle plantar flexion, hindfoot valgus, forefoot abduction

22. A patient is referred to physical therapy for the treatment of tarsal tunnel syndrome. During the examination, the therapist notes a positive Tinel's sign over the tibial nerve at the ankle. Which deformity is **MOST** often related to the nerve tension etiology associated with this condition?

- 1. Pes cavus deformity
- 2. Hallux valgus deformity
- 3. Pes planus deformity
- 4. Equinovarus deformity

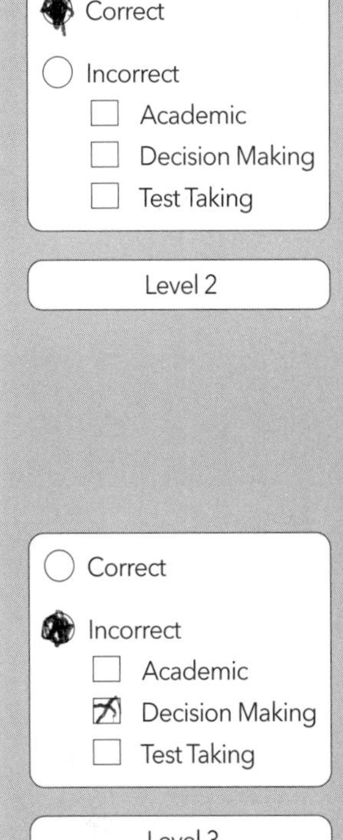

Correct
Incorrect
Academic
Decision Making
Test Taking
Level 2
Correct
Incorrect
Academic
Decision Making
Test Taking
Level 3

23. A physical therapist works with a patient on a bridging progression in order to improve the patient's core stability. The patient is able to perform single leg bridging as shown in the image. Which description **BEST** describes the next position to attain using a therapeutic ball?

- 1. Place a therapeutic ball under the patient's lower legs and require the patient to maintain a bridging position with the legs extended.
- 2. Place the patient's feet in contact with the therapeutic ball with the knees bent and require the patient to maintain a bridging position.
- 3. Place a therapeutic ball under the patient's upper back and require the patient to maintain a bridging position with one foot in contact with the ground.
- 4. Place a therapeutic ball under the patient's upper back and require the patient to maintain a bridging position with both feet in contact with the ground.

Correct
Incorrect
- [ ] Academic
- [ ] Decision Making
- [ ] Test Taking

Level 1

24. A physical therapist observes that a patient appears to exhibit excessive supination of the foot and ankle in non-weight bearing activities. Which component motions would combine to create supination in the described scenario?

1. Eversion, adduction, dorsiflexion
2. Inversion, abduction, plantar flexion
3. Inversion, abduction, dorsiflexion
4. Inversion, adduction, plantar flexion

Correct
Incorrect
- [ ] Academic
- [ ] Decision Making
- [ ] Test Taking

Level 1

25. A physical therapist completes a quantitative gait analysis on a patient rehabilitating from a lower extremity injury. As part of the examination the therapist measures the number of steps taken by the patient in a 30 second period. Which quantitative gait measure would be calculated using the described procedure?

1. Acceleration
2. Cadence
3. Velocity
4. Speed

Correct
Incorrect
- [ ] Academic
- [ ] Decision Making
- [ ] Test Taking

Level 2

26. A patient four weeks status post anterior cruciate ligament surgery exhibits persistent joint effusion. The physical therapist has been unsuccessful in reducing the effusion using cryotherapeutic agents. What is the **MOST** relevant complication of effusion for the patient?

1. Increased risk of infection
2. Inhibition of the quadriceps muscle
3. Inability to participate in active exercise activities
4. Impaired cutaneous sensation

Correct
Incorrect
- [ ] Academic
- [ ] Decision Making
- [ ] Test Taking

Level 2

27. A physical therapist performs resisted isometrics as part of a lower quarter screening examination. After testing the ankle dorsiflexors, the therapist reports the findings as strong and painful. Which interpretation is **MOST** plausible based on the test results?

1. Complete rupture of the musculotendinous unit
2. Minor lesion of the musculotendinous unit
3. Inhibition by pain
4. Neurological lesion

28. A patient diagnosed with chronic osteoarthritis is referred to physical therapy. The patient reports their current pain as a 4 on a verbal numeric rating scale ranging from 0-10. Which goal would be the **MOST** appropriate when addressing the patient's pain?

- ○ 1. Prevent pain
- ● 2. Control pain
- ○ 3. Manage pain
- ○ 4. Alleviate pain

○ Correct

● Incorrect

- ☐ Academic
- ☑ Decision Making
- ☐ Test Taking

Level 3

PERFORMANCE ANALYSIS

Musculoskeletal System

28 Questions
Time (28:00)

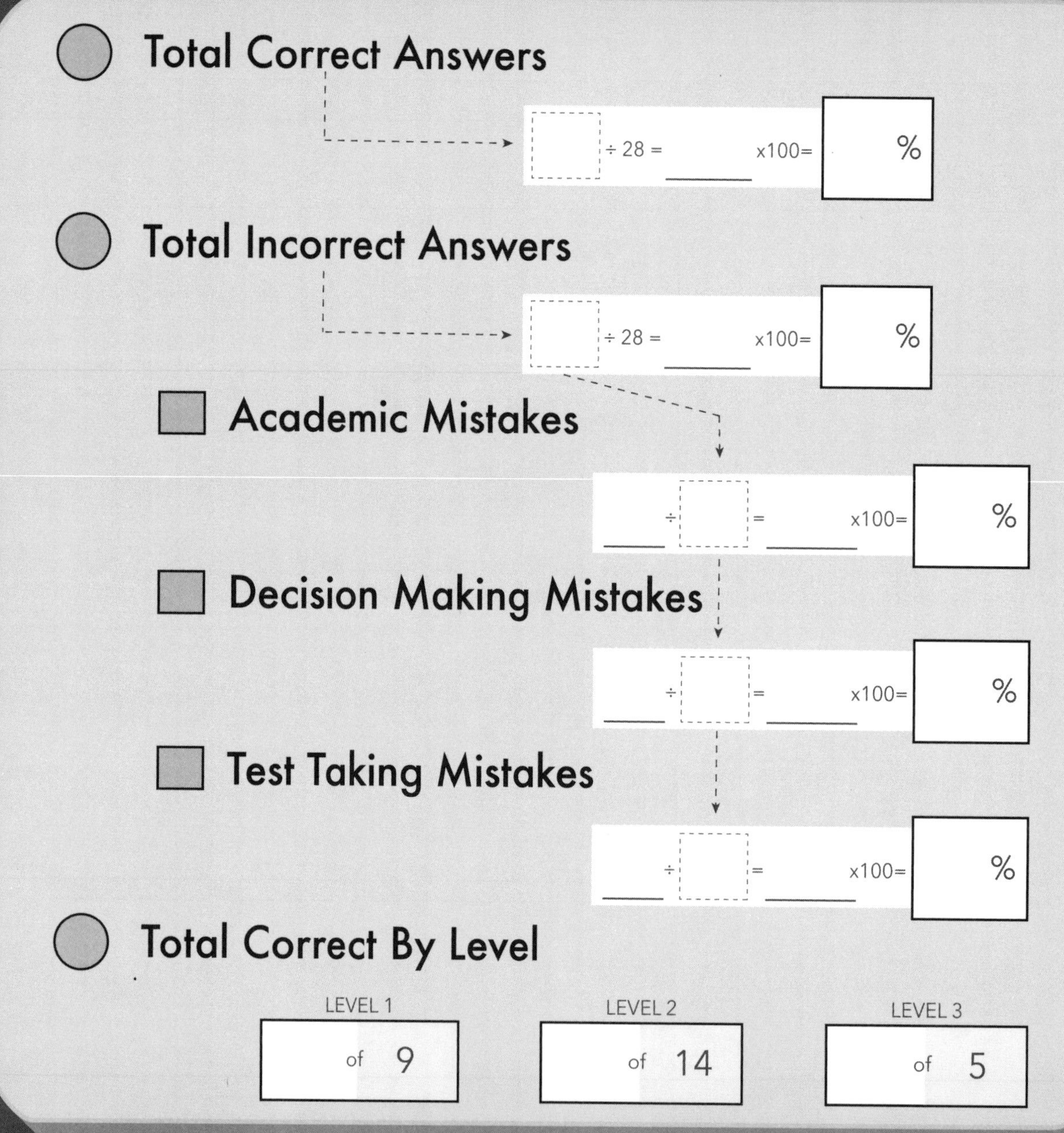

Total Correct Answers
÷ 28 = x100= %
Total Incorrect Answers
÷ 28 = x100= %
Academic Mistakes
÷ = x100= %
Decision Making Mistakes
÷ = x100= %
Test Taking Mistakes
÷ = x100= %
Total Correct By Level
LEVEL 1
of 9
LEVEL 2
of 14
LEVEL 3
of 5

"Chance favors the prepared mind."

— Louis Pasteur

The NPTE-PT is a marathon and not a sprint...

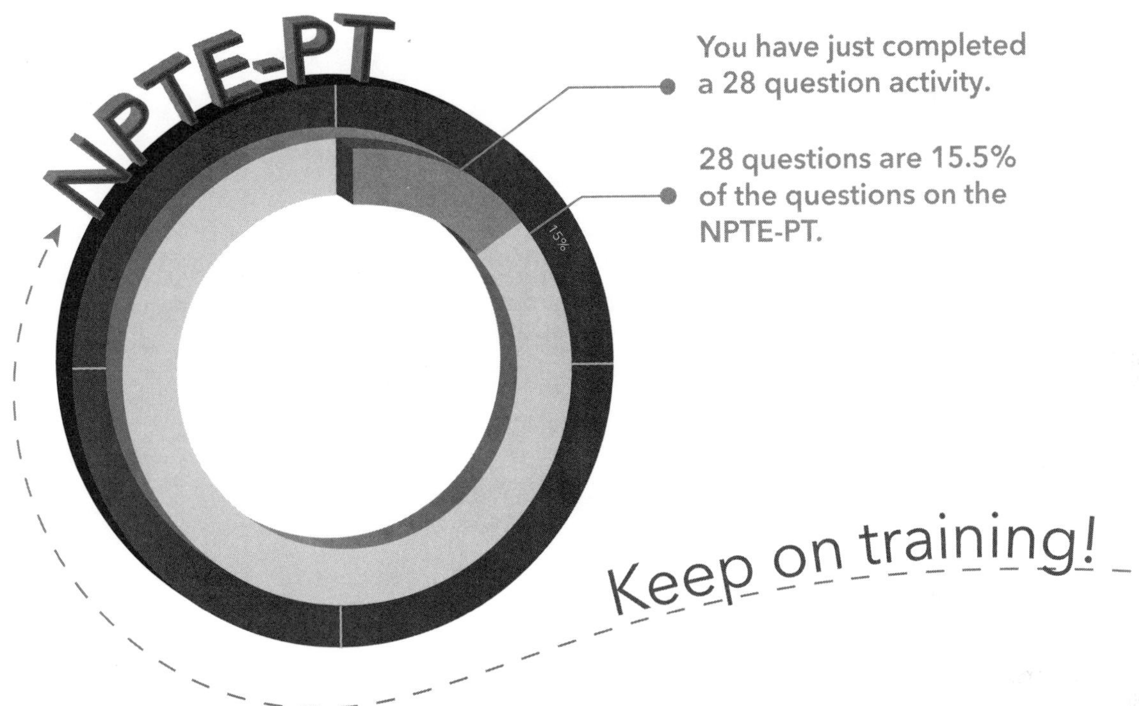
NPTE-PT
You have just completed a 28 question activity.
28 questions are 15.5% of the questions on the NPTE-PT.
15%
Keep on training!

Activity 6
Neuromuscular and Nervous Systems

Correct
Incorrect
Academic
Decision Making
Test Taking

Level 2

1. A patient has difficulty walking with variations in speed and completing an alternating finger to nose test. Which term is **MOST** consistent with the stated impairments?

   1. Asthenia
   2. Bradykinesia
   3. Dysmetria
   4. Dysdiadochokinesia

Correct
Incorrect
Academic
Decision Making
Test Taking

Level 1

2. A physical therapist completes a formal sensory assessment on a patient diagnosed with an upper extremity peripheral nerve injury. The therapist instructs the patient to close their eyes and then proceeds to place a pen cap in the patient's palm. Which discriminatory sense would **MOST** likely be assessed using the described procedure?

   1. Barognosis
   2. Graphesthesia
   3. Localization
   4. Stereognosis

Correct
Incorrect
Academic
Decision Making
Test Taking

Level 1

3. A physical therapist performing a neurological examination prepares to assess a patient's corneal reflex by directly contacting the right cornea with a cotton ball. What would be the anticipated patient response?

   1. The right eye will blink with contact to the right cornea.
   2. Both eyes will blink with contact to the right cornea.
   3. The left eye will blink with contact to the right cornea.
   4. Neither eye will blink with contact to the right cornea.

Correct
Incorrect
Academic
Decision Making
Test Taking

Level 3

4. A patient rehabilitating from a left CVA ambulates with a quad cane. The physical therapist notes right sided early heel rise during midstance followed by excessive plantar flexion into terminal stance. The patient's passive plantar flexion range of motion is 0-45 degrees and dorsiflexion is 0-15 degrees. Which of the following interventions would be the **MOST** appropriate based on the observation?

   1. Passive range of motion activities
   2. Active range of motion and mild resistive exercises
   3. Standing static and dynamic balance activities
   4. Inhibition techniques

5. A physical therapist evaluates a patient two weeks status post CVA with resultant left hemiplegia. The therapist notes that the patient has marked spasticity and is unable to perform movement outside the flexor synergy pattern. However, the patient is able to perform voluntary movements within the synergy pattern. Which stage of Brunnstrom's recovery does this scenario **MOST** accurately describe?

- 1. Stage 2
- 2. Stage 3
- 3. Stage 4
- 4. Stage 5

Correct
Incorrect
- Academic
- Decision Making
- Test Taking

Level 1

6. A physical therapist completes a screening examination on a patient with an upper extremity injury. Results of the examination reveal diminished sensation on the palmar aspect of the thumb and index finger. Motor weakness is evident in pronation and wrist flexion. Which nerve would **MOST** likely be affected?

- 1. Ulnar
- 2. Median
- 3. Radial
- 4. Musculocutaneous

Correct
Incorrect
- Academic
- Decision Making
- Test Taking

Level 2

7. A patient with a suspected head injury is assessed using the Glasgow Coma Scale. The medical record indicates the patient has maintained a score of 6 for more than six hours. What is the **MOST** appropriate classification of severity using the scale?

- 1. Concussion
- 2. Mild head injury
- 3. Moderate head injury
- 4. Severe head injury

Correct
Incorrect
- Academic
- Decision Making
- Test Taking

Level 1

8. A physical therapist develops a treatment plan for a child with Down syndrome. Which of the following therapeutic activities would be the **MOST** appropriate?

- 1. Facilitate agility and tumbling activities on a floor mat to improve coordination
- 2. Utilize inhibitory techniques in order to decrease hypertonicity of the trunk
- 3. Apply stretching techniques to tight muscles to prevent contractures
- 4. Utilize trunk rotation during play in order to elicit postural reactions

Correct
Incorrect
- Academic
- Decision Making
- Test Taking

Level 2

Correct

Incorrect

Academic

Decision Making

Test Taking

Level 1

9. A patient is referred to physical therapy after being diagnosed with multiple sclerosis. As part of the examination, the physical therapist assesses several discriminative sensations with the patient's eyes closed. Which method would be the **MOST** appropriate when assessing kinesthesia?

1. The therapist moves the patient's upper extremity and asks the patient to indicate the direction of movement while the extremity is in motion.
2. The patient moves the upper extremity and indicates the direction of movement while the extremity is in motion.
3. The therapist moves the patient's upper extremity to a selected position and asks the patient to describe the position.
4. The patient moves the upper extremity to a selected position and is asked to describe the position.

Correct

Incorrect

Academic

Decision Making

Test Taking

Level 2

10. A physical therapist treating an infant on a floor mat attempts to assess the forward protective extension reaction. Which position would be the **MOST** appropriate to observe this reaction?

1. Pivot prone
2. Prone
3. Quadruped
4. Sitting

Correct

Incorrect

Academic

Decision Making

Test Taking

Level 2

11. A physical therapist reviews a physician's note prior to initiating an examination on a newly referred patient. The note indicates idiopathic symptoms of fluctuating auditory deficits, intermittent vertigo, tinnitus, and a feeling of pressure in the ears. Which diagnosis would be **MOST** likely based on the reported symptoms?

1. Benign positional vertigo
2. Migraine vestibulopathy
3. Acute labyrinthitis
4. Meniere's disease

Correct

Incorrect

Academic

Decision Making

Test Taking

Level 2

12. A physical therapist reviews the medical record of a patient with a peripheral neuropathy affecting the spinal accessory nerve. Which objective finding would be **MOST** likely based on the patient's medical diagnosis?

1. Winging of the scapula at 90 degrees of forward flexion
2. Weak elbow flexion with the forearm supinated
3. Difficulty actively abducting the arm beyond 90 degrees
4. Apprehension with the arm in 90 degrees of abduction and lateral rotation

13. A physical therapist provides a small perturbation to a patient in standing in order to assess the patient's ability to employ motor strategies related to balance. Which motor strategy would be the **MOST** immediate after force application?

- ○ 1. Stepping
- ● 2. Ankle
- ○ 3. Lunging
- ○ 4. Hip

● Correct
○ Incorrect
☐ Academic
☐ Decision Making
☐ Test Taking

Level 2

14. A physical therapist designs a strengthening program for a patient with upper extremity weakness that incorporates proprioceptive neuromuscular facilitation techniques. Which verbal command would be the **MOST** appropriate for D1 flexion?

- ● 1. Close your hand and pull up and across your body
- ○ 2. Close your hand and pull down and across your body
- ○ 3. Open your hand and push down and away from your body
- ○ 4. Open your hand and pull up and away from your body

● Correct
○ Incorrect
☐ Academic
☐ Decision Making
☐ Test Taking

Level 2

15. A physical therapist examines a patient that sustained a head injury in a motor vehicle accident. During the 30 minute session, the therapist has extreme difficulty maintaining the patient's attention. Which area of the brain was **MOST** likely involved in the accident?

- ✓ 1. Frontal
- ○ 2. Temporal
- ● 3. Parietal
- ○ 4. Occipital

○ Correct
● Incorrect
☒ Academic
☐ Decision Making
☐ Test Taking

Level 1

16. A physical therapist completes a cranial nerve assessment on a patient in the medical intensive care unit. Which of the following methods is **MOST** appropriate when testing cranial nerve XI?

- ○ 1. Assess the patient's gag reflex
- ○ 2. Ask the patient to perform tongue protrusion
- ○ 3. Utilize a tuning fork placed at the mastoid process
- ● 4. Perform resisted shoulder shrugs

● Correct
○ Incorrect
☐ Academic
☐ Decision Making
☐ Test Taking

Level 1

Correct
Incorrect
- Academic
- Decision Making
- Test Taking

Level 2

17. A physical therapist identifies the presence of the plantar grasp reflex in an infant. Which of the following outcomes is **MOST** likely based on the presence of the primitive reflex?

1. Limited hand-eye coordination
2. Diminished balance reactions and weight shifting in standing
3. Inability to grasp and release objects voluntarily
4. Difficulty with selected protective responses

Correct
Incorrect
- Academic
- Decision Making
- Test Taking

Level 2

18. A patient with a cerebellar stroke works on improving the functional use of the involved left upper extremity. Which intervention would be the **MOST** appropriate to improve the patient's ability to use the involved upper extremity?

1. Stretch the arm prior to the practice of functional tasks
2. Have the patient reach in various directions for objects of different size and shape
3. Incorporate techniques that provide sensory stimuli to the upper extremity
4. Position objects on the patient's left side to reduce neglect

Correct
Incorrect
- Academic
- Decision Making
- Test Taking

Level 2

19. A physical therapist administers the Sensory Organization Test to a patient with compromised balance. Which type of activity would be the **MOST** appropriate to assess the visual and vestibular systems while compromising the somatosensory system?

1. Positioning a patient on a normal surface with eyes open
2. Positioning a patient on a normal surface with eyes closed
3. Positioning a patient on foam with eyes open
4. Positioning a patient on foam with eyes closed

Correct
Incorrect
- Academic
- Decision Making
- Test Taking

Level 3

20. A physical therapist working in a home health agency receives a referral for a patient with a traumatic brain injury. While observing the patient prior to formally initiating the examination, the therapist determines the patient is mildly agitated. Which action by the therapist would be the **MOST** appropriate?

1. Reschedule the patient
2. Initiate the examination
3. Request assistance from another staff member
4. Contact the referring physician

21. A patient with Parkinson's disease was recently prescribed levodopa. During therapy the patient reported lightheadedness when getting up off of the mat. Which action by the physical therapist would be **MOST** appropriate?

- 1. Refer the patient to the physician for evaluation for another medication
- 2. Suggest that the patient perform the task slowly, sitting for a few minutes before moving into standing
- 3. Perform tests and measures related to the vestibular system
- 4. Monitor the patient's vital signs without changing the method used to perform the task

Correct
Incorrect
- Academic
- Decision Making
- Test Taking

Level 3

22. A physical therapist works on preambulation activities with a child diagnosed with developmental delay. As part of the program, the therapist utilizes manual approximation at the shoulders and pelvis in order to promote upper and lower extremity stability. Which of the following developmental positions would be the **MOST** appropriate to utilize when performing this technique?

- 1. Kneeling
- 2. Half kneeling
- 3. Modified plantigrade
- 4. Standing

Correct
Incorrect
- Academic
- Decision Making
- Test Taking

Level 2

23. A physical therapist works with a patient who exhibits neurogenic claudication. Which finding is **MOST** consistent with this condition?

- 1. Pain is exaggerated when walking on an incline
- 2. Pain occurs after walking a predictable distance
- 3. Pain is relieved by resting in a sitting position
- 4. Pain seems to originate in the posterior calf

Correct
Incorrect
- Academic
- Decision Making
- Test Taking

Level 2

24. A physical therapist works with a patient that is sitting on the edge of a mat surface with their feet on the floor. The patient is asked to reach for an object placed two feet in front of them on the floor. Which pattern of muscle activity is **MOST** responsible for the modulation of movement during this task?

- 1. Concentric contraction of the spinal flexors
- 2. Eccentric contraction of the spinal flexors
- 3. Concentric contraction of the spinal extensors
- 4. Eccentric contraction of the spinal extensors

Correct
Incorrect
- Academic
- Decision Making
- Test Taking

Level 2

PERFORMANCE ANALYSIS

Neuromuscular and Nervous Systems

24 Questions
Time (24:00)

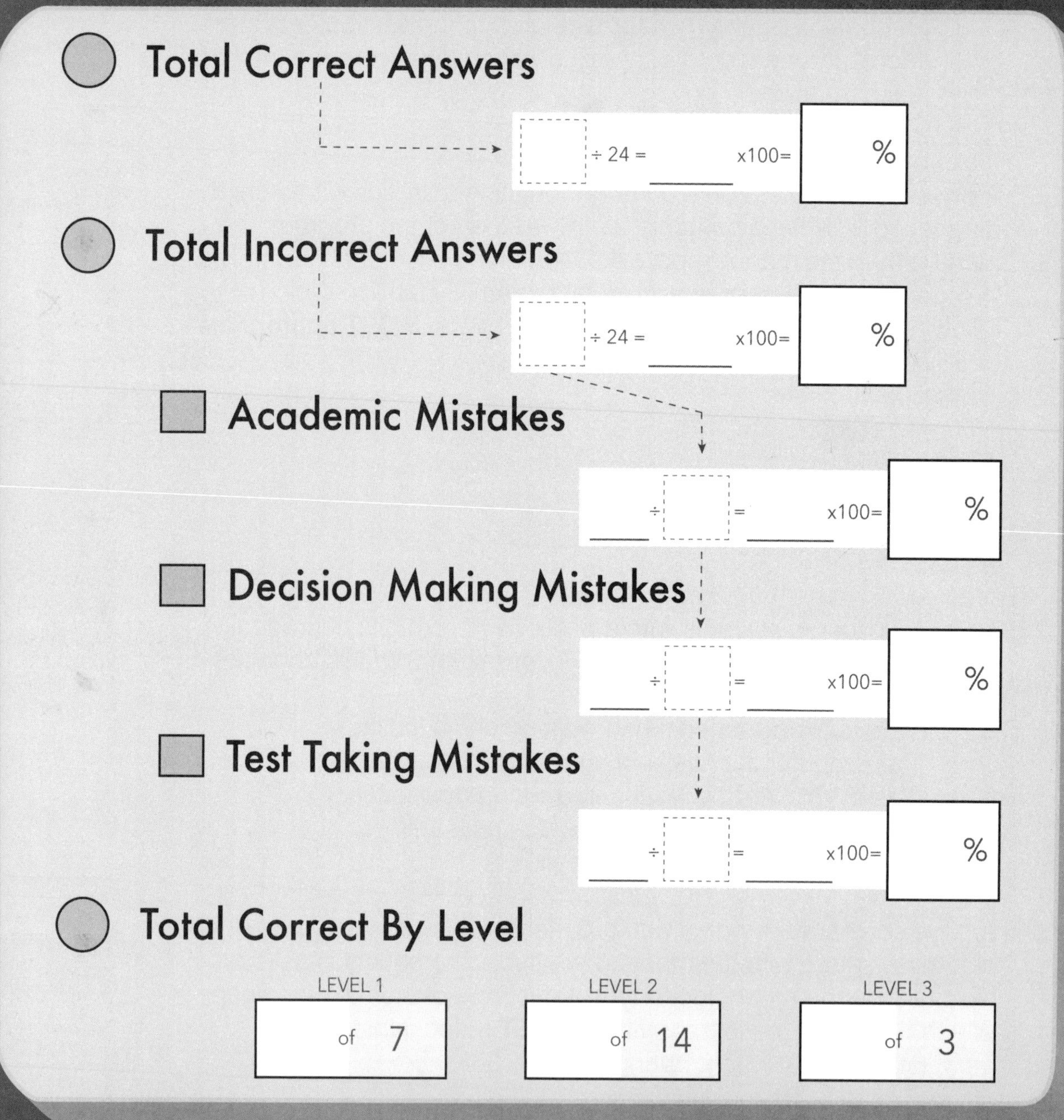

Total Correct Answers
÷ 24 =
x100=
%
Total Incorrect Answers
÷ 24 =
x100=
%
Academic Mistakes
÷
=
x100=
%
Decision Making Mistakes
÷
=
x100=
%
Test Taking Mistakes
÷
=
x100=
%
Total Correct By Level
LEVEL 1
of 7
LEVEL 2
of 14
LEVEL 3
of 3

"It is wise to keep in mind that no success or failure is necessarily final."

– Anonymous

Activity 7
Cardiovascular and Pulmonary Systems

1. A physical therapist has an athlete simulate running by exercising in the deep end of a therapeutic pool using an elastic cord attached to a flotation device and the side of the pool. Which of the following would serve as the **MOST** practical method to determine exercise intensity during this activity?

   ○ 1. Heart rate
   ○ 2. Blood pressure
   ○ 3. Respiratory rate
   ● 4. Level of perceived exertion

● Correct
○ Incorrect
☐ Academic
☐ Decision Making
☐ Test Taking

Level 2

2. A physical therapist analyzes a sputum sample after completing bronchial drainage. The sample appears to be white with a hue of pink, non-viscous, and foamy. Which term is **MOST** consistent with the described sputum sample?

   ○ 1. Frothy
   ○ 2. Fetid
   ● 3. Mucoid
   ○ 4. Purulent

○ Correct
● Incorrect
☒ Academic
☐ Decision Making
☐ Test Taking

Level 1

3. A physical therapist examines data obtained during a series of pulmonary function tests. The therapist is able to determine that the patient's inspiratory capacity was recorded as 4,000 mL, however, is not able to locate a value for vital capacity. Based on the inspiratory capacity, which number would be **MOST** representative of the patient's vital capacity?

   ○ 1. 1,000 mL
   ○ 2. 3,000 mL
   ○ 3. 5,000 mL
   ● 4. 7,000 mL

○ Correct
● Incorrect
☐ Academic
☒ Decision Making
☐ Test Taking

Level 2

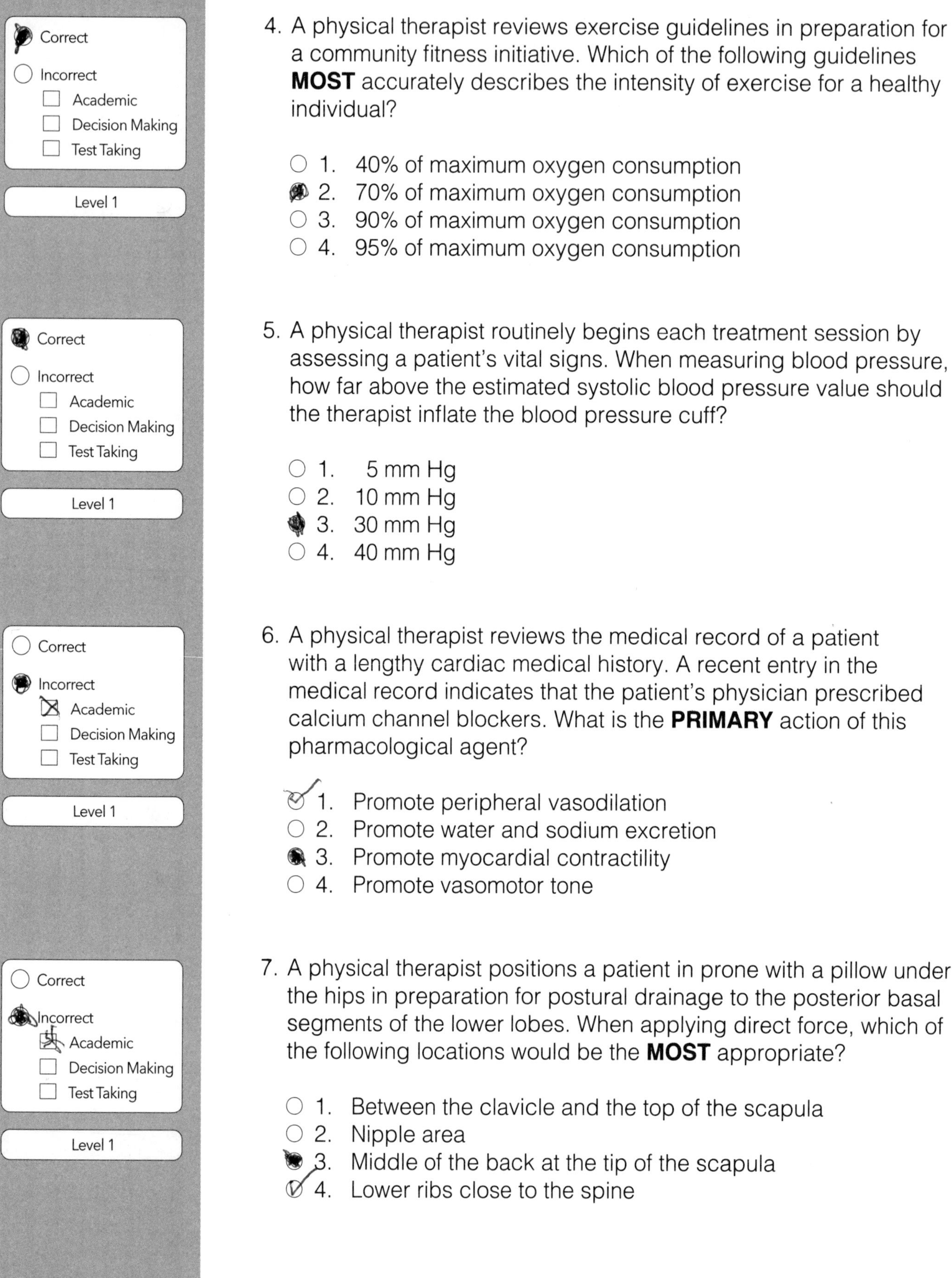

Correct
Incorrect
Academic
Decision Making
Test Taking

Level 1

4. A physical therapist reviews exercise guidelines in preparation for a community fitness initiative. Which of the following guidelines **MOST** accurately describes the intensity of exercise for a healthy individual?

1. 40% of maximum oxygen consumption
2. 70% of maximum oxygen consumption
3. 90% of maximum oxygen consumption
4. 95% of maximum oxygen consumption

Correct
Incorrect
Academic
Decision Making
Test Taking

Level 1

5. A physical therapist routinely begins each treatment session by assessing a patient's vital signs. When measuring blood pressure, how far above the estimated systolic blood pressure value should the therapist inflate the blood pressure cuff?

1. 5 mm Hg
2. 10 mm Hg
3. 30 mm Hg
4. 40 mm Hg

Correct
Incorrect
Academic
Decision Making
Test Taking

Level 1

6. A physical therapist reviews the medical record of a patient with a lengthy cardiac medical history. A recent entry in the medical record indicates that the patient's physician prescribed calcium channel blockers. What is the **PRIMARY** action of this pharmacological agent?

1. Promote peripheral vasodilation
2. Promote water and sodium excretion
3. Promote myocardial contractility
4. Promote vasomotor tone

Correct
Incorrect
Academic
Decision Making
Test Taking

Level 1

7. A physical therapist positions a patient in prone with a pillow under the hips in preparation for postural drainage to the posterior basal segments of the lower lobes. When applying direct force, which of the following locations would be the **MOST** appropriate?

1. Between the clavicle and the top of the scapula
2. Nipple area
3. Middle of the back at the tip of the scapula
4. Lower ribs close to the spine

8. A physical therapist reviews the medical record of a patient recently referred to physical therapy. Which of the following would provide the therapist with the **MOST** accurate measure of the patient's present cardiovascular fitness?

- ○ 1. Heart rate response and rate of perceived exertion
- ○ 2. Total lung capacity
- ○ 3. Maximum oxygen consumption
- ○ 4. Cardiac output

○ Correct
○ Incorrect
☐ Academic
☐ Decision Making
☐ Test Taking

Level 1

9. A physical therapist in an acute care hospital notices that a patient with known cardiovascular disease exhibits unilateral ankle edema. Which medical condition is **MOST** consistent with this observation?

- ○ 1. Heart failure
- ○ 2. Hepatic cirrhosis
- ○ 3. Myocardial infarction
- ○ 4. Venous thrombosis

○ Correct
○ Incorrect
☐ Academic
☐ Decision Making
☐ Test Taking

Level 2

10. A 38-year-old patient rehabilitating from an ankle sprain completes an exercise program designed to improve cardiovascular fitness. Assuming the primary activity in the exercise program takes 30 minutes to complete and corresponds to 8 metabolic equivalents, what is the **MOST** appropriate frequency of exercise?

- ○ 1. Two times per day
- ○ 2. Four times per day
- ○ 3. Two times per week
- ○ 4. Four times per week

○ Correct
○ Incorrect
☐ Academic
☐ Decision Making
☐ Test Taking

Level 2

11. A physical therapist performs an examination on a patient diagnosed with chronic bronchitis after completing a lengthy chart review. Which of the following methods would be the **MOST** appropriate to determine if the patient would benefit from suctioning?

- ○ 1. Chest x-ray
- ○ 2. Pulmonary function tests
- ○ 3. Auscultation
- ○ 4. Culture specimen

○ Correct
○ Incorrect
☐ Academic
☐ Decision Making
☐ Test Taking

Level 3

Correct
Incorrect
Academic
Decision Making
Test Taking

Level 1

12. A physician orders an x-ray of the lungs of a patient with suspected lobar pneumonia. Assuming the physician's diagnosis is accurate, which of the following x-ray findings is **MOST** likely?

1. Radiolucent infiltrate involving a small portion of a lobe
2. Radiopaque infiltrate involving the vast majority of a lobe
3. Radiolucent infiltrate involving the vast majority of a lobe
4. Radiopaque infiltrate involving a small portion of a lobe

Correct
Incorrect
Academic
Decision Making
Test Taking

Level 3

13. A physical therapist elects to terminate an exercise session after recording a patient's blood pressure as 165/105 mm Hg and pulse rate as 140 beats per minute. Assuming the patient's blood pressure was recorded as 125/85 mm Hg and pulse rate as 72 beats per minute at rest, which finding was **MOST** likely responsible for the exercise being terminated?

1. The systolic blood pressure response
2. The diastolic blood pressure response
3. The systolic and diastolic blood pressure response
4. The heart rate response

Correct
Incorrect
Academic
Decision Making
Test Taking

Level 2

14. Which of the following category of drugs is used in the management of heart failure because it decreases preload?

1. Calcium channel blockers
2. Sympathomimetics
3. Cardiac glycosides
4. Diuretics

Correct
Incorrect
Academic
Decision Making
Test Taking

Level 3

15. A patient diagnosed with congestive heart failure is referred to a cardiac rehabilitation program. Before the examination, the physical therapist reviews the results of the patient's recent cardiac testing. Which of the following objective findings is **MOST** anticipated based on the patient's medical diagnosis?

1. 40% left ventricular ejection fraction
2. 54 beats per minute resting heart rate
3. 100/59 mm Hg resting blood pressure
4. 12 breaths per minute with exertion

PERFORMANCE ANALYSIS

Cardiovascular and Pulmonary Systems

15 Questions
Time (15:00)

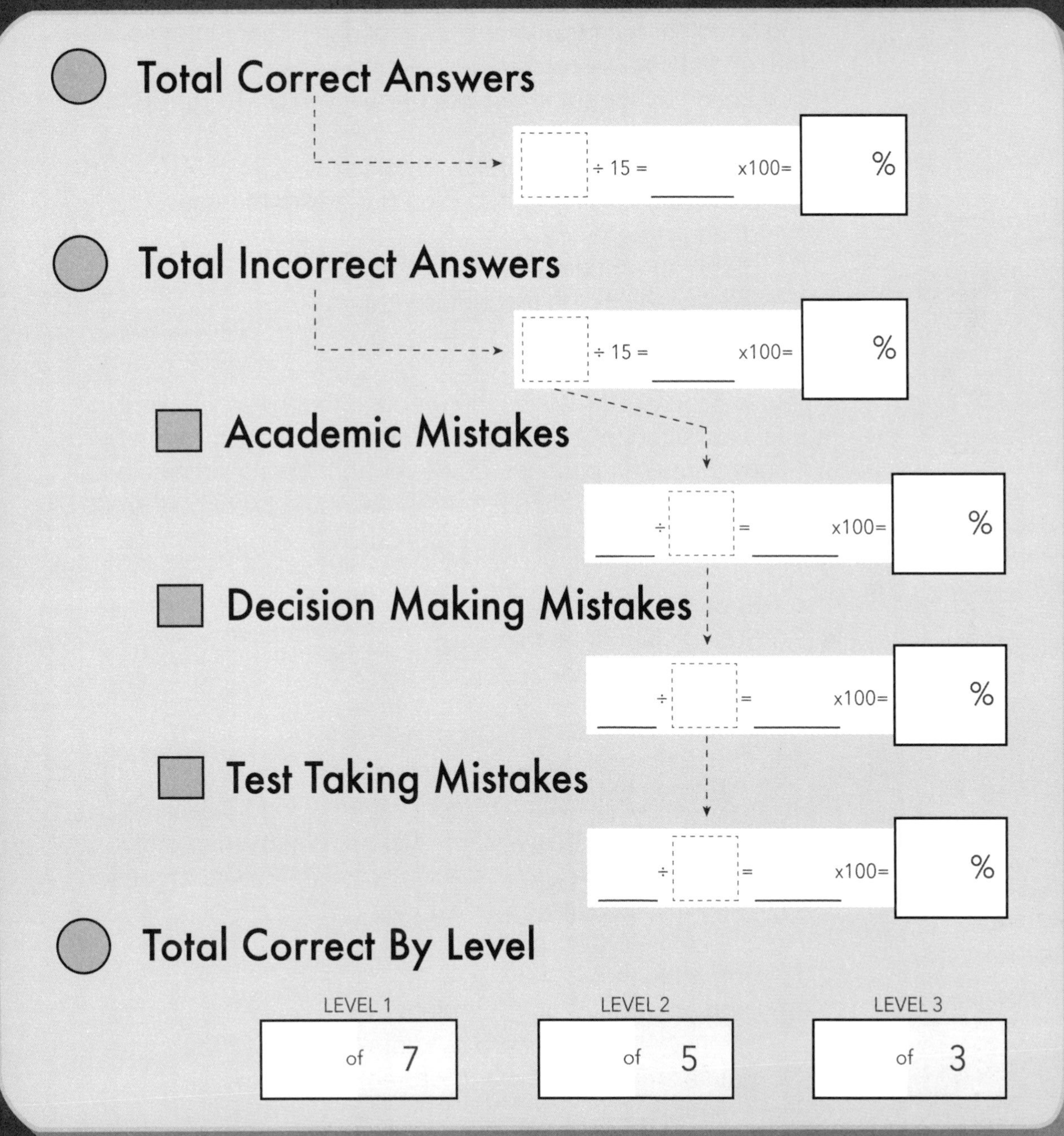

Total Correct Answers
÷ 15 =
x100=
%
Total Incorrect Answers
÷ 15 =
x100=
%
Academic Mistakes
÷
=
x100=
%
Decision Making Mistakes
÷
=
x100=
%
Test Taking Mistakes
÷
=
x100=
%
Total Correct By Level
LEVEL 1
of 7
LEVEL 2
of 5
LEVEL 3
of 3

"There is nothing more exhilarating than to be shot at without results."

– Winston Churchill

Activity 8
Other Systems

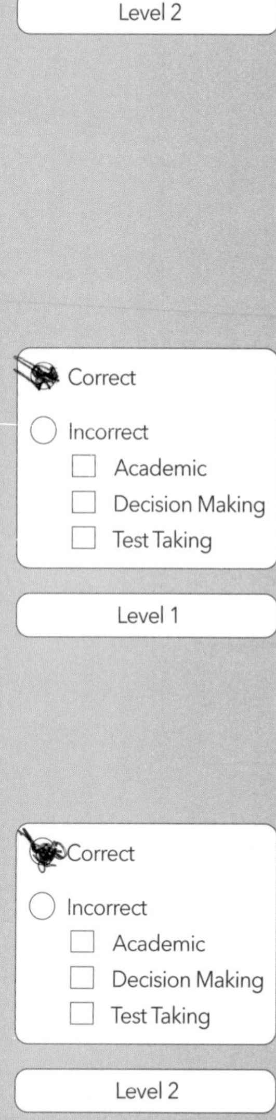

1. A 33-year-old female with a diagnosis of adhesive capsulitis has been receiving physical therapy services for three weeks. The physical therapist has been treating the patient successfully with the use of active assistive exercises and joint mobilization. Upon reporting to her next treatment session, the patient informs the therapist that she is entering her second trimester of pregnancy. Which action by the therapist would be the **MOST** appropriate?

   1. Begin a prenatal exercise program
   2. Discontinue joint mobilization due to ligamentous laxity during pregnancy
   3. Begin an aquatic therapy program
   4. Continue with the present treatment

2. A physical therapist reviews the medical record of a patient recently admitted to the hospital after sustaining extensive burns in a house fire. The patient's burns range from superficial to full-thickness. Which classification of burns would likely be the **MOST** painful?

   1. Superficial
   2. Superficial partial-thickness
   3. Deep partial-thickness
   4. Full-thickness

3. A physical therapist treats a patient with a wound classified as "red" using the Red-Yellow-Black system. Which intervention would be the **MOST** appropriate based on the wound's present classification?

   1. Debridement
   2. .Debridement, absorb exudate
   3. Remove slough, absorb exudate
   4. Maintain moisture, wound protection

4. What acute change in arterial oxygenation will a person who resides close to sea level experience immediately after ascending to an altitude of 5,000 feet above sea level or higher?

1. Arterial oxygenation is reduced due to reduced oxygen concentration in the air.
2. Arterial oxygenation is reduced due to reduced air pressure.
3. Arterial oxygenation is reduced due to increased air pressure.
4. Arterial oxygenation is increased due to increased air pressure.

- Correct
- Incorrect
  - Academic
  - Decision Making
  - Test Taking

Level 2

5. A physical therapist examines a patient diagnosed with Graves' disease. The patient presents with tachycardia, restlessness, exophthalmos, and fatigue during exercise. Which additional finding would be **MOST** anticipated based on the patient's diagnosis?

1. Poor peripheral circulation
2. Decrease in deep tendon reflexes
3. Heat intolerance
4. Disproportionate weight gain to caloric intake

- Correct
- Incorrect
  - Academic
  - Decision Making
  - Test Taking

Level 2

6. A physical therapist discusses the use of a topical moisturizer with a patient to combat dryness and itching of the skin in the area of a healed burn. Which scenario would **MOST** likely require the use of a moisturizer for an indefinite period?

1. A superficial burn on the palm of the hand caused by steam
2. A superficial partial-thickness burn on the dorsum of the hand caused by chemical exposure
3. A deep partial-thickness burn on the anterior thigh caused by contact with boiling water
4. A full-thickness burn on the volar surface of the forearm caused by fire

- Correct
- Incorrect
  - Academic
  - Decision Making
  - Test Taking

Level 1

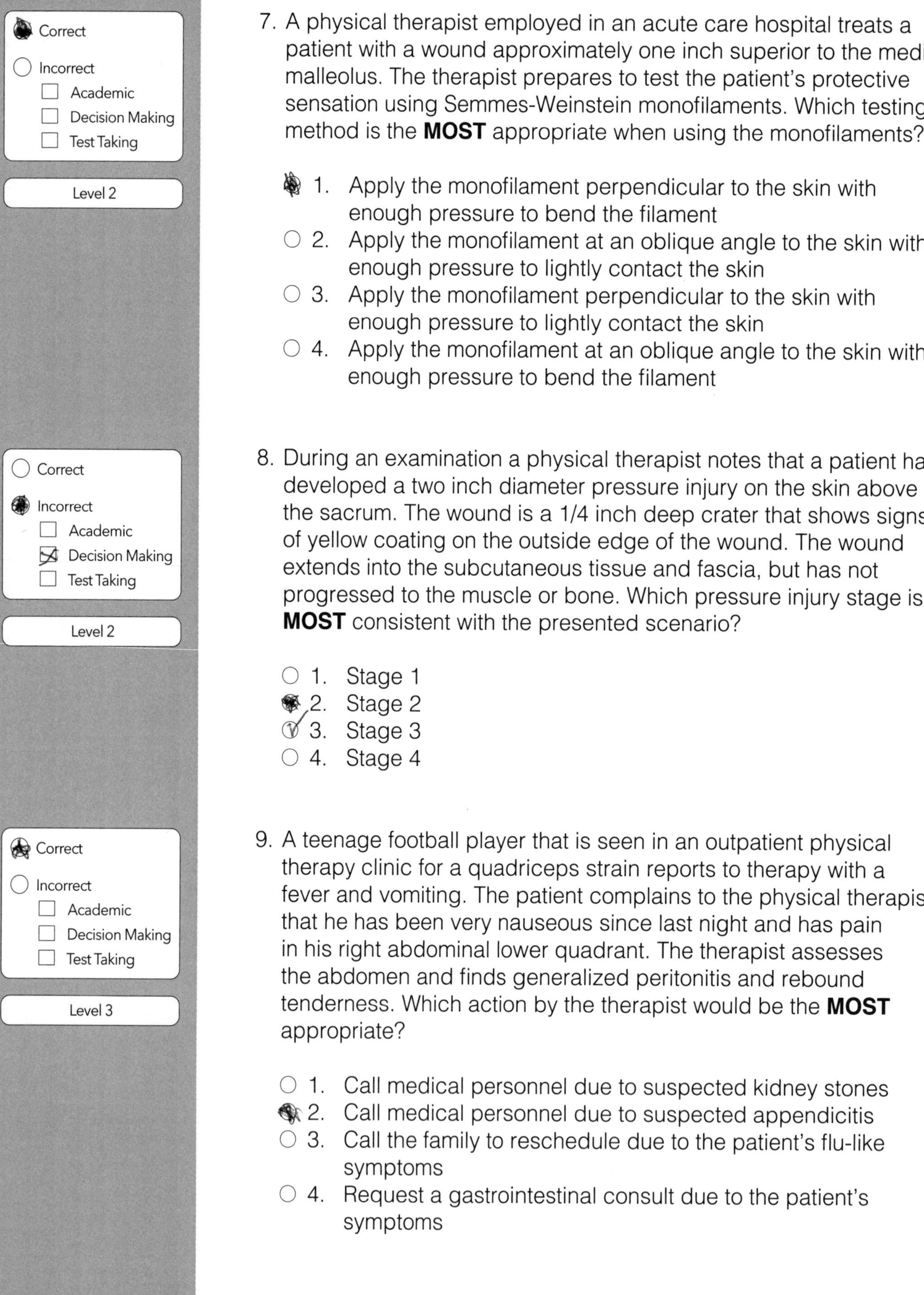

Correct
Incorrect
Academic
Decision Making
Test Taking

Level 2

7. A physical therapist employed in an acute care hospital treats a patient with a wound approximately one inch superior to the medial malleolus. The therapist prepares to test the patient's protective sensation using Semmes-Weinstein monofilaments. Which testing method is the **MOST** appropriate when using the monofilaments?

1. Apply the monofilament perpendicular to the skin with enough pressure to bend the filament
2. Apply the monofilament at an oblique angle to the skin with enough pressure to lightly contact the skin
3. Apply the monofilament perpendicular to the skin with enough pressure to lightly contact the skin
4. Apply the monofilament at an oblique angle to the skin with enough pressure to bend the filament

Correct
Incorrect
Academic
Decision Making
Test Taking

Level 2

8. During an examination a physical therapist notes that a patient has developed a two inch diameter pressure injury on the skin above the sacrum. The wound is a 1/4 inch deep crater that shows signs of yellow coating on the outside edge of the wound. The wound extends into the subcutaneous tissue and fascia, but has not progressed to the muscle or bone. Which pressure injury stage is **MOST** consistent with the presented scenario?

1. Stage 1
2. Stage 2
3. Stage 3
4. Stage 4

Correct
Incorrect
Academic
Decision Making
Test Taking

Level 3

9. A teenage football player that is seen in an outpatient physical therapy clinic for a quadriceps strain reports to therapy with a fever and vomiting. The patient complains to the physical therapist that he has been very nauseous since last night and has pain in his right abdominal lower quadrant. The therapist assesses the abdomen and finds generalized peritonitis and rebound tenderness. Which action by the therapist would be the **MOST** appropriate?

1. Call medical personnel due to suspected kidney stones
2. Call medical personnel due to suspected appendicitis
3. Call the family to reschedule due to the patient's flu-like symptoms
4. Request a gastrointestinal consult due to the patient's symptoms

10. A physical therapist examines a patient three months postpartum. The patient reports voiding small amounts of urine when she picks up her child, runs or laughs. Which condition is **MOST** consistent with the presented scenario?

- 1. Reflex incontinence
- 2. Urge incontinence
- 3. Stress incontinence
- 4. Functional incontinence

Correct
Incorrect
Academic
Decision Making
Test Taking

Level 1

11. A patient is hospitalized for a severe exacerbation of Crohn's disease. The medical record states that they are scheduled to undergo an emergent colostomy procedure. Which scenario is **MOST** likely associated with this type of surgical intervention?

- 1. Chronic diarrhea that has caused the patient to develop anal fissures
- 2. Poor absorption that has caused the patient to become malnourished
- 3. Intestinal fibrosis that has caused the patient's bowel to become obstructed
- 4. Gastric inflammation that has caused the patient to develop ulcerations

Correct
Incorrect
Academic
Decision Making
Test Taking

Level 3

12. A patient is referred to physical therapy for a fractured tibia. The physical therapist completes a chart review and notes that the patient currently takes a proton pump inhibitor medication. Which of the following conditions is **MOST** likely treated with this type of pharmacological agent?

- 1. Gastroesophageal reflux disease
- 2. Cardiac arrhythmias
- 3. Urinary incontinence
- 4. Psoriasis

Correct
Incorrect
Academic
Decision Making
Test Taking

Level 1

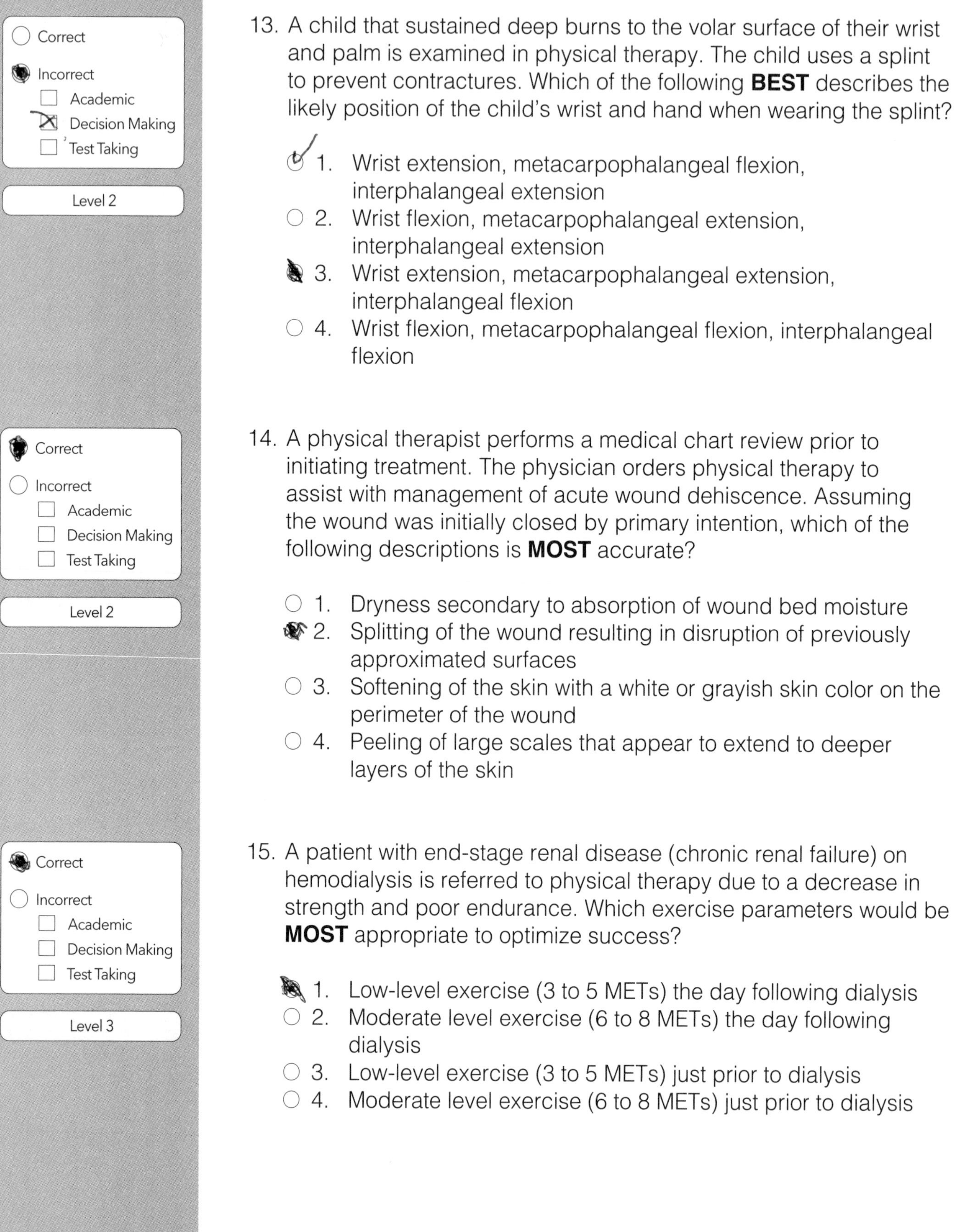

Correct
Incorrect
Academic
Decision Making
Test Taking

Level 2

13. A child that sustained deep burns to the volar surface of their wrist and palm is examined in physical therapy. The child uses a splint to prevent contractures. Which of the following **BEST** describes the likely position of the child's wrist and hand when wearing the splint?

1. Wrist extension, metacarpophalangeal flexion, interphalangeal extension
2. Wrist flexion, metacarpophalangeal extension, interphalangeal extension
3. Wrist extension, metacarpophalangeal extension, interphalangeal flexion
4. Wrist flexion, metacarpophalangeal flexion, interphalangeal flexion

Correct
Incorrect
Academic
Decision Making
Test Taking

Level 2

14. A physical therapist performs a medical chart review prior to initiating treatment. The physician orders physical therapy to assist with management of acute wound dehiscence. Assuming the wound was initially closed by primary intention, which of the following descriptions is **MOST** accurate?

1. Dryness secondary to absorption of wound bed moisture
2. Splitting of the wound resulting in disruption of previously approximated surfaces
3. Softening of the skin with a white or grayish skin color on the perimeter of the wound
4. Peeling of large scales that appear to extend to deeper layers of the skin

Correct
Incorrect
Academic
Decision Making
Test Taking

Level 3

15. A patient with end-stage renal disease (chronic renal failure) on hemodialysis is referred to physical therapy due to a decrease in strength and poor endurance. Which exercise parameters would be **MOST** appropriate to optimize success?

1. Low-level exercise (3 to 5 METs) the day following dialysis
2. Moderate level exercise (6 to 8 METs) the day following dialysis
3. Low-level exercise (3 to 5 METs) just prior to dialysis
4. Moderate level exercise (6 to 8 METs) just prior to dialysis

16. A patient with diabetes mellitus is seen in physical therapy for a general conditioning program. Which activity would be **MOST** likely to increase the risk of hypoglycemia for the patient?

1. Aquatic therapy in a therapeutic pool for 30 minutes
2. Riding a stationary bicycle at 60 revolutions per minute for 15 minutes
3. Lower extremity resistive exercises using a one pound cuff weight
4. Outdoor walking program at 1.5 miles per hour for 30 minutes

- Correct
- Incorrect
  - Academic
  - Decision Making
  - Test Taking

Level 3

17. A physical therapist uses wet-to-dry gauze dressings to remove necrotic tissue from a pressure sore located on the sacral region. What is the **MOST** significant potential disadvantage of this form of debridement?

1. Maceration of tissue surrounding the wound
2. Removal of viable tissue from the wound area
3. Release of airborne organisms with resultant cross contamination
4. Pain associated with the removal of the gauze dressings

- Correct
- Incorrect
  - Academic
  - Decision Making
  - Test Taking

Level 2

18. A patient status post right transfemoral amputation secondary to trauma is admitted to a rehabilitation hospital for prosthetic training. During a therapy session the patient reports phantom limb sensation where they can feel their foot and "pins and needles" in the portion of the leg that was amputated. Which advice would be the **MOST** appropriate for the patient?

1. Avoid wearing the prosthesis until the sensation dissipates
2. Provide tapping and massage to the residual limb on a regular basis
3. Leave the residual limb unwrapped to allow for better motion and full exposure to the air
4. Seek a referral for grief counseling

- Correct
- Incorrect
  - Academic
  - Decision Making
  - Test Taking

Level 2

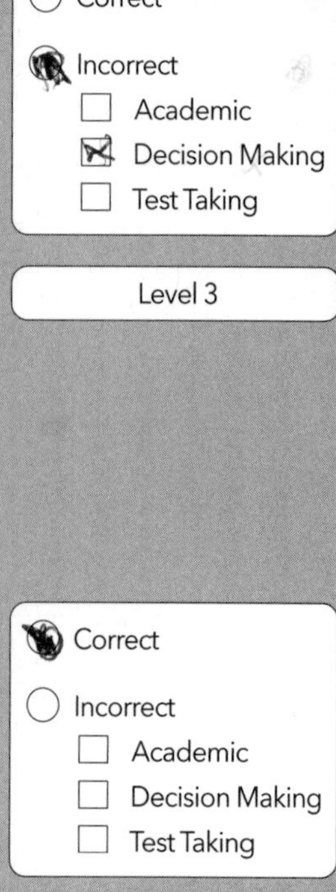
Correct
Incorrect
Academic
Decision Making
Test Taking
Level 3

19. An older adult patient with liver disease is referred to physical therapy following a total knee replacement. The patient reports that the opioid analgesic medication they are taking for pain is ineffective and that they are experiencing unwanted side effects. Which pharmacokinetic factor is **MOST** likely responsible for the patient's complaint?

1. Metabolism
2. Excretion
3. Distribution
4. Absorption

Correct
Incorrect
Academic
Decision Making
Test Taking

Level 1

20. A physician hypothesizes that a patient with lung cancer may be experiencing a partial blockage of the superior vena cava due to a tumor. Which objective finding would be **MOST** likely based on the hypothesis?

1. Diminished blood returned from the head, neck, and arms to the right atrium
2. Diminished blood returned from the lower body and viscera to the right atrium
3. Diminished deoxygenated blood from the right ventricle to the left and right lungs
4. Diminished oxygenated blood from the right and left lungs to the left atrium

PERFORMANCE ANALYSIS

Other Systems

20 Questions
Time (20:00)

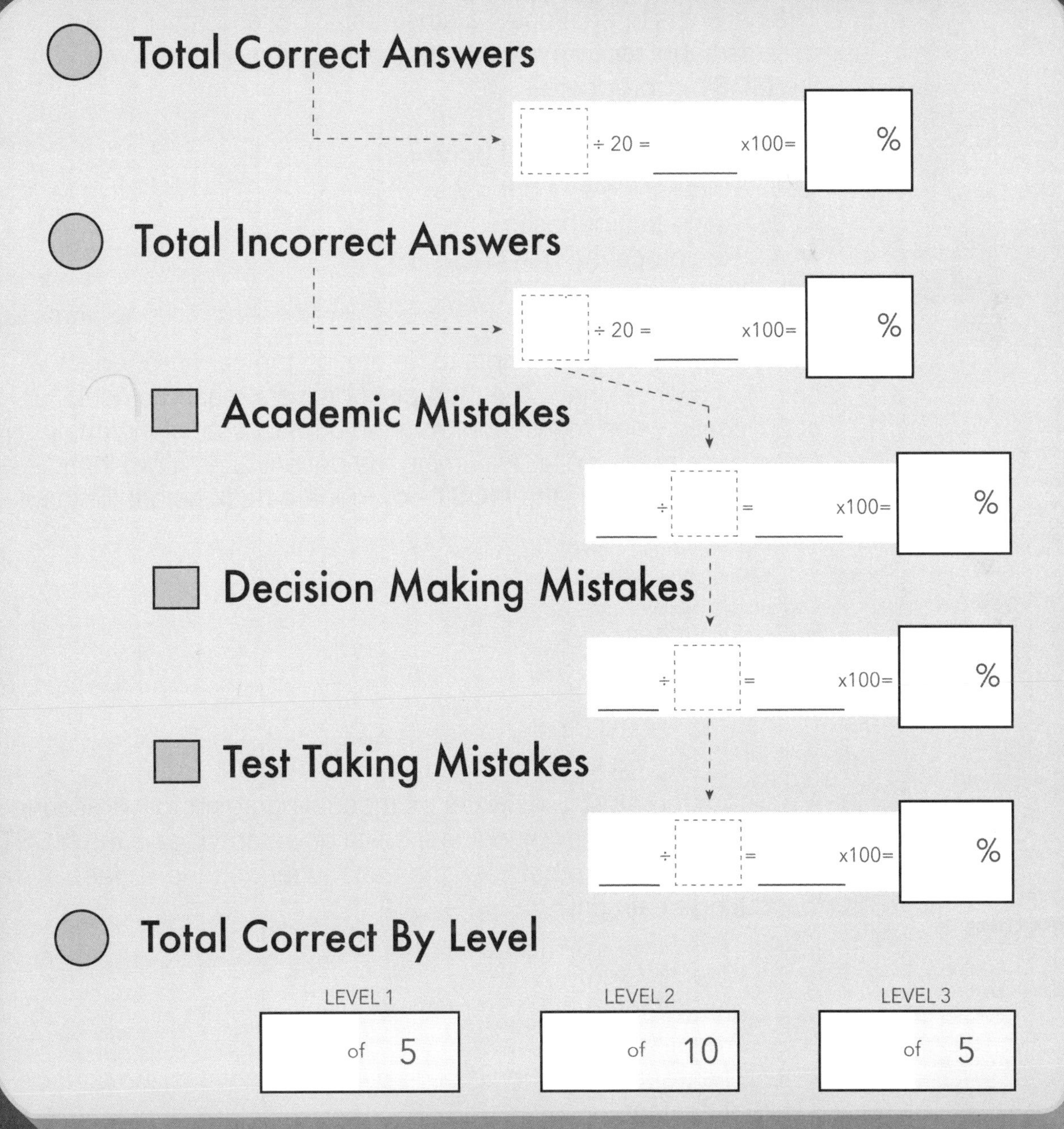

Total Correct Answers
÷ 20 =
x100=
%
Total Incorrect Answers
÷ 20 =
x100=
%
Academic Mistakes
÷
=
x100=
%
Decision Making Mistakes
÷
=
x100=
%
Test Taking Mistakes
÷
=
x100=
%
Total Correct By Level
LEVEL 1
of 5
LEVEL 2
of 10
LEVEL 3
of 5

"You can't run from your troubles. Ain't no place that far."

— Brer Rabbit

Activity 9
Equipment, Devices, and Technologies; Therapeutic Modalities

Correct
Incorrect
Academic
Decision Making
Test Taking

Level 2

1. In preparation for ambulation activities, a physical therapist orders orthoses for a patient with a complete L3 spinal cord injury. The patient is three months status post injury and has had an unremarkable recovery. Which of the following orthoses would be the **MOST** appropriate?

   1. Hip-knee-ankle-foot orthoses
   2. Knee-ankle-foot orthoses
   3. Ankle-foot orthoses
   4. Reciprocating gait orthosis

Correct
Incorrect
Academic
Decision Making
Test Taking

Level 2

2. A physical therapist attempts to determine the necessary back height of a wheelchair. The therapist obtains a measurement of 20 inches when measuring from the original seat of the chair to the base of the axilla. Assuming the patient uses a two inch seat cushion, what is the **MOST** appropriate back height for the wheelchair?

   1. 14 inches
   2. 16 inches
   3. 18 inches
   4. 20 inches

Correct
Incorrect
Academic
Decision Making
Test Taking

Level 1

3. A physical therapist uses water as a coupling agent for ultrasound by immersing a patient's foot in a basin of water. What is the **MOST** appropriate distance between the transducer and the surface of the foot during treatment?

   1. 6 centimeters
   2. 4 centimeters
   3. 2 centimeters
   4. The transducer should be in direct contact with the surface of the foot.

4. A physical therapist treats a patient status post CVA with neuromuscular electrical stimulation in an attempt to decrease flexor spasticity in the forearm. The electrodes should be placed over which of the following muscle groups to achieve this objective?

   1. Wrist extensor and finger flexor musculature
   2. Wrist extensor and finger extensor musculature
   3. Wrist flexor and finger extensor musculature
   4. Finger extensor and finger flexor musculature

Correct
Incorrect
- Academic
- Decision Making
- Test Taking

Level 2

5. A physical therapist administers ultrasound to the low back of a patient rehabilitating from a muscle strain. The therapist uses ultrasound with a frequency of 1 MHz and an intensity of 1.5 W/cm^2. After one minute of treatment, the patient denies feeling any sensation of warmth. Which of the following actions by the therapist would be the **MOST** appropriate immediate response?

   1. Increase the intensity of the ultrasound
   2. Continue to monitor the patient's subjective reports throughout the intervention
   3. Discontinue the current ultrasound and instead utilize ultrasound with a frequency of 3 MHz
   4. Discontinue ultrasound as an intervention and perform a sensory assessment

Correct
Incorrect
- Academic
- Decision Making
- Test Taking

Level 2

6. A physical therapist works with a child diagnosed with cerebral palsy. As part of the patient's plan of care, the physician orders a trial of inhibitive casting on the patient's lower leg. What would be the **PRIMARY** goal of inhibitive casting for this patient?

   1. Reduce the influence of abnormal tonic reflexes
   2. Improve range of motion in the knee and ankle
   3. Reduce pain during weight bearing activities
   4. Improve the fluidity of ambulation

Correct
Incorrect
- Academic
- Decision Making
- Test Taking

Level 1

PERFORMANCE ANALYSIS

Equipment, Devices, and Technologies; Therapeutic Modalities

6 Questions
Time (6:00)

Total Correct Answers

[ ] ÷ 6 = ______ x100= [ ] %

Total Incorrect Answers

[ ] ÷ 6 = ______ x100= [ ] %

Academic Mistakes

______ ÷ [ ] = ______ x100= [ ] %

Decision Making Mistakes

______ ÷ [ ] = ______ x100= [ ] %

Test Taking Mistakes

______ ÷ [ ] = ______ x100= [ ] %

Total Correct By Level

LEVEL 1	LEVEL 2	LEVEL 3
of 2	of 4	of 0

"Luck is not chance, it's toil; fortune's expensive smile is earned."

— Emily Dickinson

Imagine if a study plan allows you to improve your exam score by a single question for each 20 questions encountered.

This extrapolates to improving your exam score by 9 questions for 180 scored items....

IMAGINE THE POSSIBILITIES!

Activity 10
Safety and Protection; Professional Responsibilities; Research and EBP

Correct
Incorrect
Academic
Decision Making
Test Taking

Level 3

1. A physical therapist instructs a patient rehabilitating from a lower extremity injury to ambulate with crutches. The therapist positions themselves on the patient's side and utilizes a contact guard. During the session the patient slightly loses their balance and begins to drift backward. Which action by the therapist would be **MOST** appropriate?

   1. Provide manual assistance in a forward direction to the pelvis and trunk
   2. Push backward on the pelvis and trunk
   3. Pull on the safety belt to alter the patient's center of gravity
   4. Lower the patient to the floor

Correct
Incorrect
Academic
Decision Making
Test Taking

Level 1

2. A physical therapist administers cardiopulmonary resuscitation to an eight-year-old patient with a lengthy cardiac history. What is the **MOST** appropriate minimum depth to use when administering chest compressions on this patient?

   1. 20 percent of the anterior-posterior depth of the chest
   2. 33 percent of the anterior-posterior depth of the chest
   3. 50 percent of the anterior-posterior depth of the chest
   4. 67 percent of the anterior-posterior depth of the chest

Correct
Incorrect
Academic
Decision Making
Test Taking

Level 3

3. A female patient with sacral dysfunction is referred to physical therapy. During the examination, the male physical therapist becomes concerned that several examination procedures could be misconstrued as a sexual advance. Which action by the therapist would be **MOST** appropriate?

   1. Request a female therapist observe the examination
   2. Properly drape the patient
   3. Leave the door to the treatment room partially open
   4. Ask the patient if she would prefer a female therapist

4. A physical therapist determines that a patient's forced expiratory volume in one second has improved by 60 mL. The therapist recognizes that the value is greater than the minimal clinically important difference. Which definition is **MOST** consistent with this term?

- ○ 1. The smallest difference in those patients observed to have changed
- ○ 2. The smallest difference a patient would perceive as beneficial
- ○ 3. The smallest difference that could be detected as statistically significant
- ○ 4. The smallest difference detectable based on the instrument's measurement error

○ Correct
○ Incorrect
☐ Academic
☒ Decision Making
☐ Test Taking

Level 1

5. An older adult patient has difficulty communicating in physical therapy due to presbycusis. What intervention is **MOST** appropriate to improve communication with the patient?

- ○ 1. Speak with a louder voice
- ○ 2. Speak in a higher tone
- ○ 3. Speak with a lower voice
- ○ 4. Speak in a lower tone

○ Correct
○ Incorrect
☐ Academic
☒ Decision Making
☐ Test Taking

Level 2

6. A physical therapist employed in an acute care hospital discusses the progress of a patient status post femur fracture with the referring physician. During the discussion the physician indicates that the fracture should be stable enough to begin resistive exercises. The following day the therapist does not see new orders from the physician in the medical record. Which action by the therapist would be **MOST** appropriate?

- ○ 1. Continue to treat the patient based on the previous orders
- ○ 2. Discontinue physical therapy treatment until the new orders are in the medical record
- ○ 3. Document the verbal orders and modify the treatment plan accordingly
- ○ 4. Contact the physician's office

○ Correct
○ Incorrect
☐ Academic
☐ Decision Making
☐ Test Taking

Level 3

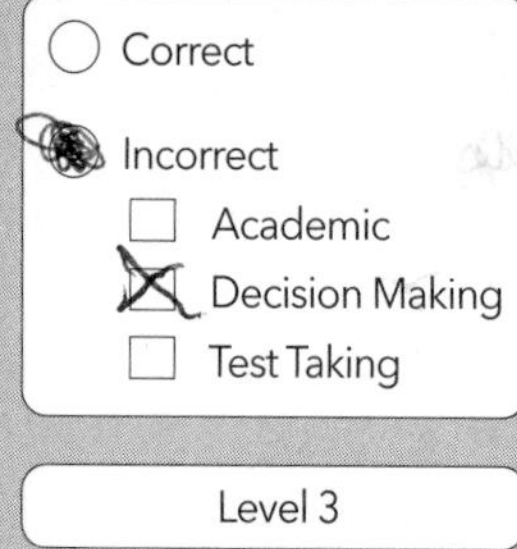
Correct
Incorrect
Academic
Decision Making
Test Taking

Level 3

7. A physical therapist is treating a 12-year-old boy diagnosed with leukemia. The parents have asked staff members not to inform the boy about his medical diagnosis. During a treatment session the boy directly asks the therapist about his illness. Which action by the therapist would be the **MOST** appropriate?

  1. Attempt to redirect the boy's attention to a different topic
  2. Inform the boy that you have limited access to his medical record
  3. Inform the boy about his medical diagnosis
  4. Suggest the boy speak to his doctor

PERFORMANCE ANALYSIS

Safety and Protection; Professional Responsibilities; Research and EBP

7 Questions
Time (7:00)

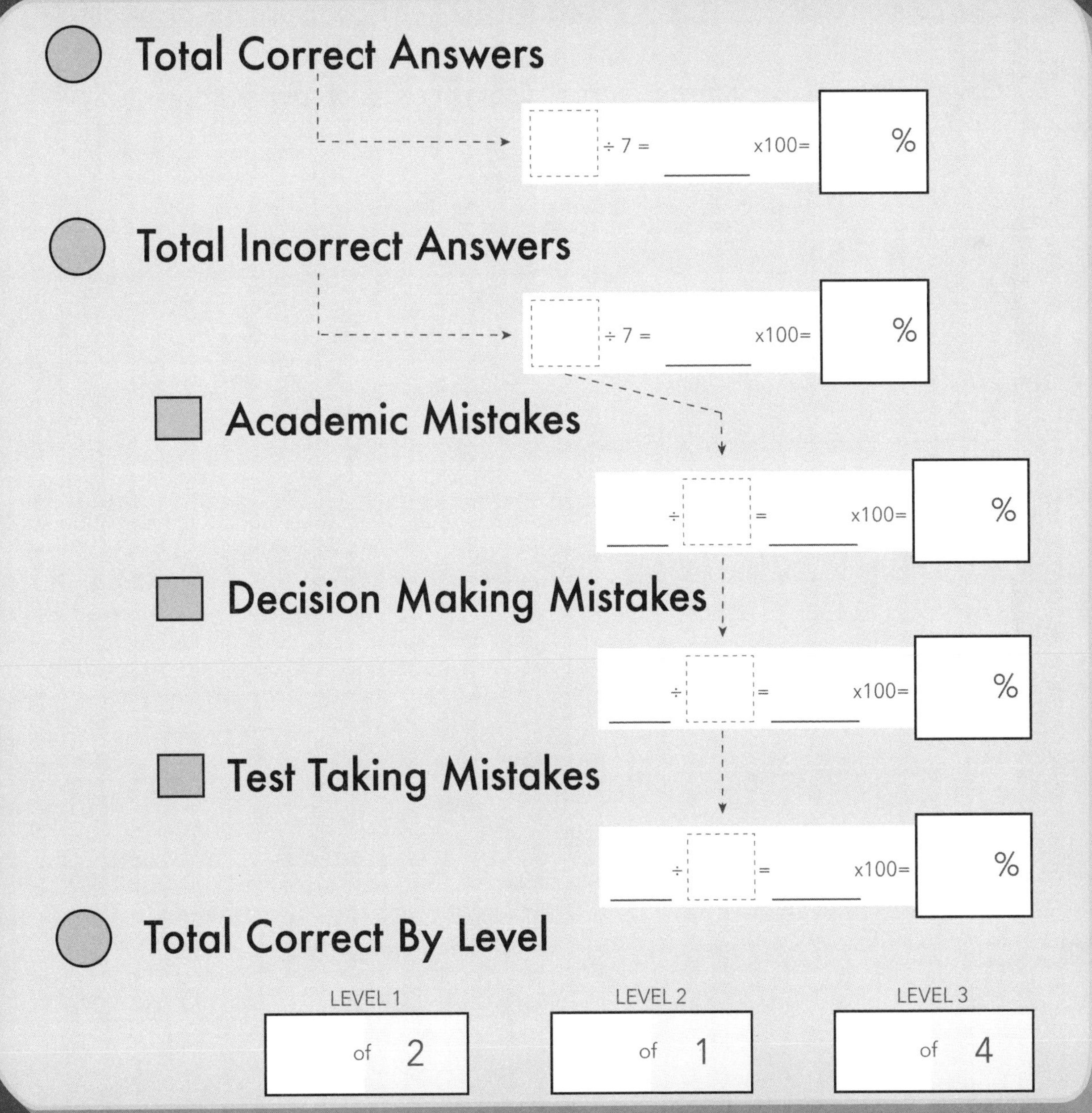

Total Correct Answers
÷ 7 =
x100=
%
Total Incorrect Answers
÷ 7 =
x100=
%
Academic Mistakes
÷
=
x100=
%
Decision Making Mistakes
÷
=
x100=
%
Test Taking Mistakes
÷
=
x100=
%
Total Correct By Level
LEVEL 1
of 2
LEVEL 2
of 1
LEVEL 3
of 4

"One of the most important keys to success is having the discipline to do what you know you should do, even when you don't feel like doing it."
– Anonymous

TO DO LIST:

DATE:

01 Become an academic BEAST – Start my free 15 day trial of Basecamp.

02 Use coupon code [ ] to save 20% on Scorebuilders' products.

03 Save 20% on Basecamp extensions using my school coupon code.

04

05

06

07

08

09

10

11

12

13

14

15

16

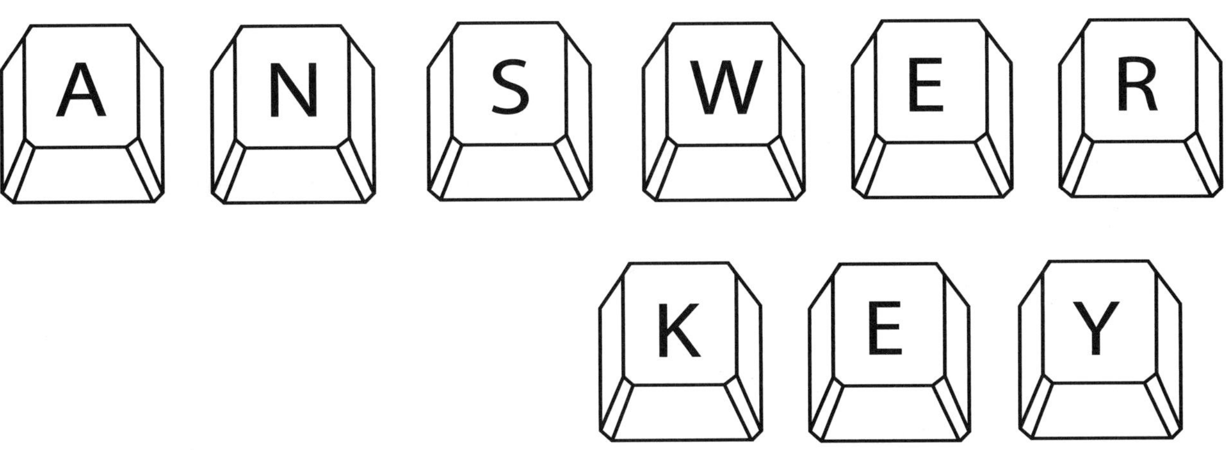
ANSWER
KEY

ANSWER KEY:
ARE YOU READY TO RUMBLE?

QUESTION	ANSWER	QUESTION	ANSWER
1	2	6	1
2	2	7	2
3	1	8	3
4	4	9	2
5	2	10	1

ANSWER KEY:
BACK TO BASICS

QUESTION	ANSWER	QUESTION	ANSWER
1	3	11	2
2	3	12	4
3	2	13	1
4	2	14	2
5	4	15	4
6	2	16	4
7	1	17	3
8	4	18	4
9	2	19	2
10	2	20	2

ANSWER KEY:
CONTENT OUTLINE

QUESTION	ANSWER	QUESTION	ANSWER
1	1	16	3
2	2	17	1
3	3	18	2
4	2	19	3
5	3	20	2
6	2	21	2
7	2	22	1
8	3	23	3
9	3	24	2
10	1	25	2
11	3	26	3
12	4	27	3
13	1	28	2
14	3	29	2
15	1	30	2

ANSWER KEY:
ALTERNATE EXAM ITEMS

QUESTION	ANSWER	QUESTION	ANSWER
1	4	11	1
2	4	12	3
3	3	13	2
4	2	14	4
5	4	15	2
6	1	16	3
7	4	17	3
8	3	18	4
9	4	19	4
10	2	20	2

ANSWER KEY:
MUSCULOSKELETAL SYSTEM

QUESTION	ANSWER	QUESTION	ANSWER
1	4	15	1
2	3	16	1
3	3	17	4
4	2	18	4
5	4	19	3
6	2	20	3
7	1	21	3
8	1	22	3
9	3	23	1
10	2	24	4
11	4	25	2
12	2	26	2
13	1	27	2
14	3	28	3

ANSWER KEY:
NEUROMUSCULAR AND NERVOUS SYSTEMS

QUESTION	ANSWER	QUESTION	ANSWER
1	4	13	2
2	4	14	1
3	2	15	1
4	4	16	4
5	2	17	2
6	2	18	2
7	4	19	3
8	4	20	2
9	1	21	2
10	4	22	3
11	4	23	3
12	3	24	4

ANSWER KEY:
CARDIOVASCULAR AND PULMONARY SYSTEMS

QUESTION	ANSWER	QUESTION	ANSWER
1	4	9	4
2	1	10	4
3	3	11	3
4	2	12	2
5	3	13	2
6	1	14	4
7	4	15	1
8	3		

ANSWER KEY:
OTHER SYSTEMS

QUESTION	ANSWER	QUESTION	ANSWER
1	4	11	3
2	2	12	1
3	4	13	1
4	2	14	2
5	3	15	1
6	4	16	1
7	1	17	2
8	3	18	2
9	2	19	1
10	3	20	1

ANSWER KEY:
EQUIPMENT, DEVICES AND TECHNOLOGIES; THERAPEUTIC MODALITIES

QUESTION	ANSWER	QUESTION	ANSWER
1	2	4	2
2	3	5	2
3	3	6	1

ANSWER KEY:
SAFETY AND PROTECTION; PROFESSIONAL RESPONSIBILITIES; RESEARCH AND EVIDENCE-BASED PRACTICE

QUESTION	ANSWER	QUESTION	ANSWER
1	1	5	4
2	2	6	4
3	1	7	4
4	2		

PERFORMANCE ANALYSIS DASHBOARD

Correct Summary

EXERCISE	PAGE #	CORRECT QUESTIONS	AVAILABLE QUESTIONS
Are You Ready to Rumble?	p. 11	6	10
Back to Basics	p. 19	13	20
Content Outline	p. 122	14	30
Alternate Exam Items	p. 153	16	20
Musculoskeletal System	p. 186	20	28
Neuromuscular and Nervous Systems	p. 194	16	24
Cardiovascular and Pulmonary Systems	p. 199	6	15
Other Systems	p. 207	13	20
Equipment, Devices, and Technologies; Therapeutic Modalities	p. 210	3	6
Safety/Protection; Professional Responsibilities; Research/EBP	p. 215	2	7
	TOTAL:	109	180

CORRECT

109 ÷180= 0.61 x100= 61%

GRAPH YOUR PROGRESS

20% 40% 60% 80% 100%

CORRECT

INCORRECT

Indicates a value obtained from a table. Simply follow the ---- line!

Indicates a mathematical computation is required. Give your mind a break and use a calculator.

% Indicates a calculated percentage. Each percentage has a corresponding graph.

Incorrect Summary

EXERCISE	INCORRECT QUESTIONS	ACADEMIC MISTAKES	DECISION MAKING MISTAKES	TEST TAKING MISTAKES
Are You Ready to Rumble?	4	2	1	1
Back to Basics	7	3	3	1
Content Outline	16	12	4	0
Alternate Exam Items	4	2	2	0
Musculoskeletal System	8	3	4	1
Neuromuscular and Nervous Systems	8	2	5	1
Cardiovascular and Pulmonary Systems	9	6	3	0
Other Systems	7	1	6	0
Equipment, Devices, and Technologies; Therapeutic Modalities	3	0	3	0
Safety and Protection; Professional Responsibilities; Research and EBP	5	0	5	0
TOTAL:	71	31	36	4

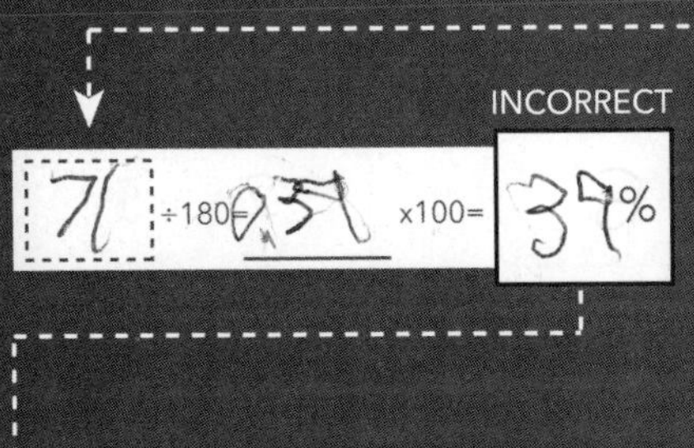

INCORRECT
71 ÷180= 0.39 x100= 39%

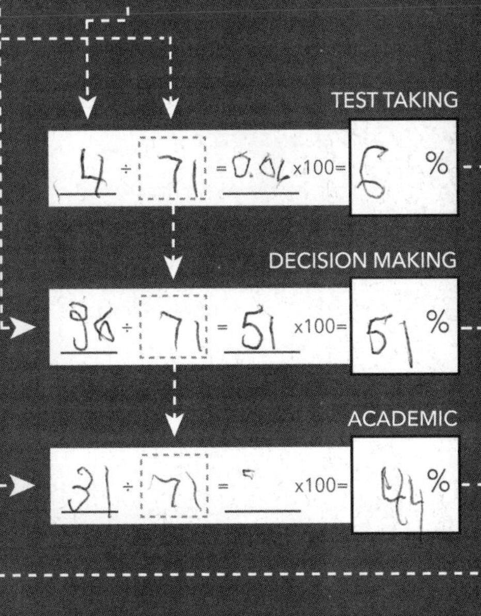

TEST TAKING
4 ÷ 71 = 0.06 x100= 6 %
DECISION MAKING
36 ÷ 71 = 51 x100= 51 %
ACADEMIC
31 ÷ 71 = x100= 44 %

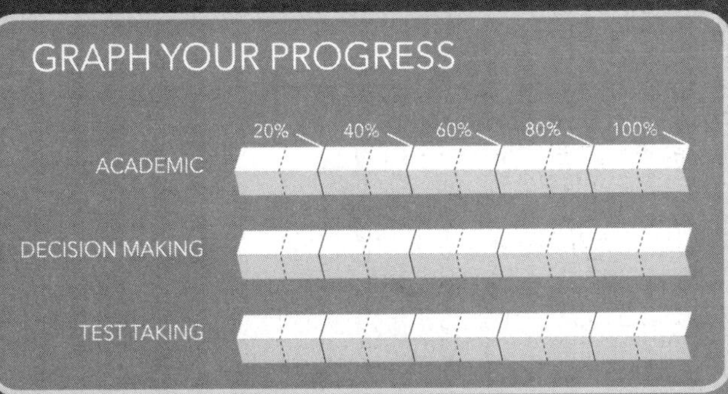

GRAPH YOUR PROGRESS
20%
40%
60%
80%
100%
ACADEMIC
DECISION MAKING
TEST TAKING

LEVEL ANALYSIS

Level Summary

Fill in the number of questions answered correctly in each level.

EXERCISE	LEVEL 1		LEVEL 2		LEVEL 3	
	# CORRECT	TOTAL	# CORRECT	TOTAL	# CORRECT	TOTAL
Are You Ready to Rumble?	1	3	3	4	2	3
Back to Basics	2	4	7	9	3	7
Content Outline	5	12	4	11	5	7
Alternate Exam Items	5	8	9	10	2	2
Musculoskeletal System	6	9	13	14	1	5
Neuromuscular and Nervous Systems	5	7	9	14	2	3
Cardiovascular and Pulmonary Systems	2	7	2	5	2	3
Other Systems	5	5	6	10	2	5
Equipment, Devices, and Technologies; Therapeutic Modalities	1	2	2	4	0	0
Safety and Protection; Professional Responsibilities; Research and EBP	0	2	0	1	2	4
TOTAL CORRECT:	____ ÷ 59 =		____ ÷ 82 =		____ ÷ 39 =	
% CORRECT:	= x 100 → ____ %		= x 100 → ____ %		= x 100 → ____ %	
	CORE		SYNTHESIS		INTERPRETATION	

TO DO LIST:

DATE:

01 Become an academic BEAST – Start my free 15 day trial of Basecamp.

02 Use coupon code [ ] to save 20% on Scorebuilders' products.

03 Save 20% on Basecamp extensions using my school coupon code.

04

05

06

07

08

09

10

11

12

13

14

15

16

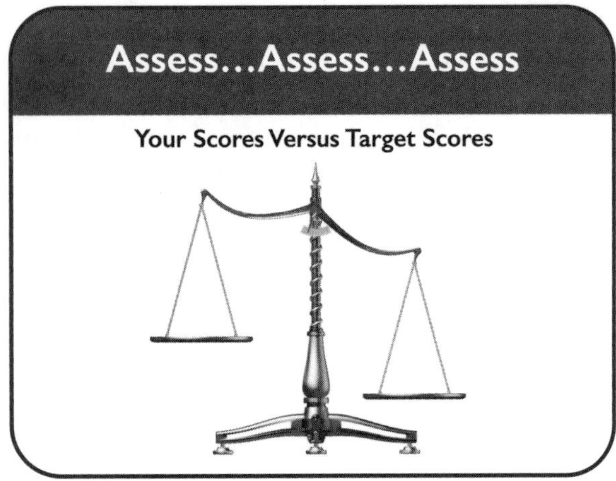
Assess...Assess...Assess
Your Scores Versus Target Scores

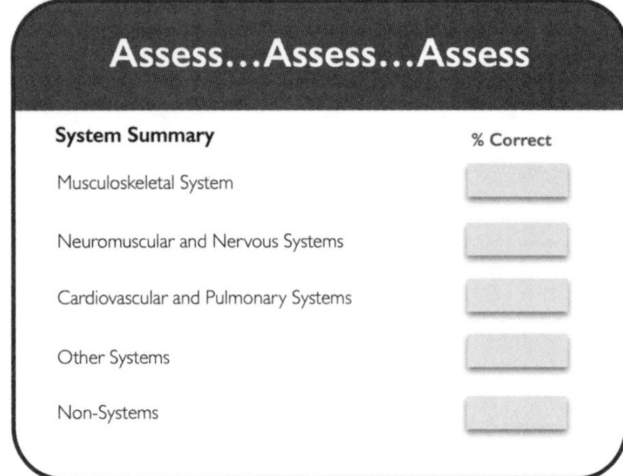
Assess...Assess...Assess
System Summary
% Correct
Musculoskeletal System
Neuromuscular and Nervous Systems
Cardiovascular and Pulmonary Systems
Other Systems
Non-Systems

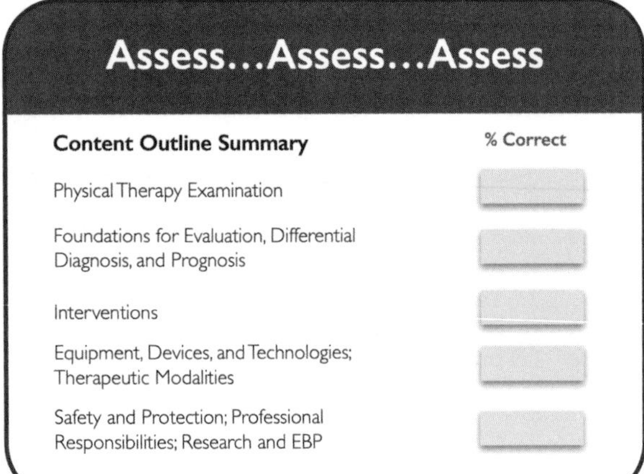
Assess...Assess...Assess
Content Outline Summary
% Correct
Physical Therapy Examination
Foundations for Evaluation, Differential Diagnosis, and Prognosis
Interventions
Equipment, Devices, and Technologies; Therapeutic Modalities
Safety and Protection; Professional Responsibilities; Research and EBP

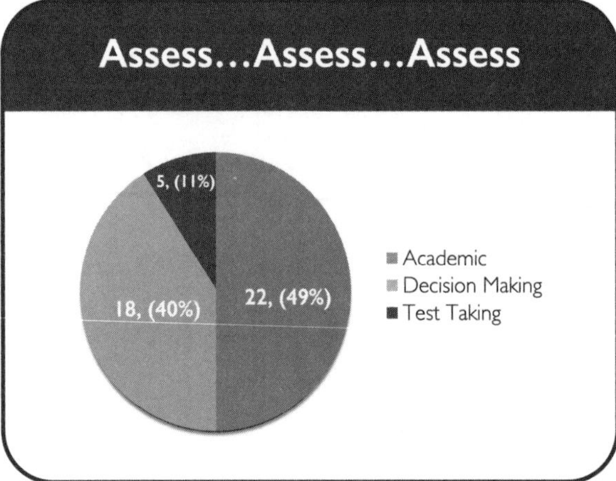
Assess...Assess...Assess
5, (11%)
18, (40%)
22, (49%)
Academic
Decision Making
Test Taking

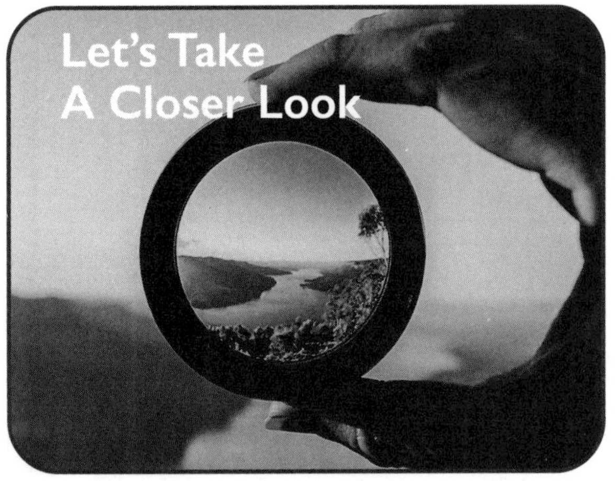
Let's Take
A Closer Look

Consider the risk associated with each scenario.

You Make The Call

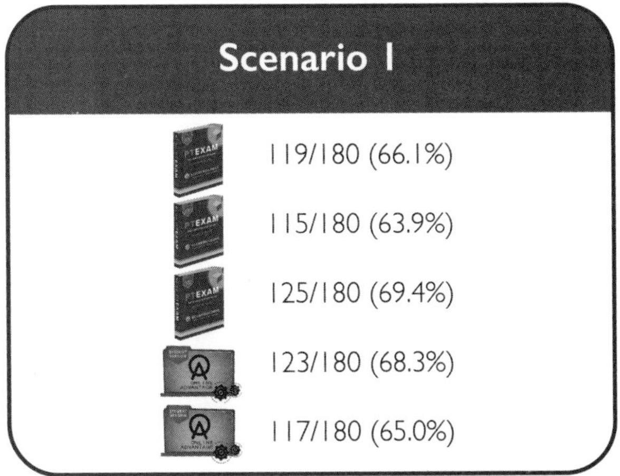
Scenario 1
119/180 (66.1%)
115/180 (63.9%)
125/180 (69.4%)
123/180 (68.3%)
117/180 (65.0%)

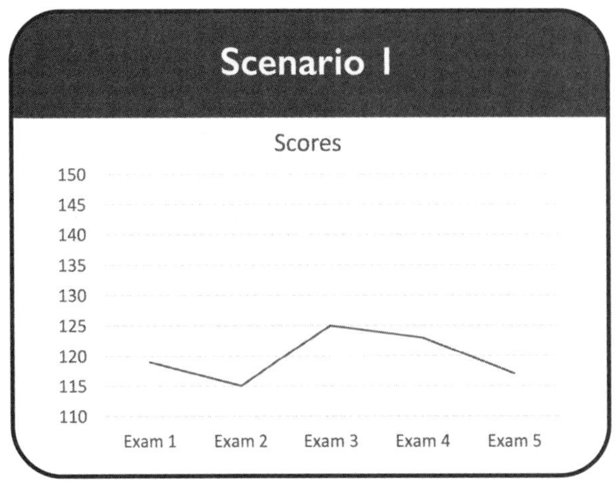
Scenario 1
Scores
150
145
140
135
130
125
120
115
110
Exam 1
Exam 2
Exam 3
Exam 4
Exam 5

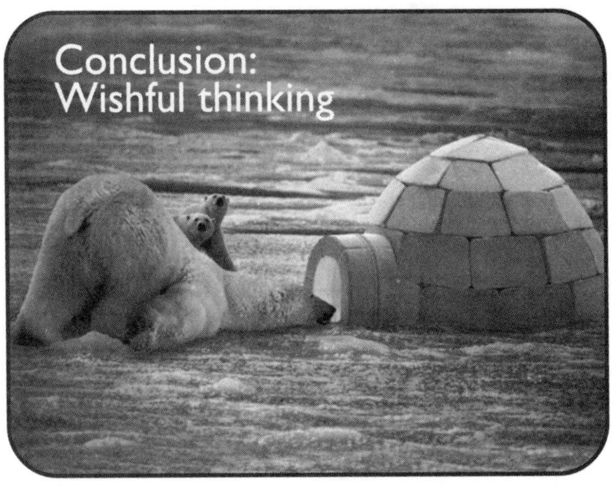
Conclusion:
Wishful thinking

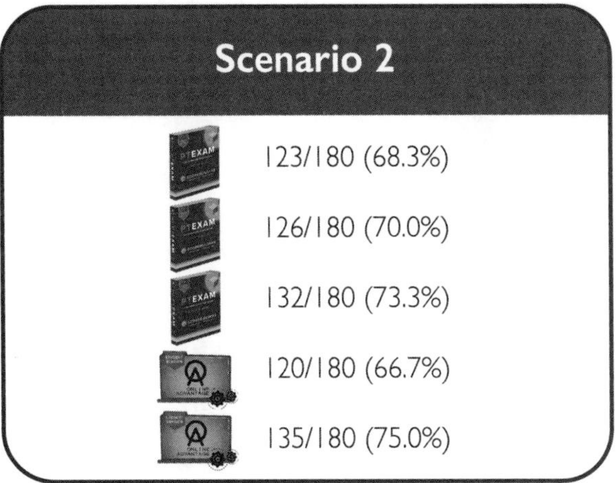
Scenario 2
123/180 (68.3%)
126/180 (70.0%)
132/180 (73.3%)
120/180 (66.7%)
135/180 (75.0%)

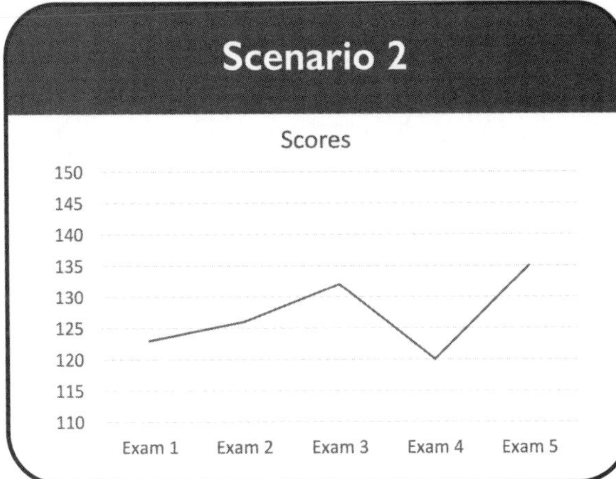
Scenario 2
Scores
150
145
140
135
130
125
120
115
110
Exam 1
Exam 2
Exam 3
Exam 4
Exam 5

Conclusion:
Rolling the dice

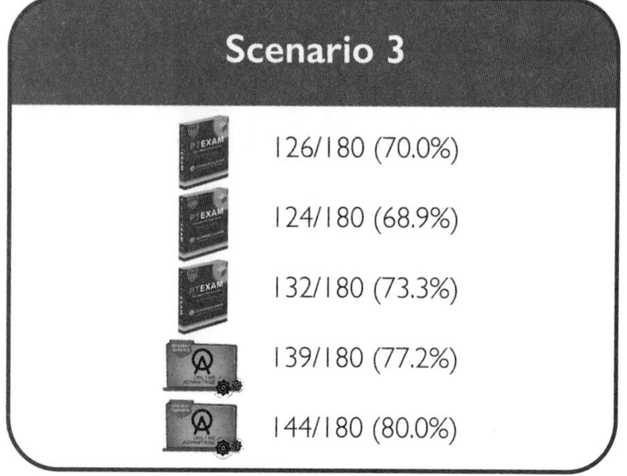
Scenario 3
126/180 (70.0%)
124/180 (68.9%)
132/180 (73.3%)
139/180 (77.2%)
144/180 (80.0%)

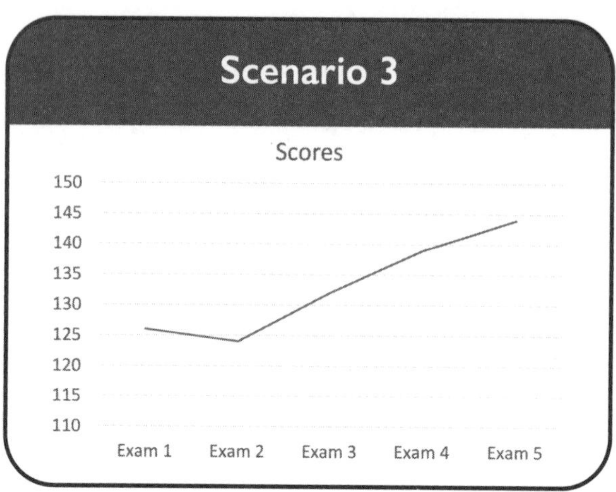
Scenario 3
Scores
150
145
140
135
130
125
120
115
110
Exam 1
Exam 2
Exam 3
Exam 4
Exam 5

Conclusion:
SHOW TIME!

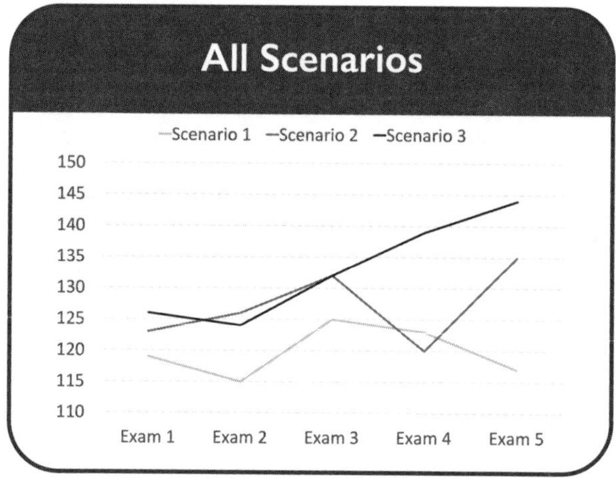
All Scenarios
Scenario 1
Scenario 2
Scenario 3
150
145
140
135
130
125
120
115
110
Exam 1
Exam 2
Exam 3
Exam 4
Exam 5

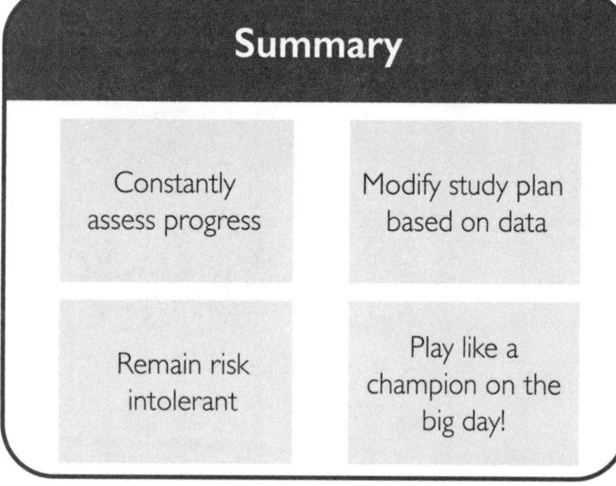
Summary
Constantly assess progress
Modify study plan based on data
Remain risk intolerant
Play like a champion on the big day!

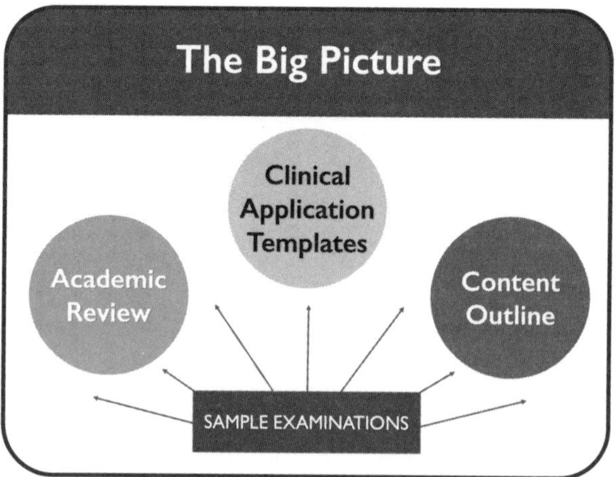
The Big Picture
Clinical Application Templates
Academic Review
Content Outline
SAMPLE EXAMINATIONS

Be Poised for Success

"Even if you are on the right track you'll get run over if you just sit there."

- Will Rogers

"Obstacles are those frightening things you see when you take your eyes off the goal."

- Anonymous

There is no point at which you can say, "Well, I'm successful now. I might as well take a nap."

- Carrie Fisher

SCOREBUILDERS
Connect with us on social media!
@scorebuilders
@scorebuildersme
/Scorebuilders

Pass on the First Attempt
PASS
PLEDGE
Support until you pass
SCOREBUILDERS
www.scorebuilders.com/passpledge

THANK YOU!

Resource List

American Physical Therapy Association
1111 North Fairfax Street
Alexandria, Virginia 22314
Phone: (800) 999-2782
Web site: www.apta.org

Federation of State Boards of Physical Therapy
124 West South Street, Third Floor
Alexandria, Virginia 22314
Phone: (703) 299-3100
Web site: www.fsbpt.org

Scorebuilders
175 Innovation Way
Scarborough, Maine 04074
Phone: (207) 885-0304
Fax: (207) 883-8377
Email: info@scorebuilders.com
Web site: www.scorebuilders.com

Preferred Academic Resources

Administration

Nosse L, Friberg D: Managerial and Supervisory Principles for Physical Therapists, Third Edition, Lippincott Williams & Wilkins, 2010

Cardiopulmonary

Hillegass E, Sadowsky H: Essentials of Cardiopulmonary Physical Therapy, Fifth Edition, W.B. Saunders Company, 2022

American College of Sports Medicine: ACSM's Resource Manual for Guidelines for Exercise Testing and Prescription, Seventh Edition, Lippincott Williams & Wilkins, 2014

CPR/First Aid

Le Baudour C, Bergeron D: Emergency Medical Responder: First on Scene, Tenth Edition, Action Training Series, 2015

Evaluation/Diagnosis/Prognosis/Outcome

Goodman C, Heick J, Lazaro R: Differential Diagnosis for Physical Therapy, Sixth Edition, Elsevier, 2018

Goodman C, Fuller K: Pathology: Implications for the Physical Therapist, Fifth Edition, WB Saunders Company, 2021

Ethics/Legal

Scott, R: Promoting Legal and Ethical Awareness, Mosby, 2009

Purtilo R: Health Professional and Patient Interaction, Eighth Edition, W.B. Saunders Company, 2014

Examination Review Books

Giles S: PTEXAM: The Complete Study Guide, Scorebuilders, 2024

General Resources

Basecamp, Scorebuilders, www.scorebuilders.com, 2024

Giles S: PT Content Master – Flash Cards, Scorebuilders, 2023

Giles S: PT Content Master – Apple and Android Application, Scorebuilders, 2024

Sueki D, Brechter J: Orthopedic Rehabilitation Clinical Advisor, Mosby Inc., 2010

Roy S, Wolf S, Scalzetti D: The Rehabilitation Specialist's Handbook, Fourth Edition, F.A. Davis, 2013

Goniometry

Norkin C, White D: Measurement of Joint Motion: A Guide to Goniometry, Fifth Edition, FA Davis Company, 2016

History and Systems Review

Bickley L, Szilagyi P: Bates' Guide to Physical Examination and History Taking, Twelfth Edition, Lippincott Williams & Wilkins, 2017

Integumentary

Myers B: Wound Management: Principles and Practice, Third Edition, Prentice Hall, 2011

Sussman C, Bates-Jensen B: Wound Care: A Collaborative Practice Manual for Physical Therapists and Nurses, Fourth Edition, Lippincott Williams and Wilkins, 2012

Muscle Testing

Conroy V, Murray B: Kendall's Muscle Testing and Function with Posture and Pain, Williams and Wilkins, Sixth Edition, 2024

Reese N, Bandy WD: Joint Range of Motion and Muscle Length Testing, Second Edition, WB Saunders Company, 2009

Musculoskeletal

Dutton M: Orthopedic Examination, Evaluation, and Intervention, Sixth Edition, McGraw-Hill Companies, 2023

Magee D: Orthopedic Physical Assessment, Seventh Edition, Elsevier, 2021

Edmond S: Joint Mobilization/Manipulation: Extremity and Spinal Techniques, Third Edition, Mosby, 2016

Neuromuscular

Lazaro R, Reina-Guerra: Umphred's Neurological Rehabilitation, Seventh Edition, Mosby Inc., 2020

O'Sullivan S, Schmitz T: Physical Rehabilitation: Assessment and Treatment, Seventh Edition, F.A. Davis, 2019

Fell D, Okasis K, Rauk R: Lifespan Neurorehabilitation, F.A. Davis, 2018

Shumway-Cook A, Woollacott M: Motor Control: Translating Research into Clinical Practice, Sixth Edition, Lippincott, Williams & Wilkins, 2023

Patient Care Skills

Fairchild S, O'Shea R: Principles and Techniques of Patient Care, Seventh Edition, Elsevier, 2023

Pediatrics

Palisano R, Orlin M, Schriber J: Campbell's Physical Therapy for Children, Fifth Edition, W.B. Saunders, 2017

Ratliffe K: Clinical Pediatric Physical Therapy: A Guide for the Physical Therapy Team, Mosby Company, 1998

Pharmacology

Ciccone C: Pharmacology in Rehabilitation, Fifth Edition, F.A. Davis, 2016

Practice

Guide to Physical Therapist Practice, Fourth Edition, American Physical Therapy Association, 2023

Research
Portney L, Watkins M: Foundations of Clinical Research: Applications to Practice, Third Edition, Prentice Hall, 2015
Straus SE, Richardson WS, Haynes RB: Evidence-Based Medicine: How to Practice and Teach EBM, Fourth Edition, Churchill Livingstone, 2011

Therapeutic Exercise
Brody L, Hall C: Therapeutic Exercise: Moving Toward Function, Fourth Edition, Lippincott Williams and Wilkins, 2018
Kisner C, Colby L: Therapeutic Exercise Foundations and Techniques, Eighth Edition, F.A. Davis, 2023

Thermal Agents/Electrotherapeutic Agents
Cameron M: Physical Agents in Rehabilitation: From Research to Practice, Sixth Edition, Elsevier, 2023
Prentice W: Therapeutic Modalities in Rehabilitation, Fourth Edition, McGraw-Hill Inc., 2011

Web-based Examinations
Online Advantage, Scorebuilders, www.scorebuilders.com, 2024

Your Sole Objective: Pass the Licensing Examination!

The Reality of Passing the Examination

- You are a licensed physical therapist
- You feel immense pride in this wonderful accomplishment
- Your family concludes you are brilliant
- You have the opportunity to take advantage of a fantastic job market
- You experience what it is like to have a positive cash flow

The Reality of Failing the Examination

- You are not a licensed physical therapist
- You are emotionally devastated and have difficulty even getting out of bed
- You question whether you will ever be a physical therapist
- You wonder why you scheduled the exam before you were ready
- You begin to doubt things you were once sure of
- You recognize the odds of passing on the next attempt are even worse than on the first attempt
- You are required to spend a great deal of money to take the exam again

Words of Wisdom

- Prepare for this exam with intensity and passion
- Find sources of motivation to "will" yourself forward even when you feel you have nothing left
- Establish a meaningful study plan and constantly assess your progress
- Take advantage of all resources (content prompts, clinical application templates, critical work activities)
- Blend academic content review and sample examinations while maintaining a focus on decision making
- Recognize that taking the exam prior to being ready is a form of legalized gambling
- Recognize you are the sole party responsible for success or failure
- Take the exam only when the outcome is virtually certain

TO DO LIST:

DATE:

01 Become an academic BEAST – Start my free 15 day trial of Basecamp.

02 Use coupon code [ ] to save 20% on Scorebuilders' products.

03 Save 20% on Basecamp extensions using my school coupon code.

04

05

06

07

08

09

10

11

12

13

14

15

16

TO DO LIST:

DATE:

17

18

19

20

21

22

23

24

25

26

27

28

29

30

31

32

TO DO LIST:

DATE:

33
34
35
36
37
38
39
40
41
42
43
44
45
46
47
48